THE PURSUIT OF HAPPINESS

The Pursuit Of Happiness

ROBERT KELSEY

BANTAM BOOKS

LONDON · NEW YORK · TORONTO · SYDNEY · AUCKLAND

THE PURSUIT OF HAPPINESS
A BANTAM BOOK : 0 553 813269

First publication in Great Britain

PRINTING HISTORY
Black Swan edition published 2000

1 3 5 7 9 10 8 6 4 2

In order to protect identities, the names, and in some cases the
distinguishing features, of all characters have been altered, with the
exception of the author, who takes full responsibility for *his* actions.
For the sake of the narrative, certain events have been amalgamated or
their sequence changed, and in some instances characters appear in
situations where they were not actually present.

Set in 11/13pt Caslon by
County Typesetters, Margate, Kent.

Bantam Books are published by Transworld Publishers,
61–63 Uxbridge Road, London W5 5SA,
a division of The Random House Group Ltd,
in Australia by Random House Australia (Pty) Ltd,
20 Alfred Street, Milsons Point, Sydney, NSW 2061, Australia,
in New Zealand by Random House New Zealand Ltd,
18 Poland Road, Glenfield, Auckland 10, New Zealand
and in South Africa by Random House (Pty) Ltd,
Endulini, 5a Jubilee Road, Parktown 2193, South Africa.

Reproduced, printed and bound in Great Britain by
Cox & Wyman Ltd, Reading, Berkshire

To my Mum

Acknowledgements

Vicky Lindsell (for tolerance), Caroline Dawnay (for persistence), Annabel Hardman (for assistance), Larry Finlay (for vision and patience), Sadie Mayne (for thoroughness), Marcus Fernandez (for saving my life), Toby Fildes (for flexibility), Mike Atherton, Clare Sutton, Kevin Wensley, Matt Hobbs, Andy Morgan, Patricia Hamzahee, Matt Main, Rheena Khana, my landlady (for being such a gift of a character), that Puerto Rican bloke in the deli on Columbus and the Ukrainian waitress in the diner on 86th Street.

BEFORE

Those little-town blues

New York is the Coke of cities. It's Mickey Mouse, Marilyn Monroe, Microsoft. No other town can brand an image like this one. You could shout 'New York' in the ear of a grub-eating Polynesian and he'd reply, 'Liberty, yellow cabs, skyscrapers, hot dogs.' Either that or he'd kill you with a poisoned dart. To me, New York looked like one great big comic-book canvas for adventure.

The city first blipped on my radar screen through TV, of course. New York was the setting for around a third of the kitschy 1970s imported US shows. The rest came from some bland suburbia – a sort of Anywhere, USA. Even as a child I noticed the difference.

Anywhere, USA was peopled by attractive versions of the English with cool but whiney accents. *The Brady Bunch* was a wholesome rendition of family life on my Essex housing estate, except they drove vast wood-panelled station wagons and had a girly netball hoop above the garage door – for the exclusive use of the boys. They wouldn't have in my estate. They'd have used the actual garage door as a goal and pummelled it day and night.

And everything seemed so perfect in Anywhere, USA. Nothing ever went wrong – even in the adventure shows.

Sure, the odd gang of furtive Cubans made conspiratorial noises down by the pleasant blue-water docks. But they were soon dealt with by Rockford, Bananacheck (or whatever his name was) and the *Mission: Impossible* gang. No-one died in the shoot-outs and the bad guy with the strange accent was sure to end up with his plan foiled and his hands in the air.

This was a clean world where the heroes wore pressed shirts and tight trousers. Only the crooks had crooked teeth and messy hair. Well, only the crooks and Columbo.

New York, on the other hand, was teeming with badly dressed cops in need of fresh underwear. They were ugly, overweight and sat in their wrecked bedlam of an office refusing to answer the phone. Coffee was drunk by the gallon and everybody shouted at everybody else – usually about answering the phone or getting more coffee.

New York was a city of furtive characters stalking filthy, graffiti-ridden streets. They were all mad and about to kill or be killed. And every night brought new, hideous ways to despatch some bum or pimp or hooker. Bodies were dumped in hallways, bedrooms, cupboards or the trunk of a car. They were found floating in rivers, slumped over steering wheels or lying on a street corner. It was utter carnage and only one man was cool enough to cope: Kojak.

Kojak would arrive at the scene through spinning lights and echoing sirens. He'd find an excited crowd, a depressed sergeant, and Stavros – who'd hand him a coffee. In the background, the body disappeared into an ambulance. In the foreground, a crazy woman shouted that she'd seen it all happen. But she was a lying bitch and the smooth dude in the flash coat would drag her off to be the next victim. Kojak would eye his town and know: it was the pimp, with the gun, in the alley – again.

To a bored kid trapped in a crap English version of Anywhere, USA, New York looked like a cops'n'robbers paradise. They could keep *The Incredible Hulk*. New York didn't need implausible plots or characters. It *was* the implausible plot and character. Danger and possible death lurked round every corner – no wonder no-one ever went home.

All my favourite movies as a kid involved New York. I wanted to be Charles Bronson in *Death Wish*, strutting around with a big fuck-off gun and blasting away at muggers and squirrels. I wanted to be a member of *The Warriors*, wearing a red headband while running scared through the streets and subways. And I wanted to be John Travolta in *Saturday Night Fever* (I'd discovered girls by now), escaping the dull suburbs for the big city nightlife.

New York movies screamed 'Welcome to hell, mother-fucker'. Oh for my dad to have said that to Auntie Norma when he picked her up at Chelmsford station. New York had ragged men warming hands on open braziers, huddled women shaking fists at passing cars, burnt-out buildings and shattered streets. It sure beat Barratt Homes and the Wimpey estate.

New York had cop-car sirens with an urgent whoo-whoo-whoo (murder-murder-murder) rather than the apologetic durr-durr, durr-durr (lost cat, lost cat) of home. New York phone calls started with a manly single ring instead of the effeminate burr-burr of England and no-one ever said 'Goodbye' when they hung up. And New Yorkers always had TVs in their bedrooms, which I wasn't allowed.

In my mind I spent most of my time in New York. I was Kojak. I carried a US-style cop badge and rode my Raleigh Chopper round the village in search of bodies. Once found I'd outline them with chalk and shout 'Get Forensics down here now, and for Chrissake don't touch anything.' Stavros would then hand me my tenth cup of coffee and I'd loosen my school tie in despair.

Occasionally my mates would catch me and I'd have to pretend I was lurking behind the village hall to spy on the ballet class getting changed.

But we all lived the dream to an extent. We all crashed down the school stairwell like Starsky and Hutch. And we all jumped off garage roofs during the day and climbed through rows of back gardens at night, dressed in dark clothes and acting out our TV fantasies. Yet I was aware that *Starsky & Hutch* was Hollywood and that New York didn't have back gardens.

A city I'd discovered through a childish need for urban excitement followed me into teen angst. New York was an unhappy metropolis full of fucked-up people wondering where it had all gone wrong. And did I do fucked-up as a teenager or what?

I was beyond TV by then. Only books could convey New York's pain and alienation and satisfy the self-obsessed miserable bleeder in me. My favourite book was *The Catcher in the Rye*. Everything and everyone pissed off the central character, Holden Caulfield. To Caulfield, life seemed so empty. No-one understood real feelings. Everyone was a phoney. Oh yes, I was Holden Caulfield all right.

But that lucky bastard got to be depressed and misunderstood wandering around the streets of Manhattan. I had to be depressed between Boots and Woolworths in Chelmsford precinct. It just wasn't the same.

In fact Caulfield was stuck out in New Jersey but took the train into New York where he could contemplate slashing his wrists in an appropriate environment. I took inspiration from this – my early knowledge of London came from scuffing along and kicking litter through East End streets: collar up, fag in mouth, dayreturn in pocket. I walked with a hardened urban-warrior yet thoughtful and poetic expression – not easy – and with my shoulders burdened by the weight of it all.

My God, I loved it.

JULY

Eng-err-land, Eng-err-land, Eng-err-land

I was a Londoner, and proud. The city defined me. It was my creed. It had given me the identity I lacked and I wore it like a badge. I spoke London, wore London, walked London. I'd learnt the streets with a cabbie's zeal and could recite every stop on the Circle Line – not that it made me more popular.

City life was great. London thrilled me. I loved the noise, the temper, the tension. I loved stalking the mean streets and watching the people. I loved lying in bed and imagining all the happenings around me. I even loved the new whoo-whoo police sirens – and that we were getting a crime rate to match.

As for New York – it was still there. I'd been a few times on business and it was all I'd imagined. I'd wandered the streets: collar up, fag in mouth, hands in pockets. And I'd stayed up late pondering the cityscape, coffee in hand. But it's not the same when there are meetings to be scheduled and conferences to attend. The mood is lost, the tension diverted, the coffee decaffeinated. And anyway, I wouldn't two-time my city. London was mine and I was London's.

So to end up in New York came as a bit of a shock. It also came out the blue. I made an off-the-cuff observation at the investment bank where I worked and before I knew it I was applying for visas and buying a one-way ticket. That wasn't my intention. I had simply pointed out an interesting fact.

We were crowded into a top-floor meeting room with a fine view of the East End, my old stomping ground. And I happened to point out that our little gathering was led by a man from Rotterdam and consisted of people from Moscow, Madrid, Munich, Dublin and Manchester – but you could see where I was born out the window. I was like Dennis Wise in the Chelsea changing room, I said: the cheeky local brought along to crack the jokes and interpret the insults from the stand.

My supposed 'wish' to work abroad found its way into the boardroom just as the directors were debating a dilemma. This dilemma centred on the New York subsidiary office, where things were not going well. It wasn't making any money and it was losing staff like an ants' nest in a flash flood. The headcount had dropped by two-thirds in just over a year and those that remained spent the day applying for new jobs or bitching about London. They were convinced head office wanted to close them down. Such feelings were not helped by a recent company merger which had meant a move out of their swanky Downtown skyscraper, with its splendid view over Brooklyn Bridge, into a building that resembled a multi-storey car park and was lost in a sleepy Connecticut suburb.

The directors had decided the way to improve morale in the New York – now Connecticut – office was to despatch a bright young thing on secondment from London. They wanted to send someone to demonstrate that the North American operation had a future. They'd send someone full of energy and enthusiasm. Someone to make people laugh and get them working as a team again. Someone too dim to realize that he was being sent

14

to a hell-hole with a working environment like the death row of a Texas jail. Then our team director remembered what I'd said while pondering the view of East London. 'Isn't it the case, I think,' he said in his confused Dutch grammar, 'that I, very much, have the person for the job.' The other directors nodded sagely while trying to unravel his strangulated syntax.

Things moved fast. I was whisked into the managing director's office and told I'd be earning a fortune. I was whisked into the Human Resources office and told to ignore the managing director's promises. I wouldn't be earning a fortune but I had to go anyway because they'd already given my London desk and gym membership to somebody else.

All the seniors came to congratulate me. I was showered with compliments like 'Your talents are uniquely suited to the environment out there,' and 'This is a great opportunity for a great guy,' (he was American) and 'Isn't it that the making of you this will be.' (He was the Dutchman).

They made all sorts of noises about remaining committed to North America and me being part of that commitment. My job was simply to improve morale. They knew I could do it, they thought I'd fit in right away, that I'd be welcomed as a breath of fresh air.

Before I knew it I'd been sent on a recce to Greenwich – the rich Connecticut stockbroker town rather than the scruffy suburb between Millwall and Charlton.

I found a department acting like it had survived a gas attack and could smell a new assault with every breeze.

I was deluged with questions. The seniors looked at me suspiciously and asked, 'Why are you here?' with a menacing 'Stay off my patch, you git' undertone. Each hid his papers at my approach and hastily grabbed his computer mouse when I walked up behind him. The juniors laughed out loud and asked, 'Why are you here?'

– knowing they'd be gone as soon as they could get a job back in New York. There was a climate of fear among the seniors and a dark gallows humour from the juniors. Both thought they were turning out the lights on a lost empire and that I was here to nick the light bulbs.

Indeed, once their side of the water, my role did look odd. It was difficult to offer energy and enthusiasm to a group of paranoid Americans convinced that London had sold them down the river. While the North American head tried to reassure me that the words 'America' and 'future' were not mutually exclusive, it didn't take long to work out that his team was beyond morale boosting, their every paranoia fuelled by the fact that he was a Yorkshireman. He developed a philosophical outlook when pressed about my usefulness in the States. 'Son,' he'd say, 'just enjoy yourself', or 'Son, see it as an adventure' – an interesting development from the advertised 'great opportunity'. In fact, I felt my main role was to cheer him up while he faced down the hostile natives.

But he'd have to wait. The World Cup was about to start and I knew the UK's saturation coverage would, in the US, translate as the 'World What?' I delayed my departure until after the final. Yet my timing was off. England played Argentina in the second round of France '98 on the last afternoon of my recce. I was told of an Irish pub on Manhattan's Third Avenue showing the match and arrived early to find it already full of anxious-looking men wearing a variety of dated England shirts. In fact quite a lot about these guys seemed dated. Many sported footballers' haircuts from the golden age of the Chris Waddle easy perm.

This lot had clearly lived here too long. My attempt at a rousing 'Eng-err-land, Eng-err-land, Eng-err-land' was greeted with blank stares and I soon resigned myself to shouting at the TV along with the others.

Not that I minded. The game was a thriller and by

extra time the bar was nicely tensioned. It was just like home. Several real English thugs had been thrown out, the floor was sticky with beer and someone shouted 'Get your tits out' at a passing female. They also shouted at David Batty as he sent his penalty into the hands of Carlos Roa. Another glorious England defeat passed into history and my last emotional tie to home was severed. New York had their man.

One of our Blimps has gone AWOL

Perception is everything when judging an investment bank. A positive perception leads to confidence and trust. And once an investment banker has your confidence and trust, he can fuck you over and make a killing.

But my department had a perception problem. In fact it had about as big a perception problem as it's possible to have within an investment bank: people wondered whether we were investment bankers at all. As a rule, investment bankers never lend their bank's money – they lend someone else's – and they charge the client a fortune for the privilege. But my department was handing over its own dosh and charging next to nothing. This is the world of the commercial banker – a stuffy bore who goes home at five, wears brown shoes and earns less money. A lot less.

Most of the big names in banking have both a commercial and an investment bank but the line between the two is blurred. And our department was one of those whose function was most furiously argued over. Our greatest fear was that the heads of the investment bank were going to say, 'Yanno wat, you guys just ain't cuttin' it here wit ya brown shoes and ya one-hour lunches. You guys are headin' for the commershoil bank.'

17

There were two things that kept us in the investment bank. We were a steady source of income and we were rather clever, if we could just stop handing over the bank's money at giveaway rates and discard the Hush Puppies.

Our department's role was to take simple banking deals – lender gives money to borrower sort of stuff – and make them much more complicated. We'd bring in insurers and trustees and special-purpose vehicles and equity holders and leasing companies and Uncle Tom Cobley and all.

The chief means of demonstrating how complicated we could make something was to draw large and intricate box-and-arrow diagrams. These were supposed to show the relationship between different parties in a transaction but were really to try and confuse the client. We'd spend many happy hours drawing these charts – to the point where a simple and trusting client would look in wonder at his funding plans as they sprawled across a whiteboard looking like a map of the London Underground. By the time we'd finished explaining it he wasn't sure whether to repay his loan or change onto the Piccadilly Line.

These charts looked great and could confuse anybody, including the company gods. In the good old days one of the bank's chiefs would occasionally wander by to see what we were up to. We'd happily walk him through some labyrinthine chart until his eyes glazed over. He'd soon find an excuse to leave saying 'Excellent, excellent,' in a way that meant 'I haven't got a clue what you're on about, I just pray you know what you're doing'.

As I say, those were the good old days when our investment bank was run by a group of old British bankers. They liked our department. We handed out the bank's money to our old and trusted clients – many run by their old and trusted schoolfriends. Sure we added whistles and bells to a simple loan but that's what we were paid for. These were big loans – you needed insurers and trustees and those little branch lines that looked like they went to Epping or Amersham.

But these chaps weren't sure about this investment banking carry-on at all. They preferred the certainties of a high-street clearing bank, boring as it may be. Cheque books and overdrafts, that was their idea of banking – not barrow boys gambling millions on pork-belly futures. They really only kept an investment bank for the image. They saw it as their sports car – a foxy little number ready for the weekends. It cost a fortune to maintain and its workings were a mystery, but the kudos was terrific and the clients loved it.

Yet while our sporty number had a sleek body, something was amiss under the bonnet. It had been created from a series of expensive purchases of even smaller and sportier independent companies. These specialized financial houses are universally known as boutiques, although the word still fills my head with 1960s' girls sorting through racks of hot pants. And the theory was that the bundling of these specialist boutiques, gelled by generous scoopings from the boring old commercial bank, would create one King's Road of an investment bank.

Fine in theory. Fine, in fact, in practice, until the investment bank succumbed to a typical rogue-trader scandal. A poorly monitored individual indulged in some creative accountancy and an unexplained hole appeared on our balance sheet. Soon the top brass were muttering about the cost and risk of investment banking and the chief executive, who'd run up an impressive bill out shopping for boutiques, fell on his sword. This left a power vacuum.

Enter the Americans.

One of the top man's boutique buys was in Greenwich,

Connecticut. This was a bond-trading house run by a gang of buddies who'd enriched themselves buying and selling bits of paper on Wall Street. Now married with kids, they thought commuting from their five-acre spreads a drag, so they clubbed together and set up a dealing room overlooking a wooded harbour off Long Island Sound. From here they earned even greater piles of cash.

They also created a pleasant working environment for themselves. They built a boat-mooring outside the office, adopted a casual dress code and bought some gear for a spot of fishing after the markets closed. Meanwhile, they were two minutes from the golf course, ten minutes from the family and two hours from the ski slopes. What could be better?

And these guys were good. So good that when the power vacuum appeared they felt confident enough to throw in their hat for a chance at running the whole investment bank. It was a game of power poker between the best of British and the cream of America.

On one side of the table sat a group of stiff-upper-lipped public school-educated British chums who knew a thing or two about the importance of trust and name. Indeed, many had silly names themselves given to them by the Queen. Their days were simple: some tinkering in the office first thing, a spot of lunch with an old friend and a decent claret, and an afternoon snooze at the club.

On the other side of the table sat a group of savvy, sharp-witted New York hustlers. These guys didn't eat lunch and rarely drank. John Bull – actually Sir John Bull (later Lord Bull of Lickey End) – and his pals thought them rum young guns but reckoned they had the measure of these yanks. They may be flash but they had no bottom – the lack of lunch being the probable cause.

But this wasn't *The Persuaders*. Roger Moore didn't

match Tony Curtis across this card table, oh no. Tony took the whole goddam investment bank and left the Blimps wondering what the hell had happened.

Here was the result: Pall Mall 0, Wall Street 5 – it was one hell of an away win.

But now the Americans had a task on their hands. They had to create a fully cooked investment bank from the stale ingredients and shiny kitchen utensils they'd been left with. They spent the first weeks opening jars and cautiously smelling the contents, or picking up strange wire implements and mouthing to each other, 'What's this?'

One of our problems had been that the bank seemed to do everything. If a company rang up and asked, 'Do you do X?'

'Hey, do we do X?' we'd reply. 'We're the best Xers in the business.' We'd put down the phone, look up X in the *Dictionary of Investment Banking* and go buy the best company of Xers we couldn't afford.

This was soon to change. 'I want to make the best chicken in town and not worry about hamburgers,' said our new American head.

I assume someone then pointed out that, er, he was now in charge of an investment bank and, er, not his local diner. And I assume he then explained that he knew damn well he was in charge of an investment bank but what he meant was we should concentrate on what we were good at and get rid of everything else. All the burgers, in other words.

This was the cue for every department to run around flapping its wings and laying eggs, especially us. We were in the blur, and blur equals burgers unless we could grow some feathers – fast.

This was where I could make a difference. I was going to cluck around the Greenwich farmyard with all the energy and enthusiasm I could muster. I'd sprout

21

feathers and wings and even those flabby red bits on my head. I'd do whatever was necessary to convince the Americans we were plump, succulent and ready for plucking. That's plucking, with a PL.

Groundhog Day II – the Boring Sequel

'Go and work in the New York office,' they said.

Great, I'd love to.

'Oh, but did we tell you it's now in a sleepy small-minded town like the one you grew up in.'

Oh, great.

There are no songs written about Greenwich, Connecticut. There are no TV shows – unless there's one called *Life in a Boring Town* that never made it across the Atlantic. Greenwich is a monastery within twenty miles of the world's greatest permanent circus. And this is where I had to live, at least until I found my Manhattan apartment.

By my third week living in the Greenwich Harbor Inn I thought I was starring in *Groundhog Day II – the Boring Sequel*. Everything seemed to roll round and round. The old couple had the same bickery argument each break-fast about whether the Greenwich Harbor Inn was as nice as the Old Harbor Inn around the next bay, which appeared to be where they'd spent the first half of their lives. The same waiter came and offered the same coffee. And I occupied the same seat, gazed out of the same window, and had the same staring contest with the same seagull standing in the same seagull shit.

Around the hotel, time seemed to drip by. It was only occasionally punctuated by old ladies' conferences or tacky weddings. Each week brought a change of grannies booked in for the Colostomy Bag Convention or the

Incontinence Forum. The causes changed but they didn't. They staggered around in tight knots, descending stairs slower than a glacier or conducting noisy group sessions in a corridor. And every Saturday saw a wedding. The bride always looked shocked by the number of badly dressed people she didn't know and the band always sounded as if they'd met for the first time an hour ago.

The hotel itself seemed determined to box above its weight. The architecture was pure red-brick toilet block but it tried desperately to create the atmosphere of an exclusive yacht club, complete with a wall dedicated to the Royal Yacht *Britannia*. Of course this only worked with people not already members of an exclusive yacht club. People like the diners at the restaurant. They were mainly out-of-towners, in Greenwich to celebrate their anniversary somewhere relatively posh.

The hotel had a harbourside restaurant where they could eat while admiring the impressive cruisers and yachts moored alongside. The diners would marvel at the decadence in front of them, passing comment on each boat and picking their favourite. And they could pause between the crab starter and the lobster main and quietly ponder what might have been, had they married better.

And this was some parade. Each evening these great floating palaces glided into position, sporting flags from a variety of obscure British colonies. Although called yachts there wasn't a sail, nor sailor, in sight. But there was a definite pseudo-nautical hierarchy. Larger than the size of your average bungalow, the boats were fitted with sitting rooms of white leather sofas and came with jet skis attached. Those in the detached family house range also had blackened glass and an internal dock for smaller vessels, while the five-bedroom mansion boats came with a tanned, uniformed crew and the occasional helicopter.

And, of course, the bigger the boat, the better-looking

the women the cheerful white-haired owner with too much skin was able to attract. And by the way he clutched the bikini-clad beauty, I guessed she wasn't his niece.

It's impossible to be too rich in this country. One evening a yacht the size of a bus sat in splendour by the restaurant, its owner lording it with the locals at the bar. He was soon shamed, however, as a vessel only slightly smaller than the hotel turned up and loomed over his pathetic craft like a mighty swan over a moorhen. His mood changed. He quietened down and started saying please. And by morning his boat was gone. He'd crept out under the cover of night, no doubt cursing his poverty.

But don't let the posh boats and fast women fool you into thinking Greenwich a racy place. The pace of the town remains that of an antique clock – slowly grinding out a summer's afternoon. While hubby's on Wall Street doing his Master of the Universe act, the trim wife with her intelligent hairdo drives down the quaint Greenwich Avenue in her 'Sports Utility Vehicle' (read Jeep). She parks in front of the twee branch of Saks of Fifth Avenue and buys a little number for the Thompsons' gathering on Friday. And in the evening the Cherokee Jeeps line up outside the station loaded with smiling spouses, excited kids and wagging dogs (all natural blondes), waiting for the square-jawed one back from adding to his pile.

It's a perfect image for a perfect town. This place squeaks it's so clean. It even avoids scruffy urban street furniture like traffic lights, preferring a policeman instead. He shouts when you may cross and barks 'Stay on the curb you Limey piece of shit' if you try and jump him.

The shops are mostly crafty, antiquey-type places run by bored wives. Practical shops are kept to a minimum and the housekeeping stuff is left to the Mexican au pair. She drives the family's fourth car to the out-of-town '*maauull*' while the Jennifers and Lauras browse for Italian trinkets and French underwear down the cute tidiness of the Avenue.

The exclusivity of the shops, however, is nothing compared to the beaches. To gain access to the 'public' beaches in Greenwich you need to own a citizens' card. Greenwich residents even have their own private island. Ferries leave from opposite the hotel – coveted card holders only. Having befriended several locals – not solely for this purpose you understand – I went to both the island and one of the beaches. I anticipated suave Riviera-type fare. What I found was a classic American beach, complete with fat families and barbecues. I also found a distant and misty view of the Manhattan skyscrapers – an eerie sight like a brooding warship almost lost over the horizon. Its relative presence explained the resident-card policy. Greenwich is the first decent resort out of New York, and to grant general access to the beaches would invite the great unwashed to pour out of the metropolis and pollute the water every summer weekend.

And if the locals-only diktat required reinforcement, Greenwich received a taste of the hell awaiting it when the Powerball masses arrived. Powerball is America's largest lottery, inflated by twenty small states clubbing their local games into one. The nearest Powerball state to New York is Connecticut, and the first town over the border is good old Greenwich. By mid-July, and after several rollovers, the lottery prize stood at a cool $300 million.

Cue pandemonium. For a few days our beloved and serene corner of this blessed land became the centre of the universe. Actually, it was more like Ellis Island after a famine. The town was in utter chaos. The Interstate 95 backed up five exits as noisy, knackered Oldsmobiles and Lincolns, full of lottery-crazed New Yorkers, rattled into Greenwich. The police had to be redeployed from shouting at crossing pedestrians to controlling six-hour line-ups outside the newsagents.

The most curious element was the racial divide. While not exclusively white, Greenwich is certainly challenged when trying to locate significant numbers of blacks or Latinos not bussed in to mow the lawn or make the beds. Given this, Powerball was the anthropological equivalent of Hurricane Hugo. Hispanic or black to a man, woman and child they lined up as a people who knew how to queue.

They also knew this town despised them, although the residents couldn't resist walking by the TV news vans. They were the uncomfortable reminders of the other America – people who'd bet the rent money on a one in eighty million chance of winding up half as rich as many Greenwich citizens.

I wanted to go up to them and say, 'Don't blow two hundred dollars on this no-hoper. Take the wife to a nice restaurant. Take someone else's wife to a nice restaurant – just don't throw it away paying more tax.'

But what did I know? To the dirty men, fat women and screaming kids in the queue I'd already won the lottery. These guys wouldn't waste $200 on one meal. Rice and beans would do, just like last night. They saw $200 as the chance of getting the hell out of their rat-hole housing project in the Bronx. After the draw, and with a winner found in Ohio, the Bronx must have seemed that much bleaker.

And now the rent money had to be found.

Bristling chest hair and glitter-glazed painted nails

Everyone in our Greenwich office loves the place. I've yet to meet someone from outside our sulky department not delighted to be working out here on the wooded fringes of New York. They're also content to work in a building that resembles the rejected design for a nuclear war command centre. Even those transferred from the swanky Manhattan skyscraper say they were more than happy to make the swap. It's a ten-minute drive from home. It's a nice location. So what if it's a concrete carbuncle?

And I'm trying to like it – I really am. It's a happy place, with happy people – all happy to be here. And I too can be one of these happy people. If only I'd let myself. But I can't. I hate it. I don't want shady fucking suburbia. I want the urban fucking apocalypse. I don't want bobbing fucking boats. I want the teaming fucking anthill. And I don't want some squat fucking bunker. I want a piercing fucking skyscraper in the heart of the fucking action. Bugger a ten-minute drive. I want to be part of the vortex, not resisting the pull like a contestant in a dodgy *It's a Knockout* game.

I'm sorry, but I cannot understand how anyone can live next to New York and not at least work in it. It's like living next to Copacabana Beach but always swimming at the local leisure centre. Sure the beach is dirty, sure it's full of tourists and muggers and sure it's salt water and sticky sand. But it's Copacabana, for Chrissake – fuck the leisure centre.

New York is forty minutes by train and the most commonly stated comfort for the Greenwich workers is the removal of that awful cattle-truck journey. But so what? Once you've hit Grand Central you're in New York, the world's greatest neurotic experiment. In New York looking out the window is an adventure – just think what you can do in your lunch hour.

For my first lunch break in Greenwich I checked out the boats. By day two I'd seen enough boats for a lifetime and by day three I realized why nobody takes a lunch

27

break – there's nowhere to go and nothing to do.

In fact, I lie. Greenwich does have a lunchlife and a nightlife. It's just a bit thin. Let's start with lunch. Other than the in-bunker cafeteria there are two joints within a two-minute walk or, this being suburban America, a thirty-second drive from the office.

Just across the street is Manero's Steakhouse, a ropey diner that tries to elevate itself through some aggressive marketing. 'Try our Gorgonzola Salad,' shouts one poster, 'it's World Famous'.

Now I don't know about you but I had to be shown Greenwich, Connecticut on the map. Manero's was certainly off my beaten path and their Gorgonzola Salad really didn't figure at all. But what do I know? Maybe there's a school in Mongolia right now reciting the modern wonders of the world and ranking Manero's Gorgonzola Salad alongside Niagara Falls and the Great Wall of China.

Manero's is one of those restaurants that considers itself a local landmark because it's been around for more than ten years. It displays faded photographs of the place in the Neolithic age when scary-looking men stood for the camera wearing muddy boots and droopy moustaches. I'm talking about the 1970s.

But landmark or not, it would be a cheapskate mayor who bought a passing president lunch at Manero's. Better to take him to the Atlantis Restaurant – my breakfast room at the Greenwich Harbor Inn. By lunchtime the hard rolls and brittle bacon have given way to oysters and crab-cakes at forty dollars a pop. The restaurant spills outside in the evening and the tables are lent an exotic air by the yachts and the mock-Caribbean shack that acts as the hotel's summer bar.

The bar is the centre of our after-work nightlife, such as it exists. While most workers head for their families and what youngsters there are flee back to New York, the residual single and suburban crowd end up here. And by 6p.m. the outside bar is usually full of the company's finest and the town's finished.

The Friday night margaritas flow freely and pretty soon both crowds blend in rather well. At closing they stagger off to the hotel's karaoke lounge in one happy throng, leaning into each other for support. The karaoke lounge is called Pier 92 although local wits call it Pier No IQ. And while not the centre of Greenwich nightlife, it has a notoriety as the bar with the latest licence – as well as the thickest people.

Nightlife in Greenwich is indeed a little anaemic. However, two places did manage to demonstrate that this town is not dead from the neck down. And both hint at a certain sexual frustration in the prim-hedged nook that is Greenwich, Connecticut.

First up is the Dome. No escape here from that sharp Greenwich wit – its nickname is the Do Me. The other hang out is Baang! up on Putnam Avenue. As you might expect, the Do Me contains what there is of the Greenwich singles scene. By midnight Friday the place is awash with bristling chest hair and glitter-glazed painted nails. The two seem destined to tangle as the hormones are pumped up full-volume by too many seabreezes.

Despite its name, Baang! is the more serene of the two. The decor has that cool Spanish feel and the menu talks some crap about Pan-Asian American Fusion – bloody expensive noodles to you and me. And don't the beautiful people of Greenwich lap it up? What they really love is the fact that Baang! has a large car park and a position on the widest, fastest street in the town, perfect for a wheel-spinning entrance in the Porsche while the trophy girlfriend clings on to the remains of her hairdo.

There's no falling off your barstool here. Baang! is about being seen and being seen at your best. You can forget Beverly Hills 90210. This is Greenwich 06830: the nails are manicured, the teeth are white, the talk is small and the underwear silk – and that's just the men.

Other than Baang! and the Do Me, Greenwich can struggle. I worried for my impending birthday. To avoid spending it watching yuppies chatter or drunks sing I accepted my boss's invitation to a bootleg Beatles concert.

We stood in the local park on a warm evening, a long way back from the band. I'd forgotten my contact lenses so for the first forty minutes I could have been watching the Beatles themselves. At this distance the sharp suits and pudding-basin haircuts looked authentic. And they certainly sounded good – even the mock-Scouse accents would have been undetectable to an American ear. My mistake was to have a closer look at the band. From twenty yards they were too old, overweight and more like the Three Stooges than the Fab Four.

The spell broken, I wandered back to the Harbor Inn, marvelling at the fireflies as they flickered around my bare ankles. Their glowing tails blazed a green line through the dark and, I noted to my delight, they exploded with a frenzied flash when squashed against the fence by my programme.

As I walked through the hotel the strangled strains of Pier No IQ wafted out. But I resisted – it may have been my birthday but what kind of sad bastard spends it alone in a pissed-up karaoke bar? And besides, tomorrow was a big day – I was heading for New York to find my hip Manhattan apartment.

Stung

Be careful of the insects in America. An evening's sock-less walk in the park and my ankles looked like a volcanic archipelago for weeks. Those fireflies filled their bellies on my flesh and the bites fizzed in the summer heat. Liberal applications of insect cream failed to ease the mad itching and I rubbed the lotion in so hard, and for so long, even I realized it was a cover for a good scratch.

I could have done without the bites – I was irritated enough. Trying to find an apartment in Manhattan is an exercise in frustration and humiliation. It makes flat-hunting in London seem like a warm afternoon in the park. Forget behaving like sensible adults – you're soon trying to jump queues and discredit rivals. Forget value for money – rents in New York no longer border on the ridiculous but are lost three days into the interior. And forget any sense of privacy – forms require you to divulge your last five addresses, your last five jobs and all your bank accounts and savings.

The forms also make you state your earnings. I resisted. My broker (forget hunting alone, this guy's carved it up) told me I'd see no apartments until he had the figure. He then folded his arms like a spoilt child.

I wanted to say, 'That's none of your business, wanker,' but instead chose something very British.

'I'm afraid I'd rather keep that private,' I said. 'If you don't mind.'

I stiffened my lower jaw.

But forget hiding behind any British veneer. He had people offering him sex with their mothers to see an apartment and he sat stony-faced until I told him. I coughed it up as if clearing a fly from my throat.

'There,' he replied, smiling sarcastically. 'That wasn't so hard, was it?'

He knew his game. An idea of my income took the top 50 per cent off his list immediately. Actually, make that the top 80 per cent – this town ain't cheap.

Because of my 'reverse commute' to Greenwich, my first-choice area was around Grand Central Terminal.

31

But this is slap in the heart of Midtown and my housing allowance, which by London standards was generous, put me in cardboard-box territory round there.

I was shown what I was told were spacious studios which were no more than one-room cupboards. For $2,000 a month I could rent one of these walk-in wardrobes sufficiently high up to have a moderate view over Manhattan or in a sufficiently nice building to have a gym on the roof. Under that and the window looked on to a light well containing 1980s' litter and 1970s' building materials. And if I was lucky I'd have a great view of the guy opposite plucking his nasal hair.

But the rents weren't the only surprise. By the day's end I'd decided the 9a.m. appointment was worth a second look. It had gone. On the market, renter found, lease signed, deposit paid, the lot – all in one day.

And the longer I left it the worse the situation became. I saw one apartment where I had to meet a freelance agent outside. By the time she arrived, eight groups of viewers lined the sidewalk and were arguing over who'd arrived first.

It didn't help that the broker showing this place was barking mad. While most of the brokers were normal post-college kids, doing the job to make some money and toughen themselves up, this broker was born to broke. Constantly talking loudly – as if showing people round a stately home – she was virtually in tears as she described its fine features. She even gave me a little hug to sympathize with my dilemma.

My dilemma revolved around the fact that every American adult has a credit history. These are built from their early teens with American kids obtaining store cards and kiddies' bank accounts purely to build up a history of good credit.

And 'good credit' in the US requires a positive report, not simply one that isn't negative. To have no credit, therefore, is to have no credit history, which gives you the creditworthiness of Robert Maxwell's bookie. And, of course, a foreigner has no credit history and is, therefore, not creditworthy.

In the US I was *persona non grata*. And although my company offered to guarantee the rent, this offer was weakened by the move to Connecticut. Many landlords saw a guarantee from an out-of-town company as invalid. An out-of-state company and you may as well write it on the back of a lottery ticket.

But if my broker thought he was spending time and splashing out cab fares on a handicapped horse, he didn't say. He stuck with me and I saw the inside of a lot of New York apartments.

I hated everything. New York apartments are tiny and have crap cubby hole kitchens or no kitchen at all. They also come with nothing: no carpets, no curtains, no light fittings. And you can forget furniture. I'm surprised I didn't have to pay extra for a front door.

I was going to have to pay extra for a doorman. Now I'd lived in major cities all my adult life and I'd yet to realize the one thing I'd been missing was a doorman. As far as I was concerned the last thing I wanted was some jocular witness to my Friday-night behaviour. Was he supposed to say 'Good evening, sir' as I crawled through the lobby on all fours dribbling kebab?

After seeing a hundred places with a doorman I finally turned to my broker and said, 'No more doormen.'

I knew what I wanted – a brownstone. I'd wanted to live in one of these Victorian redbrick town houses ever since I'd bought the *St Michael Traveller's Treasury New York* from Marks & Spencer with my pocket money when I was twelve. According to the book they were the height of Manhattan sophistication. They boasted a myriad of features such as lattice ironwork and stone sculpting. New York's aristocracy lived in a brownstone, it said. But

33

New York's aristocracy lived in a whole one, while my budget extended to what was once the coal store.

Still, as soon as my broker started showing me brownstone apartments I was on firmer territory. Gone were the thin soulless passageways with a hundred doors. The brownstones all had ornate wooden stairwells that were a pain to climb but looked and felt like old New York. Gone were the bland interior white walls of the tower blocks. Brownstone apartments came with exposed brickwork and half-height wood panelling. And gone were those fucking doormen with their false smiles and dodgy moustaches.

Brownstones had been relegated to 'walk-ups' in broker-speak as they obviously made them less money. To me they encapsulated the image of residential New York. Brownstone terraces occupied quiet tree-lined streets with big boxy cars parked by the kerbs. Old men in trilby hats stood having animated conversations involving jerky arm movements, sudden chest expansions and exaggerated mouth downturns. Skateboarders scooted by dog walkers in fur coats. And groups of black kids with wild Afro hair sat on the front stoop shouting 'yo bro' at passers by – the Marks & Spencer book of New York sure had a lot to answer for.

Brownstones stretched for thirty blocks north of 66th Street on the Upper West Side. This was my New York.

I waited a week before I was shown something out of the William Morris room of the V&A. It had twelve-foot high ceilings, parquet floors, wood panelling, exposed brickwork and a fireplace in which Henry VIII would have happily farted.

It was steeply priced for a one bedroom, but bollocks – it was the only place I'd seen with any soul. It even had a beautiful Spanish girl staying there temporarily. She had eyes you could fall into and a manner you wanted to

34

take home. But she didn't persuade me, oh no. Even her underwear – strewn round the bedroom in fascinating little bundles – had no effect on the decision. I mean, come on – I realized she wasn't part of the deal.

I'm not that sad.

The search for Jaclyn Smith

A month in Greenwich and I was thinking about sex. All the time. I could be in a serious meeting and my mind would suddenly fill with writhing, naked women – a major problem if the meeting ended abruptly.

The trouble was that America was full of American women. And all that childhood TV had convinced me that American women were the best. In fact, my first wet dream occurred while Charlie's Angels were climbing through my pubescent mind. They had told me to take off my pants and were giggling and squirming appreciatively. Then Jaclyn Smith pouted her lips and took me in hand. I woke up sweating and with some explaining to do to my mother.

American women seemed so smart, so confident and, of course, so sexy. And they were all so beautiful – at least the TV gave that impression. I assumed they all looked like Marcia from The Brady Bunch: bright eyes, full smile, white teeth, flowing hair. The hair capped it. It was as if they were in soft focus, like the women in the Silvikrin ads.

And get this. The USA has 130 million females. Sure some of them look like Barbara Bush, but just as many look like Jackie Kennedy in her prime. And I wanted one to be mine – just one. Somewhere in the USA was my Jaclyn Smith or Marcia. But there was a problem with this plan. The very things I found attractive about New

York – its urban grit, its realism, its well hard murder-a-minute madness – did not make for attractive women. Jaclyn Smith didn't hang out in Brooklyn. Marcia was not from the Bronx. Cagney and Lacey were from New York and those two had the sex appeal of leftover washing-up. 'Hey, ya gonna fuck wit me or wat?' would've been the nearest these two could muster by way of a seductive come-on.

Luckily that's only one side of New York womanhood. The other side is the cool metropolitan sophisticate in charge of her own destiny. Women like Daryl Hannah in *Wall Street*: arty, confident, rich, and tasty as you like. This was the goal – a New York yuppie for the wife.

My superiors saw things differently. It wasn't that they expected me to do nothing but work. They just saw my venture as more Shag-a-Round than Find-a-Spouse.

'You're on a mission', said the departmental head as he poked me in the chest, 'to bag as many women as possible.'

He'd spent time in New York and saw himself as a retired Lothario. Now married to an ex-model – natch – he expected to live vicariously through my sexual exploits.

'Get out there and get yourself laid,' he said. 'That's an order. I want a regular update.'

It wasn't the sort of order I was inclined to disobey. I also saw the two missions as wholly compatible. Somewhere in this certain bed parade would be the wife – I'd simply put blow-job technique on the list of required wife skills.

God knows what Mandy would have to say about all this. Mandy was from the London office. She's the sort of Essex girl that wiggles round City offices turning heads. She had flirty eyes, a vacant gaze and a sweet voice that melted your heart but left you certain you'd yet to meet Mastermind. Indeed Mandy was one of those people who thought Homer was alive and well and living in Springfield – but she had great tits.

Mandy and I worked in different departments and met through co-operation on a deal. It turned out we both supported West Ham and would chat about their weekend performance on Monday mornings. After West Ham had been knocked out of the cup I suggested a commiserating lunch, but didn't follow up. I'm pretty crap with women in this respect. I expect a major green light if I'm to make my move.

Mandy finally lost patience and made the move for me in the Bishopsgate Pitcher & Piano. 'So what happened to that lunch you were going to buy me?' she snapped, narrowing my escape route with her body.

I reddened and looked nervously round the room. 'I think you were just teasing me,' she said. 'You know I fancy you and you wanted to test my reaction.'

Blimey, that was a bit direct.

I struggled to find excuses but she didn't really care. She'd been giving positive signals for months and it was about time this idiot responded. At last I got the hint, took her to a nightclub and snogged her on the dance floor.

I'd been seeing her for two months when I discovered I was bound for the US.

I took her to Jamie's wine bar in Broadgate and told her straight. 'I'm going to live in New York.'

Her large floppsy eyes looked down and her mouth creased. She sighed a deep sigh.

'Bit of a bombshell,' she said.

Oh how I loved her. I loved her because she was completely different to the women I usually went for. Being an angst-ridden pseudo-intellectual, I'd always sought mind compatibility. I wanted a woman who could discuss Voltaire and Marx and felt strongly about global issues. Notwithstanding that, I wanted a great shag.

Yet by the time I'd met Mandy the real world had crashed in and I just wanted a great shag. I'd grown up. I'd become embarrassed by my own nonsense-intellectualism and the shite I spent my younger years spouting. Mandy thought Voltaire and Marx were high-street fashion chains and that was fine by me.

But two months is no time to corrupt a life-changing decision. I had a one-way ticket to New York and she wasn't invited.

This lent an ominous air to the few weeks we had left before my departure. And as D-Day neared her eyes became doughier, her sighs became longer and, more and more, I'd catch her looking at me as if memorizing my face for posterity. And to my amazement I started doing the same to her. The time we spent together became very special. Each moment was precious – grasped and elongated. This lasted right until the final meal, at Bibendum, the final champagne, and the final early night.

By the morning of the flight her eyes were such deep pools of sorrow I felt I'd inflicted an unspeakable cruelty upon her. She cried. I cried. She cried and laughed. I cried and laughed. I said goodbye and made for the door. She stood in a black silk dressing gown looking lost. I turned back and hugged her, kissing her tearful eyes, holding her tight, feeling the press of her breasts.

I felt the press of her breasts again. I took off her dressing gown and said goodbye to her breasts individually. I said goodbye again (to her face). She cried again. I cried again. I left – and sat in shock in the back of the taxi.

I'd not promised to be faithful. How could I with the head's orders? And neither of us had made any definitive statement about our relationship. The nearest we'd come was a conversation while walking to a dinner party in Parson's Green. She began it in a 'where do

I stand when you're gone' kind of way.

'Oh, you know,' I said. 'We'll remain friends and I'm sure we'll get it on when I'm over.'

'We'll get it on when you're over,' she repeated sarcastically.

I'd cringed when I said it. I didn't particularly want to hear it again.

'We'll get it on when you're over,' she said again.

'Look,' I said, trying to prevent a third repetition, 'I'm simply saying I can't promise to be faithful. Sure we can carry on but fidelity's out of the question.'

But Mandy had a selective memory about such statements. And at one point later on I monumentally fucked up. After arriving in the US the debate continued via e-mail. Mandy wanted further definition of what I meant by 'fidelity's out of the question' – although it was pretty clear to me, I have to say.

Typically I lapsed into arsehole-intellectualism.

'The dictionary gives the following definition of fidelity,' I wrote in one e-mail. '1) devotion to duties, 2) loyalty and devotion to person or cause, 3) sexual faithfulness to one's spouse or lover, and 4) the degree to which an amplifier accurately reproduces the characteristics of the input signal. I have no problem with definitions 1, 2 and 4.'

What a ponce.

Within minutes I had a reply.

'If you can't manage number 3, then you should forget number 2 as well.'

I didn't hesitate. I flashed back, 'I have no problem with number 3.'

I meant to say number two. I had no problem with number two – not number three. I hadn't noticed my mistake and the other end went dead. Mandy had the reply she wanted and the message was stored in a special folder.

But if I was back on the hook I didn't know it. And meanwhile I furiously fished, even if temporarily, in the smaller pond of Greenwich.

My first bite came in the Do Me, from Bernadette. Although blonde, Bernadette was from Marseilles and had that dark-featured Latin look to her. Yet the most remarkable thing about Bernadette was that a South of France upbringing and a Greenwich, Connecticut, adulthood had conspired to give her a strong Brooklyn accent.

She didn't only talk in this strange way – her stance and mannerisms were also strictly Brooklyn. It was the oddest thing – having dinner with a sophisticated-looking woman brandishing a fork clutched in her fist and with this Mafia/boxer/bouncer spiel pouring from her mouth doing a reasonable impression of a washing machine.

Still, she owned a white Porsche convertible and it was great to be driven at astonishing speed by a blonde, hair flowing madly, George Michael on the CD and the streets of Greenwich flying by like the *London-to-Brighton in 10 minutes* film. Junctions, malls, churches and overpasses flashed by as the skin on my face pressed against my skull.

As we drove at this worrying pace she spoke of her ex-boyfriend Dave, a six-foot-five bodybuilder who kept shagging other women but beat up any man seen with her. Great. She also spoke about being on anti-depressants. When she took them she would suddenly become very drowsy. Great. But that was better than when she didn't take them, because then she felt reckless and suicidal – especially when driving. T'rific.

delighted to be working out here on the wooded fringes of New York. They're also content to work in a building that resembles the rejected design for a nuclear war command centre. Even those transferred from the swanky Manhattan skyscraper say they were more than happy to make the swap. It's a ten-minute drive from home. It's a nice location. So what if it's a concrete carbuncle?

And I'm trying to like it – I really am. It's a happy place, with happy people – all happy to be here. And I too can be one of these happy people. If only I'd let myself. But I can't. I hate it. I don't want shady fucking suburbia. I want the urban fucking apocalypse. I don't want bobbing fucking boats. I want the teaming fucking anthill. And I don't want some squat fucking bunker. I want a piercing fucking skyscraper in the heart of the fucking action. Bugger a ten-minute drive. I want to be part of the vortex, not resisting the pull like a contestant in a dodgy *It's a Knockout* game.

I'm sorry, but I cannot understand how anyone can live next to New York and not at least work in it. It's like living next to Copacabana Beach but always swimming at the local leisure centre. Sure the beach is dirty, sure it's full of tourists and muggers and sure it's salt water and sticky sand. But it's Copacabana, for Chrissake – fuck the leisure centre.

New York is forty minutes by train and the most commonly stated comfort for the Greenwich workers is the removal of that awful cattle-truck journey. But so what? Once you've hit Grand Central you're in New York, the world's greatest neurotic experiment. In New York looking out the window is an adventure – just think what you can do in your lunch hour.

For my first lunch break in Greenwich I checked out the boats. By day two I'd seen enough boats for a lifetime and by day three I realized why nobody takes a lunch

27

break – there's nowhere to go and nothing to do.

In fact, I lie. Greenwich does have a lunchlife and a nightlife. It's just a bit thin. Let's start with lunch. Other than the in-bunker cafeteria there are two joints within a two-minute walk or, this being suburban America, a thirty-second drive from the office.

Just across the street is Manero's Steakhouse, a ropey diner that tries to elevate itself through some aggressive marketing. 'Try our Gorgonzola Salad,' shouts one poster, 'it's World Famous'.

Now I don't know about you but I had to be shown Greenwich, Connecticut on the map. Manero's was certainly off my beaten path and their Gorgonzola Salad really didn't figure at all. But what do I know? Maybe there's a school in Mongolia right now reciting the modern wonders of the world and ranking Manero's Gorgonzola Salad alongside Niagara Falls and the Great Wall of China.

Manero's is one of those restaurants that considers itself a local landmark because it's been around for more than ten years. It displays faded photographs of the place in the Neolithic age when scary-looking men stood for the camera wearing muddy boots and droopy moustaches. I'm talking about the 1970s.

But landmark or not, it would be a cheapskate mayor who bought a passing president lunch at Manero's. Better to take him to the Atlantis Restaurant – my breakfast room at the Greenwich Harbor Inn. By lunchtime the hard rolls and brittle bacon have given way to oysters and crab-cakes at forty dollars a pop. The restaurant spills outside in the evening and the tables are lent an exotic air by the yachts and the mock-Caribbean shack that acts as the hotel's summer bar.

The bar is the centre of our after-work nightlife, such as it exists. While most workers head for their families and what youngsters there are flee back to New York, the

AUGUST

A marauding longboat under Brooklyn Bridge

'Afternoon,' said a little East European-sounding man. He was with his mate and they stared guiltily at me. 'You here afternoon. Not now. Landlady say.'

I'd taken my apartment key out of the envelope and made to ceremonially open the door for the first time. But the door fell open without the key. Inside, these two were sweeping up.

'Landlady wrong,' I replied. 'And what the fuck's this?' I pointed at the space beyond the French doors where there was supposed to be a terrace.

I'd been persuaded to pay $2,300 a month for a tiny one-bedroom apartment without a separate kitchen because of the private terrace. On viewing, the landlady had pledged furious construction to meet my arrival date. But not a trowel had been lifted. A pair of beautiful French doors opened on to a void above the garden below.

But that wasn't the half of it. The landlady had agreed to leave the living-room furniture – an imposing mahogany dining-room table and chairs and a seductive leather couch. Gone. They'd been replaced by a small metal garden table and two equally crappy chairs not fit for a Dagenham beer garden. And the couch had been

41

swapped for a sofa scavengers wouldn't have bothered burning.

The place was also filthy – I even had the Spanish girl's pubes in the bathroom as a reminder of her beauty. The cooker was grimy, there was a layer of dust on every surface and the windows were mottled with dirt. These two goons had hardly touched the surface with their soporific sweep.

Oh, and there was a gas leak coming from the cooker.

'Window open, must,' said the brains of the outfit.

But the only window was in the bedroom and it had a broken catch. Without a prop it slammed shut. This meant leaving the door to the void permanently open. This was fine because, once open, it refused to close.

I wasn't in the best frame of mind to deal with all this. It had been a bad morning. Bernadette had turned up late with a trunk full of beach gear. She seemed irritated that I had any luggage at all, as if moving home meant the usual open-top cruise in a cotton shirt and sunglasses. I growled as I stuffed one bag behind my seat and put the other on my lap.

In fact I became grateful for the buffer. Bernadette was not in the best frame of mind for a sedate drive to the city. Dave had turned up the night before and they'd been shouting and throwing things at each other to the point where the neighbours had called the police. Dave was carted off while Bernadette carried on ranting. She trashed the remaining breakables, threatened to take all her anti-depressants at once and got herself in such a state the neighbours wished they'd gone away for the weekend.

She retold the story as we drove, becoming more and more animated as her anger mounted. We raced towards New York at breakneck speed with vehicles diving out the way at our approach. As we flashed by they'd stare in amazement at the sight of a blonde driver taking no notice of the road and gesticulating wildly at her passenger, who stared intently ahead of him and looked like he was about to touch cloth.

And I had a storming hangover.

As I say, I was not in the best frame of mind to deal with the state of the apartment.

I lost it. I paced the apartment ranting like Barry Fry after a cup defeat.

'There's no fucking terrace,' I shouted. 'The furniture's fucking gone. The place is fucking filthy. And there's a fucking gas leak. I'm stuck in some wanking shit-hole hotel while you geezers were s'posed to sort it and I find this load of fucking bollocks.'

They didn't answer. By the end of my rant I'd lapsed into cockney and neither Bernadette nor the Tweedles had a clue what I was talking about. They just looked on open-mouthed.

Eventually one of the men said, 'Nice apartment, very nice. Clean, yes,' and continued sweeping up.

I was spared violence by the arrival of the removal men. These two large black Americans spent the first ten minutes moaning that they couldn't park outside and would have to carry everything from the corner. After this they huffed and puffed on every trip, saying things like 'Man, those stairs, man that door, man that walk, man this awkward box, man that crazy dog'.

Eventually I realized their game. They were after a tip – the hazards being pointed out as the value-added element that deserved a gratuity. This continued until I heard a loud splintering crash on the stairs followed by shouting and swearing. Finally they hauled in my favourite antique chest, with the wrapping torn and the wood smashed along the edge. Fucking great – now these fucking clowns had buggered my pride and joy.

To my amazement they denied it.

43

'No sir, that weren't us, no. No, no, no. Hell, no. It was like that in the truck. Yep, yep, yep. Yep, yep. Mmmm yep.'

The two of them – muscular giants with arms like tree trunks and necks you could ride a tank over – stood looking sheepish and guilty. They stared at the floor.

Jesus Christ – now I had four naughty schoolchildren denying patently observable facts.

What a welcome to New York, although it was only the beginning. After the goons had departed Bernadette used the loo, naturally locking the door so this pervy-looking English guy wouldn't burst in. We then went shopping to return an hour or so later. By now I was desperate for a slash but the bathroom door was locked – from the inside. Bernadette hadn't released the doorlock and it had bolted when she closed the door behind her.

With my bladder ready to explode I hopped about like a man on hot coals. I considered using the sink but doubted Bernadette would be impressed so I knocked up the neighbours. I prayed for the early formalities to be brief enough to stop me wetting myself. But, of course, this is New York where madmen stalk every corner and you trust nobody – especially a guy with a strange accent and with his hand tightly gripping something in his trouser pocket. But they didn't mind a bit and it broke the ice in the most charming way.

Keith and Liz were from Michigan. They'd recently moved in and his parents were staying the weekend, so we now had two burly Midwesterners who loved nothing more than a manly problem like a door locked from the inside. The tools were out and the two of them were racing for a solution as if against *The Krypton Factor* clock. They had the hinges off before you could say 'all Englishmen are fuckwits.'

If only the landlady could have shared the spirit. This

frail old woman had actually flirted with me when we first met, touching my arm, fluttering her eyelashes and cooing at my accent. This lasted until I moved in. She then mutated into the wicked witch of the Upper West Side.

The bitch told me, 'You're welcome to repair the window yourself' – meaning she wouldn't – and on the gas leak she was less generous.

'The leak could have only been started by someone moving the stove,' she said. 'And as it wasn't Serge [the brainy sweeper] it must have been you. It's therefore your responsibility.'

I couldn't believe it. This crazy old hag had promised me a terrace and nice furniture and had delivered a broken window, an insecure door, a gas leak and furniture not fit for a wino to piss on. I went mental. I poured forth such a stream of pure Anglo-Saxon she must have thought a marauding longboat had moored up under Brooklyn Bridge.

'Mend that fucking window, secure that fucking door and repair that fucking gas leak or I'll tear up the fucking lease and get such a pack of fucking lawyers on the case you won't know what fucking hit you.'

The threat of lawyers was enough, although no doubt the swearing helped. She mutated back into a frail old lady and said, 'You're obviously very angry about this. I'll send Serge round.'

If we ever ended up in court it was clear who'd come out looking like a granny-bashing head case.

God's gazebo

No city is so in your face as New York. It's so *There*. Whether viewed from a distance or from within the glass

45

canyon streets of Manhattan there isn't a yard of it that doesn't grab you by the collar and say, 'Hey busta you're in *Noo Yoirk* now, yanno wat I'm saying?'

This starts with the first journey in from the airport. Manhattan rises from the suburban sprawl like a distant craggy mountain. Rather it's two craggy mountains with two peaks. Downtown is topped by the dual square chunks of the World Trade Center, while the Midtown peak, about three miles north, is New York's spire – the Empire State Building. And like other mountain ranges there are smaller satellite peaks. Downtown has the bland Chase Plaza and the Gothic Woolworth as apostles to the World Trade Center. In Midtown the Empire State falls away to the sleek point of the Chrysler, the broad slope of Citicorp and the ragged cliff of the old Pan Am Building.

Closer in, the pale blue waters of the Hudson and East rivers become visible. Manhattan now looks more like an exotic volcanic island – the smouldering steam from the larger buildings warning of new eruptions. It could even be a massive ship moored up to Brooklyn by the fat ropes of the bridges and waiting for the signal to glide out into the Atlantic.

Whatever the comparison, it doesn't look real. People can't surely work and live and walk their dog on what looks like a scale model of a city. Any minute some obsessive school-teachery giant is going to kneel on Long Island and plonk down a skyscraper he completed on the kitchen table or lift up the Statue of Liberty for a bit of a polish.

He must have been proud of Liberty, although he may worry it's a little out of scale – he was given it early on by a friend. Still, he's placed it far enough offshore for its size not to look too cumbersome and it makes the harbour look magnificent. She stands guard over the entrance to the city, her arm raised like an Arsenal defender on his way to a toga party. Imagine that sight after a rough crossing on an immigrant steamboat. You'd be so inspired you'd work day and night the rest of your life – as well as appeal to the ref for offside.

Once on Manhattan all changes. The most common way to get to the island is by tunnel. You emerge, not in the chaos and noise you'd expect, but in a relatively peaceful grid of streets. The surprise is due to the limited routes onto Manhattan. This concentrates the traffic into a series of bad-tempered entrances. It's like walking into a department store. The crowds at the entrance immediately disperse through the grid of perfume counters.

The impact of the skyscrapers is also diminished at close range. The landmarks of New York aim to be noticed from a distance and concentrate their features above the sixtieth floor. At ground level the front doors all look the same and you walk by with little consideration. And rubbernecking to see the tops is the quickest way to reveal you're a tourist.

Not that I minded one bit. During my early days in New York I happily skipped along with my head skyward. I'd become so absorbed with the rooftop scenery that I'd occasionally knock into hot-dog stands or collide with a lamp post.

But New Yorkers never look up, oh no. They hustle about like ants on the forest floor, ignoring the magnificence above them. And their reluctance to look up, as well as the sheer density of the skyscrapers, results in many fantastic buildings having the recognition factor of a Tory shadow minister.

Buildings that would be the symbol of lesser cities sit ignored and forlorn in New York. Take the Worldwide Plaza on Eighth Avenue. The building rises to a noble black Gothic summit from a broad brown base. It's as if the architect was tapping the flat end of a pencil looking for inspiration when his eyes paused on the tip. Yet nine out of ten New Yorkers couldn't identify it.

In fact one out of ten ain't bad. Some Midtown buildings aren't recognized by the people that work in them. Sixty-five East 55th Street is the uninspiring name of a smooth neo-Egyptian stack that deceptively folds in towards the top in an easy, majestic manner. It's a blue glass treat that would be a must-see sight in London. In New York you could show a picture of it to the janitor and he'd probably deny all knowledge.

Downtown is equally endowed with knock-your-socks-off buildings. There are four dark versions of Canary Wharf on the Hudson River waterfront. They're about the same height and are clearly by the same architect, yet they nestle in the shadow of the twin towers of the World Trade Center like children on an outing. They are all but ignored, except by me.

I couldn't be mature and blasé about New York – it was too visually exciting. Every meeting in Manhattan would challenge my attention. The view from Downtown or Midtown offices onto these canyons of glass took my breath away. To me it looked like the skyscrapers' graveyard. Towers from past epochs sat in shabby dereliction, their gilded features faded and crumbling. Others appeared fashioned like French chateaux of the Loire or German castles of the Rhine that had journeyed to Manhattan for their final resting place.

Different buildings amazed me for different reasons: the intimate carvings of the Woolworth, the elliptic curve of the Lipstick, the Chesterfield top of the AT&T (now Sony), the brutal vertical lines of the Rockefeller and the classic chrome arcs of the Chrysler. I soaked them up and revised them like French verbs.

The view could be so distracting that in meetings I quickly learnt to position myself with my back to the window. It took all my willpower, but it had to be done. The final straw was a meeting held Downtown. It took place in a boardroom with a fine view over the harbour. I was dreamily watching a silent ferry cruise by the Statue of Liberty when I realized I was talking. An expectant audience had listened to two of my three points and I no longer had a clue about the third.

But bugger it – I couldn't help but get excited. I had lunch at the top of JP Morgan at 60 Wall Street, itself one of the handsomest new buildings on Earth. As we ate, mist enveloped the city below leaving only the top of the 40 Wall Street skyscraper visible – a Gothic 1930s' palace of banking with a fairy-tale pinnacle roof. It sat on the clouds like God's gazebo. I'd never seen anything like it. My companion shrugged it away with a comment about traffic in the rain but I was enthralled. I didn't expect Superman to appear – I expected angels.

Relax, dammit

New Yorkers never live on a street – they live on a corner. Ask for an address and they'll answer 'third and forty-second' or 'Lex and ninety-sixth'. My corner was Central Park West and eighty-eighth. This was a cool corner – it included the world's most famous city park.

Central Park is Manhattan's jungle clearing. It's the 'play hard' bit of the New York psyche, with a frenzied beat to match. Nobody's playing at playing here – everyone's relaxing just as hard and fast as they can.

The park is a vast open-air activity centre. Artists paint the lake, traditional dancers twirl the fountain and masseurs tout the paths. Every bench has a poet, every grass bank a singer, every wood a family picnic. There are Tai Chi classes and Asian wedding photo calls. There are

Buddhist prayer meetings and bare-chested men's groups. There are models posing, old men fishing, boaters boating. Add A-Level French and Pottery for Pleasure and it could win a grant as an adult education centre.

But the key activity is sport. Basketball, volleyball, baseball, football, fishing, skating, cycling, chess, tennis, hockey, badminton. All are pursued with New York's usual vigour and all are played to a standard likely to intimidate any happy-go-lucky have-a-go.

African Americans play basketball on dust courts near The Mall. At first glance the games look informal and a free-for-all. But don't even think about joining in. The standard is astonishing. Street kids play ball as if for the Knicks. To be part of it is to know the rhythm of the street and to have the cool posture and poise that's your reward for twenty years of New York living.

But it was the volleyball that was difficult to stop watching. I stood for an hour witnessing a titanic struggle between two all-girl teams. It was a fascinating encounter – helped by the fact that a dozen women not wearing sports bras kept jumping in the air.

The park is bursting with beautiful people, and nowhere is more beautiful than the roller-disco. Again, novices should sit it out as everyone moves in a tight circle and follows a fast, complex dance beat – while wearing wheels. The men are seriously muscled up, with smooth oily chests hidden by the skimpiest of vests, while the women are toned goddesses. All wear buttock-hugging Lycra shorts.

The non-dancing roller-bladers are content with the ten-k loop. This is a road that winds its way round the whole park. At weekends it's closed to traffic and becomes a one-way racing circuit for bladers, cyclists and joggers. On hot Sundays it's packed. Crossing pedestrians have to gingerly pick their way between the onslaught as determined yuppies bear down, ignoring the traffic lights.

This great tide of people, all moving anti-clockwise, only thins out at the top of the park. This isn't due to the northern end being in Harlem, but because the park ends with the Great Hill and there's a tempting track cutting off the climb. Once in the know it's difficult to endure the hilly climax to the park only to greet less knackered runners emerging from the rat-run.

But one of the great mantras of Central Park is that all are welcome and this is especially so on the loop. Even having a baby in tow is no problem. Simply put the little darling in a baby stroller. These are designer tricycle prams with big bicycle wheels, an aerodynamic design and a sharp-looking mother. She jogs the loop while pushing a sleeping sprog.

A significant minority of the roller-bladers are over fifty. The men have Warren Beatty looks and charge round showing off their firm stomachs and hairy shoulders. The women have pony-tailed blonde hair and appear to be eighteen from behind. But they are mere kids compared with some of the joggers. There are plenty of white-haired, crinkly old buggers who look like they should be dribbling their food and wearing incontinence pants – not belting round the park at a pace that shames me.

Central Park isn't all relentless activity. Some of its delights are the hidden recesses where people can sit peacefully and soak up the rays. Small copses open out to enclosed rocky clearings, perfect for posed isolation with a Walkman and a pretentious book of poems. Even the lakes have some isolated shores where women can sunbathe undisturbed.

Most of the sunbathing, however, occurs on the great stretches of grass: the Great Lawn and – my favourite – the Sheep Meadow. This is the singles spot of the park.

Bikinied girl pairs lie on towels strategically placed to scan the widest horizon. Sharking single men encircle them. Both wait for the opening: a stray frisbee, a pecking bird, a noisy beer-seller. Hormones rage behind a cool façade and an unread copy of the *New York Times*.

Even without the bikinis, the Meadow has some of the best views. While other spots reveal West Side apartments rising above the lakes, the Meadow has the Midtown skyscrapers leering over the park like a row of American footballers. The Essex House Hotel is my favourite. Its rooftop sign of simple stand-alone letters is the symbol of this part of Manhattan. The name is a New York attempt at refinement although I can't help imagining pissed-up tarts shouting ''ere Trace' as they stagger back from the disco.

The Sheep Meadow's tendered lawns seem a long way off at the top of the park. The Harlem end has rough patches of grass and no lawns, but, as stated, it isn't a Harlem-gets-the-shit thing. The northern half is genuinely more rugged and natural. Waterfalls cascade over mossy stones as rocky walks of wild flowers lead to small wooden footbridges spanning bubbling brooks. The birds sing, the squirrels rustle and the sun pierces the trees. Only the occasional used condom brings you back to reality.

Such scenery exposes the popular New York myth that Central Park is a totally man-made landscape. Sure, they planted the trees and dug the lakes, but there isn't equipment now that could shift the huge escarpments of granite visible up here, let alone in the 1850s. I expect the only landscaping involved wheelbarrows full of dynamite, a match and a gang of navvies standing well back.

One of the best things about this end of the park is the lack of statues. Victorian America's inferiority complex is on full view lower down. Some of the most obscure characters are awarded statues. Medieval Polish kings, English bards, Scottish poets, even romanticized hunting savages – all honoured with grandiose monuments that look out of place in such a people's park. The most apt monuments reflect the park's democracy. Alice in Wonderland sits on a bronze toadstool and clambering kids make her lap shine. A bronze duck observes a story-telling Hans Christian Andersen, his open book the shiny climbing target. And Balto the husky dog stands proud with a perky tail, although his shiny hind-shanks are slightly disconcerting.

And the buskers haunt the very spots the planners wanted sublime. Rock, jazz or drum bands pound out music across the formal walks and arches. I even saw a Turkish belly-dancing troupe that had acquired a following of dubious middle-aged men. Some bands are so large and informal it seems anyone can join in. They congregate by the fountain for hours on end and create a clamour that thumps around the park, the noise echoing off the distant trees like the beat of an African village rumbling across the savannah.

Oh how those stuffy Victorians wanted to tame the park and turn it into a worthy rectangle for their parading. The skeletons of their pretence linger in the overblown Bethesda Fountain and the straight anal lines of The Mall. But the living soul of New York now dances round them in a thriving, writhing, chanting mass.

The Noddy and Big Ears School of Economics

My banking experience centred on a single product – Receivables. And while I could use box-and-arrow diagrams to make Receivables look as complex as a computer circuit board, it was really very simple. We lent money to someone – 'A' – and someone else – 'B' – paid us back. How 'A' and 'B' reconciled their differences was where the diagrams came in, although even that was pretty simple. 'B' was a customer of 'A' buying the gear or commodities that 'A' produced. But when 'B' took delivery of their purchases they wouldn't pay 'A' – they'd pay us. And that would repay 'A's' loan. Like I say, simple stuff.

'B' would be one of our clients in the West, such as a big oil major. 'A' would be a cash-strapped company in a poor country. In fact 'A' was the sort of company most bankers would cross the road to avoid. But not the Receivables team, oh no. We loved them – as long as they had a 'B' to repay the loan.

But if they didn't, we weren't too worried – we'd pair them up with one of our clients. We were like a dating service. 'Hey, Debbie you should meet this guy: he's a Cancer, he's tall and he likes dancing. Oh, and he produces fifty thousand barrels of oil a day – just your type.'

To date, most of our matchmaking had taken place in Russia with the newly privatized oil companies. And boy, were these companies in a mess. They might have possessed oil reserves worthy of a BP or a Texaco but they had paid no wages in months, no tax in years and no attention to the environment since the day they started drilling for oil.

Not that we worried. The Western oil giants had thrown in their hat in an effort to secure oil supplies, and their presence was our comfort. All the Russians had to do was supply oil to tankers owned by the Western majors. And as the Russians possessed so much oil that they allowed most of it to leak over the countryside, we assumed they could manage this. Then the Western oil giants would ship it to their refineries and pay us the cash that would repay the loan. It was simple, it was clever, it could grow wings and lay eggs.

My primary role in the US was to see if the Receivables product would fly over there. We'd look to Latin America to provide the 'As' and our North American client base to provide the 'Bs'. I couldn't wait. I relished the idea of wandering round Rio and Buenos Aires offering everyone I met lots of money. I'd have the odd meeting, a spot of lunch and then head for the beach to watch some women's volleyball, oh yes.

But I reckoned without Alexander Livshits. This unfortunately named individual wrecked my chances of hanging out on Copacabana Beach. He was Boris Yeltsin's financial adviser, although must have been trained at the Noddy & Big Ears School of Economics. Wherever it was, he'd been taught the best way to finance an economy was to borrow lots of money. And when it came to repayment day on the loans the answer was to borrow some more and meet the payments with the new cash.

Now I used to do this when I was a student with a credit card. I'd use the credit card to withdraw cash from the cash machine and I'd use the cash to meet the minimum payment on the card. I knew it was a dodgy way to run my finances but I had no choice. I had no idea I was following sound patterns of international economics.

Of course I was also following a path to economic self-destruction and even as a smelly student I realized I could only get away with this for a couple of months before the credit card company would work it out and demand more than its own money being handed back to them.

Yet the Russians had been doing it for years. Eventually – in fact soon after I arrived in the States – the lenders demanded some real cash before carrying on the charade. But the Russians said they didn't have any real cash. Well, raise taxes, said the lenders. We've tried that, said the Russians, but parliament kicked it out. And anyway, people won't pay up. Well repay us from your foreign reserves, said the lenders. If we do that, said the Russians, our currency will collapse. See if we care, said the lenders – we want our money or the babushka gets it.

In response the Russians did what they do best. They told the West to go fuck itself and suspended all international loan repayments.

This didn't immediately kill off our Receivables deals. While Russian companies couldn't repay their loans, we were saved because we didn't need them to. 'B' paid off our loans once 'A' had shipped the oil. As long as 'A' wasn't prevented from shipping oil we were safe, weren't we?

But while our structures meant no loss of money in Russia, for now, it would be an optimistic banker, to say the least, that handed the buggers more of the stuff. And not just Russia. Most Third World countries were in hock up to their eyebrows and international lenders, worried the borrowers would think the Russian school of international economics a good idea, were retreating from these loans as fast as their legs would carry them.

Every non-Western country was being hit. Asia had gone, Eastern Europe had collapsed and panic was sweeping Latin America. Brazil was being whacked – just as the volleyball team were preparing for my arrival.

Stay in school. Don't do drugs. Stop killing

I'd been cycling through Harlem every day, and every day the meaning of this graffiti bothered me a little more.

'Stay in school' suggested the message was aimed at kids still in school. 'Don't do drugs' implied they had yet to do drugs. And 'Stop killing' indicated they'd been knocking off people left, right and centre and it was becoming a bit of a pain.

That violence is a casual way of life above 110th Street is a given in New York. Indeed, each time I revealed my eccentric route to work I was offered raised eyebrows and knowing smiles, especially in the office.

And this being America, raised eyebrows consisted of yelling across desks.

'Hey Ted, you heard?' they'd shout. 'This guy cycles through Harlem every day. Is he nuts or wat?'

Then I'd be treated to some anecdote confirming my madness.

'My Uncle Frank knew this guy who got lost in Harlem,' the story would begin, 'and he got blown away. This crazy pulled out a gun and BLAM. Took him out – just like that.'

This is typical. Harlem is regarded with near hysteria by the rest of New York. OK, I assume that someone, at some point, did unexpectedly stumble into Harlem and was shot by a nutter. But, blimey, this guy knew a lot of people. Given how popular he was I wonder what he was doing in Harlem in the first place. I expect he became lost staggering between one of the six parties he was trying to cram in that evening. And they must have held the funeral at Yankee Stadium.

Granted, the area is visually shocking. Many streets do a reasonable impression of Dresden after an RAF visit and plenty of blocks are nothing but weeds. But it doesn't feel dangerous. If anything, much of Harlem feels empty, especially at 7a.m. when I pedal through – supposedly the time when the crack dens are shutting for the night and the police have finally bagged and zipped the last of the slain.

The Connecticut commuter line – hidden below Park Avenue flowerbeds south of 96th Street – passes right over Harlem on its way to Greenwich. And the first stop out of Grand Central is 125th Street, Harlem's main shopping thoroughfare and home of major landmarks such as the Apollo Theater and the Cotton Club.

Not that the Uptown 'reverse commuters' would know. Although most run the one-block gauntlet of begging cup-shakers to the Subway station, some can't even face this. They scurry nervously from the train into the waiting 'gypsy' cabs.

'Upper East Side,' they shout. 'Quick. Don't stop at the lights.' Then they bury themselves in the fading upholstery.

To flag a gypsy cab, just stick your hand in the street. Any Harlem street at any moment. Wiggle it up and down and a car will stop, guaranteed. Drivers giving their mother a lift home from the hospital will turf her out for your fare, or at least stuff her in the trunk.

Gypsy cabs operate in the vacuum left by the yellow cabs – ubiquitous in every other Manhattan district but virtually absent here – presumably because yellow cab drivers all knew Uncle Frank's mate.

Cycling is easily the quickest way to and from the station, as well as the cheapest and healthiest. But it can be dangerous – and not because of lurking gunmen. City Hall seems to have decided that roads in Harlem function just fine without any maintenance whatsoever. In fact they think it fun to dig a hole, slap a badly fitting metal sheet on top and indulge in some collective municipal amnesia.

'Darn it,' they'll say eventually, 'where did I leave that damn hole?'

Once you've negotiated the appallingly pot-holed roads, you have to confront the stairs at 125th Street station. While millions of dollars have been spent restoring Grand Central to reveal its glorious architectural splendour, 125th Street looks like an experiment in bad design and neglect. There's one rusting staircase for each platform and it's so thin two people can barely pass each other. Hauling a bike up and down those stairs each day is not fun, especially when the fat mama from *Tom and Jerry* is trying to go the other way.

And the foot of the stairs is no place to navigate a bike in the evening, when 125th Street has degenerated into bedlam. Cab-grabbers shout for your business and street peddlers sell pathetic wares off blankets. And every store and car throws out hardcore hip-hop. These are pounding rap tracks usually involving politically incorrect nouns glued into incoherent sentences with words like fuck. A typical hip-hop line, therefore, runs something like 'Yeah, yeah, the bitch fucks a nigger and a nigger fucks a cop. Nigger's in the chair while the bitch gets a job.'

But even at night 125th Street seems no more dangerous than the Kingsland Road or Brixton Hill. My only slight concern occurs at the junction of Lenox and 125th, right by Sylvia's Soul Food Restaurant. This is the spot for the Islamic fundamentalists. They stand on tables and shout to the shoppers, usually about the evil of the white man. Yet it's difficult to take them too seriously. It's not what they're saying – it's how they look. They're dressed like extras from *Sinbad the Sailor*, sporting Arabian robes and tasselled headgear. In fact they look more likely to climb on a magic carpet and join the Downtown traffic than cause me problems. And anyway, they're usually fending off some shopping-laden old woman and I pass by unnoticed, able to complete yet another event-free cycle through the world's most notorious neighbourhood. Uncle Frank's mate would be amazed.

Constipated by runner beans

With the Russian default on their loans, market confidence evaporated – and with it the normal practice of international banking.

'Normal practice' is where one banker is the 'Arranger' of a loan and where lots of other banks 'Participate' by lending small chunks of the total amount. So while the cake might say Barclays on the icing, in reality Barclays were lending about 5 per cent of the total and Tom Bank, Dick Bank and Harry Bank carved up the rest. This way if you tripped over the dog and the cake went flying, all the banks suffered but no-one was seriously hurt. It was an unstated rule of the financial markets. You take a slice of my cake and I'll take a slice of yours. But with banks now refusing to take these slices, no-one was going to do any baking for fear of getting stuck with the whole cake while the dog snoozed at the foot of the stairs.

Too bad I'd just baked my first American cake. I'd put $30 million on our books with the aim of selling slices to all our rivals back in London. It was my début American Receivables deal and was intended to consolidate our cake stall in the US market.

In fact it wasn't my cake at all – it was just a large slice of someone else's and I was selling even smaller slices to banks back home. For this service a bank is normally given some ego-soothing pseudo title like Co-Lead Arranger that sounds good but in reality means 'mug that stumped up more cash than the others'. But I intended creaming off some of the interest rate, for services rendered, and selling the lot to small European banks, mostly German regional savings societies. We'd end up with nothing, fulfilling the basic investment banking criteria of lending other people's money.

The deal was classic Receivables. Our 'A' was a Brazilian company that produced soya beans and shipped them to the US. Our 'B' was a big American soya-bean processor that paid us for the beans once they'd docked in the States – thus repaying the loan.

Our Credit Approval department had little argument with the deal. They could see all the 'As' and 'Bs' and knew that within weeks we'd have no risk as we'd have sold the lot to other banks. The only hitch in the approval process was when someone asked, 'So, how are soya beans grown?'

All eyes fell on me. Hmmm – beans. All I could think of was the runner-bean field adjacent to my childhood home in Essex. It was a series of vines growing up string and cane frames through which we used to race, wrecking the farmer's crop while wallowing in jungle-war fantasies.

So I substituted the word runner for soya and described the runner-bean field. I banged on about the vines, the thick green pods and the pale speckled beans. Eventually someone asked, 'Did we get all the financial statements?' and the debate moved on. I sat back, amazed. It's the only time in my life I've wanted to thank my parents for a rural Essex upbringing.

We signed over the money and were poised to sell down to our range of Co-Lead Managers – or whatever fancy title we'd invented for them. But at that very moment the Livshits hit the fan and the Russians defaulted. The loan market closed as fast as the white vans could reverse, load up and belt off.

Now, to be stuck with something that cannot be sold, even at a loss, is an investment banker's worst nightmare. And our new American masters looked on in horror as I failed to sell a cent of the deal into the market. It didn't look like chicken from where they were

61

sitting. It looked like two all-beef patties, lettuce, cheese, special sauce, pickles, onions in a sesame seed bun – with fries.

But the global financial apocalypse was not the only reason the deal wouldn't sell. A couple of the German regionals were mad enough to still be interested, secure from the chaos in their wholesome little towns with buxom Fräuleins pouring jugs of frothy yellow beer. But, being German, they wanted financial information on every party in the transaction: the soya producers, the buyers, the tractor driver, the processor's factory cat, the lot.

A fair request until delivered to the treasurer of the borrowing company – a man who had obviously learnt his English from watching *The Sweeney*. 'Bastard,' he shouted down the phone in a heavy Brazilian accent. 'I just don't believe it. This is why I didn't want bastard banks in the deal. I only wanted banks I could trust, banks I knew. Not bastards that would sell a little piece here and a little piece there. We are a private company,' he continued, 'and I don't want any bastard bank going over our figures. They will go straight to the bastard competition.'

With that the Germans declined and went off to the beer haus to chat up the chunky Fräuleins and order some sausages.

I became desperate. I tried any connection I could think of. I tried the Portuguese banks, because they spoke Brazil's language, and Spanish banks, because they nearly did, and Italian banks, because it was all the same sort of language really, wasn't it? I tried the Argentinian banks, because they must like their neighbours, and Mexican banks, because they eat a lot of soya, I think, and Miami banks because they liked Latin America, didn't they?

Not a bean. I was stuffed.

The road to Mountain-mart

Mandy and I developed a telephone ritual. My first job on arrival at work was to ring her. It wasn't soppy shit, it was more like ticking the register at school. 'Still here, still alive, haven't packed you in yet.'

And within a week of my arrival she started talking about her 'first' visit. I made a casual suggestion about a late-August drive to Vermont and wham: holiday booked, tickets bought and swimwear purchased before I could say, 'I only half meant it.'

I hadn't the heart to tell her Vermont had mountains, not beaches.

My task was to hire a car and drive to Greenwich, where Mandy would join me at the end of the day. She arrived at the Greenwich office around 7p.m. looking as gorgeous as ever, if a little ruffled by the journey. One thing I loved about Mandy was her ability to look apprehensive and vacant at the same time. It always stirred my loins and after six weeks and a zero on the scoreboard I couldn't wait to find a hotel – although I'd promised myself we'd make it to Vermont that night.

With hormones raging the drive seemed that much more of a drag. Once away from the coast the roads are dead straight and stretch for horizon after horizon of unused countryside, punctuated by the occasional neat New England town.

The only break from the boredom comes from the trucks. These monsters rumble by at eighty miles an hour and seem to suck your car under their thundering loads. Yet even travelling at scary speeds they are seriously cool. They have chrome exhausts that look like pipe organs and lovingly painted engine hoods – so much nicer than the lorries back home.

Between trucks I searched in vain for a radio station not playing 1970s' super-hits. Having failed I bored Mandy by musing about the place names. It seems the pilgrims named every town after the one they'd left back in England. And while this must have led to some confusing conversations it also led to some surreal New England geography. Signs tell you that Sunderland is a couple of exits on from Northampton, Enfield is just before Windsor and while you go right for Colchester and Norwich, this is via Glastonbury and Manchester.

But even that killed only thirty minutes and I was soon too bored and too horny to carry on. We'd got as far as the Vermont-Massachusetts border and that was enough for one drive. We decided to look in the road atlas for a nice place to stop.

And it was here that I finally lost patience with US road atlases. They are organized on an alphabetic state-by-state basis, rather than the UK method of having the country mapped out on continuing pages. While I'm sure the publishers find it convenient to place Georgia next to Hawaii it's fucking annoying when trying to drive from Connecticut to Vermont, via Massachusetts. You have to change page at the end of each state with only a vague idea where the new state is located. This is aggravated by certain clumps of states being banded together on one map, forcing you into a guessing game to discover the publishers' whimsical state-bundling policy. Vermont is found under New Hampshire as if it were simply a poxy add-on of a state, and Massachusetts is found under Connecticut, even though Massachusetts is the largest state in the region while Connecticut is no larger than Kent.

Also, the atlas changes tack occasionally and decides to have a few pages of city maps before going back to the states. Not that you care by then – the fucking thing's gone out the window.

So we guessed where to get off and plunged straight into a soulless strip of motels and super-stores. All the motels looked seedy. They had signs with blown bulbs, wonky letters, faded paint and crap names like Shangri-La. And all the stores were called something mart: K-mart, Wallmart, Petmart, Babymart, Martmart. I suggested we drive on but Mandy became excited by the idea of a genuine US motel, like in *Thelma & Louise*, and we decided to pitch up.

I was quite happy to hit the bed straight away but Mandy said no. She wanted a shower, some food and for me to treat her like something other than a sex object. I figured this would take an hour. But we couldn't find a single bar serving food and all the restaurants had closed, despite it being no later than 9p.m. Only the Exxon garage remained open, so our evening meal ended up consisting of tortilla chips and salsa eaten in front of a badly tuned TV.

It was hardly hors d'oeuvres for a major sesh, but it had been too long to let such irritations clutter our mood, or my lust. We moved onto the bed and fed the chips to each other, with dirty food snogs in between. I then decided that the salsa should really be eaten from Mandy's belly button – forget the chips. Then I thought the correct way to eat it must be a dab on each nipple. Finally I thought bollocks to the salsa.

You've got a mighty pretty mouth, boy

State law requires Vermont men under forty to grow a large bushy beard that sprawls down to their chests. State law also dictates that the bearded ones wear denim

65

dungarees, usually patterned by machine oil, paint and any other shit they can find. Of course state law says nothing of the kind; there are just so many hippies in Vermont you'd think it was the world's first fundamentalist hippieocracy. Beneath the filth and the mass of facial hair they look healthy and sound well educated – they just act like extras from *Deliverance*.

The women fail to hide their suburban middle-class roots so effectively. They may also sport dungarees and have long unkempt hair but they have no beard to hide their clear skin and straight teeth and they cannot disguise their natural beauty behind unshaven legs and hairy armpits. And, anyway, you get the feeling they'll grow up and marry an accountant on their thirtieth birthday.

I'd been told the state was developing an air of sophistication thanks to the number of ski resorts favoured by New York professionals. In summer, however, it was as redneck as a hog in a heatwave. Pick-up trucks rattled along hill-country lanes with dogs standing proudly on the tailgate. The trucks sported bumper stickers with statements such as 'If I wanted to listen to an asshole I'd fart', and other pearls of intellect unlikely to have Oscar Wilde roaring at a dinner party.

The general stores also revealed Vermont as an evolutionary laggard. More a barn than a store – with open timber ceilings and rough plank floors – they were usually run by an inbred-looking couple wearing those ubiquitous dungarees. An unshaven old man eyed you from the corner while tugging on a corncob pipe and a dopey looking kid spent the whole time staring as if you'd just sprouted a second head.

The irony is that the locals are concerned their lifestyle is being corrupted by townies searching for a rural idyll. Oh yeah – if it stops them shagging their sisters they should treat it as a blessing.

But an idyll it is. Our favourite pastime became searching for swimmable waterfalls (Mandy was determined to use her new swimsuit). We'd follow the bubbling rivers upstream, passing through steep wooded canyons and timber-roofed river bridges. Eventually we'd come across a few parked VW camper vans and we'd know – follow the path down to the river and there'd be a clutch of hippies swimming in their dungarees.

The falls were never spectacular and had occasionally been spoilt by graffiti but the sparkling clear water was a delight, even if very cold. To swim right up to the falls required a major effort as the current became stronger the closer to them you swam. Eventually you had to swim for your life just to stay put and the slightest pause sent you careering back.

I quickly realized that the joy of actually swimming under the falls was beyond me, although it wasn't beyond the hippie kids. They'd come at it the other way, floating downstream to plunge over with a delighted '*whoo-eeee*'. Oh to have been given this as a childhood playground rather than a garage door and a runner-bean field.

The other major summer Vermont pastime is hiking. We eagerly approached a log cabin information centre on the edge of one of the national forests. The bright-eyed assistant was over-helpful. 'This walk goes via the Jobby Falls and takes two days,' she enthused. 'Or this one goes to the Dodah Hump Thingy and can be done in around fourteen hours.'

Was she taking the piss or what? Did we look like we were geared up for a two-day trek through the wilderness? Were the fucking Sherpas outside or something?

'Err, we were thinking around an hour,' I said.

She looked crestfallen.

'Ohh,' she snapped. 'Well the track here leads to a woodshed. That takes about an hour.'

Well that's the one for us, then.

Vermont's gentle mountains rippled into the misty distance like an unmade bed. It was an enormous, featureless landscape – an undulating ocean of tree-tops smothering the detail below. But the trouble with hidden detail is that my imagination fills the void, and my void soon became filled with fugitives. America is full of nutters and the real psycho-babble brigade will have completely lost it and headed for the hills. And these were the hills. They'd be armed to the teeth and unlikely to welcome visitors.

Then I remembered the bears, snakes, wild cats and all the other hostile creatures that hang out in American forests. And what about the insects – handing out fatal diseases that force you to spend the brief period before your painful death crapping into a colostomy bag?

I was rapidly going off this forest. This wasn't a friendly stroll in the woods like in England, with the occasional squirrel or robin, and ending with a duck pond, a car park and a pint of Abbott Ale in The Jolly Foresters Inn.

Within twenty minutes I was a nervous wreck. Every creak of a swaying tree, every snap or breezy rustle, every buzz of an insect or twitter of a bird sent a shudder of concern rippling through me.

Mandy didn't notice. 'These woods are boring' was her view, so I agreed to turn back – making lots of 'I'm doing you a big favour' noises.

Mandy wasn't here to walk in the woods or swim in waterfalls. She was here to shag me senseless. And we pitched up at a picturesque weatherboard farmhouse B&B with the intention of doing little more than having a quick bite before indulging in all sorts of strange sex. She'd bought two bottles of duty-free Veuve Clicquot, we borrowed a couple of glasses, opened one in the bedroom and tucked in to get us in the mood.

I was soon feeling pretty amorous and tried to

persuade Mandy into giving me a champagne blow job –
I'd read about them in a novel and was curious to say the
least. But Mandy said she wanted to eat first. She said
she always preferred sex after dinner and that she didn't
find my response about getting her chops around this
very amusing. We had a playful cuddle on the bed with
me hopeful of bringing her round to the idea of pre-
dinner nuptials but Mandy stood firm – as did I.

The first bottle disappeared in no time and we pol-
ished off most of the second as well, leaving just enough
for the blow-job later. Then we staggered down to dinner.

Only one other, very sober couple occupied the dining
room.

We said 'Good evening' and smiled, probably a little
too dopily as their stares lingered while we clattered into
the table and sat down heavily.

'Would you like a drink before dinner, sir, madam?'
said the matronly-looking owner.

'Yes please. Sherry,' I demanded.

Mandy turned her nose up.

'No, it's lovely stuff,' I protested. 'Had it in Spain –
luvverly jubberly.'

Mandy started giggling.

'Luvverly jubberly, luvverly jubberly,' I repeated at the
top of my voice.

'Ssshhhh,' she hissed.

The owner seemed a little uncomfortable with our
behaviour and kept glancing over at the other dining
pair, who were clearly on their way to the 'Hang All Loud
Drunk Idiots' rally up in Nuremberg, New Hampshire.

The sherry was duly demolished. We ordered a bottle
of wine with the dinner, two further glasses to keep us
topped up during dessert and rounded it off with a couple of ports. We then staggered upstairs for our great
sesh.

Mandy was wearing her sexiest underwear and she

69

stripped me naked before lying me on my back to give me the champagne blow job. I lay back and relaxed – ready to accept my jollies like a rock star after a concert.

'What the—' I woke with a jerk.

'I don't believe you,' shouted Mandy, hitting me. 'You've fallen asleep. I've never been so insulted in all my life.'

She pushed me to one side, climbed under the covers and wouldn't speak to me until morning.

SEPTEMBER

Latino girls and Guido men

For the last day of Mandy's visit we decided to head back to New York and explore Coney Island, one of the great temples of Americana.

The train emptied at a scruffy suburban terminal and large gangs of lumpy people waddled down foul-smelling tiled corridors towards the main road and the funfairs beyond. The street must have been one of the shabbiest on Earth. Not a single shop looked capable of withstanding a minor gale and most were selling utter shite such as unlikely looking sections of household plumbing or suspiciously stained mattresses.

Between this street and the beach were two rival funfairs – one dominated by a roller coaster and the other by a big wheel. A third plot sat abandoned. This was also dominated by a roller coaster now broken and rusting, and proving an excellent trellis for ivy. In fact the whole plot was so overgrown and hauntingly quiet next to the noise and colour of the living funfairs that it looked incredibly spooky – the perfect set for a million episodes of *Scooby Doo*.

The working funfairs had everything you'd expect from such places: bumper cars, waltzers, ghost rides, silly rotating spaceships on sticks, shooting galleries,

71

throwing galleries, hooping galleries, hot-dog sellers, candyfloss sellers, shit T-shirt sellers. They also had lots of gangs – hard black and Latino youths – who smooched around with exaggerated tough-but-cool walks. They wore baggy Tommy Hilfiger and had bizarre patterns razorcut into their cropped hair, bumfluff moustaches, double earrings, back-to-front baseball caps and raucous voices.

Coney Island also had two types of gum-clicking girl gangs – pretty girls who clattered around in high heels, tight mini-skirts and tight tops with their arms folded below their breasts and their eyes scanning for boys, and bigger girls who wore figure-hugging black leggings and huffed around like cattle on the range. These girls were hard and mean and they so scared the hell out of me I nervously clutched Mandy's arm at their approach.

To avoid the gangs we decided to have a go on the roller coaster. And it was here that we came across that global breed, the funfair-ride operators. They looked just like the tattooed skinhead boys and fat-gut dads in Southend or Clacton but spoke in pure Brooklyn 'fuck yoo' accents instead of the ''ow's yer farver' *Luuunden* I was half expecting.

The roller coaster was run by an especially fat dad. He was so gross his stomach could no longer cope and the fat tumbled down his legs in grotesque rolls. He sat joking with his sons and throwing banter at passers-by, all the time swearing like a navvy, his stomach and legs wobbling with his jollity.

We clanked up the steep slope with me paying little attention to the ride. I was still fascinated by the abandoned roller coaster and an adjacent rusting steel tower that looked like a helipad on stilts. I'd read about the vast funfairs of old Coney Island but I wasn't expecting to see the abandoned corpse of one laid out beside me. As we slowed near the top the sheer size of the plot became apparent. I couldn't understand why it hadn't been redeveloped. I also remembered I was on a roller coaster.

It slid over the top with a powerful lurch. My stomach decided to stay put as the rest of me careered south. My facial features became floppy and seemed to flap about with my hair. Flashes of blurred light and colour shook by.

I felt sick.

We hit the bottom and veered sideways – the flimsy car surely inadequate protection against me tumbling out. My only response was to repeat, 'Oh fuck, oh fuck, oh *fuuucck.*'

Life became very simple. All I wanted was for this fucking thing to stop.

It started a second loop and momentarily slowed. My stomach caught up with the rest of me and my face stopped flapping around – for a second – before we plunged down again and I resumed my 'oh fuck' mantra.

After an age, the car shuddered to a stop. Peeling my hands from the bar I tried to ease my stomach by concentrating on something very still ahead of me. I avoided looking at the fat guy. It worked and I was spared the humiliation of the public hurl – just.

I climbed from the car a shaken man and said through gritted teeth, 'Let's head for the beach.'

Only the British and Americans can bugger up beach resorts this well, and Coney Island wins the prize. It's beyond tacky – it's mind-blowingly trashy. The boardwalk is lined with foul-smelling food joints and stalls that give new meaning to the words 'cheap' and 'shit'.

Drunks staggered from counter to counter arguing with the fixed-featured workers. And these drunks weren't the gangs of happy-but-like-a-fight thugs you see in Blackpool. These drunks were real professionals. They had beaten-up faces, big red noses and music-hall walks.

73

They clung to the bars or lay flat out on the many benches, their bare chests revealing sagging skin and fading tattoos.

But the drunks didn't make it to the beach. The wide stretch of golden sand was surprisingly clean and dipped gently to clear blue water – visible through the crowds that stretched away into the distance like a whole nation awaiting a biblical migration in their swimwear.

There must have been several hundred thousand people on the sand, milling about in tight little knots and all experiencing their own little dramas.

The Latinos appeared to be in family units. They surrounded a radio broadcasting jerky, brassy salsa tunes. Posing Latino girls wiggled around in g-string bikini bottoms while women a little older shouted at their kids. Adolescent boys called to the girls in Spanish and beckoned them over. Dads lay on their stomachs and watched.

But they were a minority. Italian-Americans dominated the beach. Bernadette had told me that everyone in New York calls Italian-Americans Guidos. And Guido man's natural habitat is the beach, where he can display his over-muscular chest, copious chest wig, and his greased-back hair.

Coney Island had lots of Guido men. They strutted around the beach like peacocks, flexing muscles and clenching buttocks at any passing female. Guido man wears only very tight Speedo trunks, has the stance of a gorilla and the mouth movements of a bison.

Whatever the ethnic edge to the beach the occupants had one feature in common – the gear. Each family appeared to possess enough equipment for the liberation of Europe. Cool boxes, low-slung chairs, inflatables, windbreaks, mats, umbrellas, flags – it must have taken all morning to load the car. I'm surprised they didn't bring a coffee table and some rugs. They did bring the hi-fi and the occasional small TV, usually broadcasting a baseball game.

Despite all the noise of the beach and boardwalk, Coney Island does have a relaxing side. The pier is a no-frills extension of the boardwalk and remains a peaceful sanctuary for walkers and fishermen. And both are wide enough to avoid the worst of the crowds.

Mandy and I strolled the boardwalk like contented lovers. We watched the karaoke and laughed at the wrecked renditions of Motown favourites from the bikinied singer as she writhed around furiously to an audience of admiring men. It looked like *Opportunity Knocks* at an open-air Stringfellows. And we stopped for chilli dogs at the famous Nathan's stall – although their fame didn't make them taste any less disgusting.

Mandy and I knew this was our last day for a while and she held my hand that little bit tighter. We had yet to solve the great questions about our relationship. Were we a couple? Was I still her boyfriend? Was I allowed to shag anything that moved in New York?

We avoided the subject and she departed the next morning in tears and with our time together unsullied by big issues such as the impracticality of it all.

Sex on tap

Back in Manhattan and with Mandy safely in London, I decided to hit the town with an Australian colleague and Upper West Side neighbour. Barry was the most laid-back banker in the Northern Hemisphere and not keen on New York's ability to turn an evening drink into a stressful experience. And our first port of call couldn't have been more intense.

We thought Drip was just an ordinary bar-cum-coffee

shop when we first walked in. It certainly looked normal enough. It had beaten-up armchairs and sofas and Formica tables, like a sixth-form common room or a youth hostel sitting room. Yet no-one seemed relaxed. Couples were engaged in over-smiley conversations, as if at a posh cocktail party, while single-sex groups were busily filling in forms.

At first I thought we'd walked in on a quiz night but everyone was concentrating so hard on these forms that the night's quiz paper must have been the Harvard entrance exam. Then I noticed the ring binders. Folders labelled 'Women Seeking Men' and 'Men Seeking Women' were stacked on all the low tables. Barry made for the door, but I begged him to stay.

The questionnaires asked you to describe your ideal partner and tick whether looks 'matter', 'don't matter', or 'matter but shouldn't'. Of course, everyone in the binders was trying to sound like a nice person but nobody wanted to end up on a date with someone looking like a constipated baboon, so the 'matter but shouldn't' statement was almost universally chosen.

You also had to describe your perfect weekend. No-one had written, 'sex on the beach with someone I fancy'. Instead they put, 'relaxing with friends, dining out, theatre,' and other neutral shite.

It was entertaining stuff and Barry and I spent half an hour chuckling our way through the folders. We stopped to find two women smiling at us from across the coffee table.

'Are you from *Great* Britain?' one of them asked, ''cos your accent's so neat.'

Blimey, it was true. American women do love the accent. Barry kept quiet about his nationality – so as not to confuse matters – and I put on the best Eton, Oxford and the Guards voice I could muster.

'Oh yes,' I said in an aloof tone. 'The United Kingdom

of Great Britain and Northern Ireland, to give it its correct title. Are you, perchance, from the Republic of the United States of America?'

They giggled like flirty schoolgirls.

'So have you found anyone you like?' I asked.

'Well, not in the folders,' one fluttered back, oh yes.

That came from the small one. She went especially gooey when I spoke. She was called Zoe and had the sweetest face and the straightest long blond hair. She also looked the type to completely fall for the Hugh Grant charms of an Englishman, so I laid it on thick for ten minutes while Barry shot me the odd bemused look.

I suggested dinner somewhere nice at the weekend and said she should buy me flowers to make the date especially romantic. I was in full Hugh Grant mode and Zoe loved it. She left happy she hadn't had to pick a date with someone who'd written 'looks matter but shouldn't' and whose ideal weekend involved the theatre.

I also filled in a form. I ticked 'looks matter' but made amends by describing my perfect weekend as 'an old country cottage, a roaring fire, a good red wine and a woman in my arms.'

That should get them sliding off their seats.

Of course, the system is geared to make you use the bar. If chosen, Drip rings and you visit to check the form of the interested party. If you like what you read they set up a date – at the bar. It was a great idea and within days I had two dates in two nights – Zoe on Saturday and someone called Sarah on Sunday. By Sunday night my New York cherry should have been well and truly popped.

Zoe and I corrupted the system and met for dinner at the restaurant beneath her Midtown apartment. She looked lovely and wasn't the slightest bit annoyed I was five minutes late. She just smiled and handed me my flowers. Zoe was remarkably good company and we even secretly took the piss out of the waiter. On hearing my accent he boasted about also being European. He said he was Croatian, although he sounded like he came from Zagreb, Pennsylvania to me. He assumed we were both visitors and wished us a good flight when we left, which had us laughing all the way up her stairs.

So there I was, in Zoe's apartment – with Zoe's roommate. And blimey, were these two enemies. Zoe had complained over dinner that she was a bitch and her joy evaporated as the sour-faced cow continued to watch TV rather than evacuate the living room. We ended up in the stairwell and only managed a quick snog.

Never mind, I arranged to see her again and, besides, it was Sarah on Sunday – a woman who had described herself as 'very beautiful' and agreed that 'looks matter'. She obviously liked my arrogance.

I spent Sunday trying not to think about the date. But the words 'very beautiful' kept appearing in my head. Anyone who could describe herself as very beautiful was obviously seriously confident. I needed to look my best.

With three hours to go I started getting ready. I had a bath and a shave and put on too much aftershave. I washed my face to get it off. Then I put on some more.

I tried on all sorts of clothes combinations. I opted for laid-back jeans and a Euro-style, sophisticated, open-necked dark-blue shirt. I changed my mind and put on chinos and a polo shirt.

I wished I'd had a haircut. I nearly bolted for the barbers but changed my mind, remembering that it looks terrible for the first fortnight after a cut. So I washed it, blow-dried it, thought it looked too bouffanty, and wet it again to let it drip dry.

Then I thought the chinos were too scruffy and put on a pair of Hackett trousers – *Essential British Kit* and all that – but they'd developed a dodgy crease so I went back to the jeans and the relaxed look.

I cleaned my teeth twice, gargled with Listerine,

worried I'd smell of Listerine and not aftershave, so put on a bit more aftershave. Then I fanned my face so the smell would dissipate.

After a last-minute shoe faff I realized I looked shit and was wearing the wrong gear.

I eventually left the apartment at five to seven and had to jog to Drip to make it on time. I arrived puffing and with my hair fully bouffanted from the wind. I was nervous as hell.

Sarah stood coolly by the bar wearing scruffy jeans, sneakers and a T-shirt. She also had some shopping. She greeted me as if being introduced to someone at work. Then she pointed at the drinks board behind the bar, indicating we'd better get something. I stood nodding furiously, oh yes, we'd better get something. It took a moment for the penny to drop. *I* had better get something.

'Oh, er, what would you like?'

She said something that sounded like, 'Blahdeblah tea.'

'Sorry?'

'Blahdeblah tea.'

'Er, sorry.'

She smiled thinly and told the guy serving. She said it very clearly the third time, determined that he wasn't going to miss it and I'd feel a complete arse. But it still sounded odd, like 'Ham and pickle tea', or something.

'And what would you like?' she asked, completely taking over.

'Oh, I'll have the same,' I said. 'It sounds very interesting.'

'You won't like it,' she said firmly.

'No, no. It sounds great.'

I tried to inject some levity into my voice but it was gone. I came across like a little boy caught wanking by the matron.

After several evolutionary eras, two pink iced teas arrived and we tried to find a seat. But Sunday night was obviously top meet-new-date-at-Drip night because the only seats were at the back where a gang of loud Americans were whooping along to a New York Giants game.

We sat down and tried to have a conversation, although it was noisy and she spoke very quietly, which seemed to be part of this cool persona she was trying to project. Sure she was pretty but her face showed so little emotion that her beauty was lost. She looked stern and disapproving, like a Victorian governess.

She talked about work and I quickly realized the part of my form she'd read with most interest was the line 'investment banker'. She was checking me out for cash. But I was reluctant to talk too deeply about work because it wasn't hot-shot stockbroking or bond trading. Instead I rambled on about doing deals in Russia and trailed off when I noticed she wasn't listening. It was all going very badly. This disgusting tea didn't help.

After five minutes I asked the fatal question.

'Why did you choose me?'

'Oh, I can't remember your form,' she said dismissively. 'You were one of about five I picked and expect to meet.'

Oh burst my fucking balloon why don't you?

Then she looked at my watch.

I was wearing a $10 fake Tag from one of New York's ubiquitous fake-gear sellers, having mislaid my real watch. Not only was it an obvious fake, the Tag badge on the face had come loose and was now stuck on the underside of the glass at a crazy angle. It didn't seem to interfere with the hands so I was happy for it to stay – but it proved the last straw for Ms Wannabe Rockefeller. 'I have to go Downtown to meet a friend,' she said. 'Now.'

'Oh,' I said shocked, and like an idiot, asked, 'What shall we do?'

What do you mean what should we do? You should take the hint, tell the money-grabbing bitch to go hang and get pissed in front of the TV. That's what you should do.

But no, I asked for her number.

'I don't give out my number,' she replied curtly.

She should have added, 'at least, not to losers like you.'

Four bosses and a cubicle

My Greenwich office wasn't an office at all. It was a cubicle. These partitioned workspaces are everywhere this side of the Atlantic and they're probably the worst invention in history. They have all the disadvantages of the open-plan system – you are disturbed by your neighbour and there's no privacy to ring your girlfriend or phone round for a new job – and all the disadvantages of the office system – you feel like a loner and can't see the party happening on the other side of the partition.

Mind you, it was a very nice cubicle. It had a glass front and walls that came to within three feet of the ceiling. But it had no door, no sense of privacy and acted like an echo chamber, broadcasting my voice far and wide. Whether I was cooing to Mandy in London first thing, arranging dates in New York at lunchtime or being such a sweet boy to my mum in the afternoon, the Assistant Vice-Presidents could hear it all.

The cubicle's designer had some strange notions of office storage requirements. I had a neat row of overhead cupboards that looked ready to store crockery or breakfast cereals, and I had a handy little table and chairs where I could eat my breakfast and read the paper. It felt like I spent my day in a mock Ikea or MFI kitchen. I half expected newlyweds to wander in, open and close all the cupboards and look around for an oven.

I was a Vice-President, hence the cubicle – although I suspect Al Gore's is larger. But everyone in America is a Vice-President of one form or another. Those below me were *Assistant* Vice-Presidents (no cubicle) and those above me were *Senior* Vice-Presidents (real office with a real door).

But I had a plant – a great big umbrella plant where I poured my stale coffee – and I had a printer. 'VPs shouldn't have their own printer,' I was told by one SVP. Her tone said 'joke' but her eyes said 'pissed off'. She'd come sniffing round to see how I was settling in and to make sure the distinction between our grades was apparent. She also regarded the plant with envious eyes.

She could have it. I didn't want to be responsible for the thing's death. And she could have the printer. It was crap anyway. It printed one-page spreadsheets on three hundred and forty-seven pages and spent most of the morning flashing 'warming up'. It was clearly the runt printer of the department. That's why a mere VP was allowed the fucking thing in the first place.

In London we'd done away with all this bollocks. We'd even got rid of the offices, apart from the managing director who needed somewhere private to sack people. Hanging TV screens had also been installed for that trading-floor buzz – although one had been tuned to the Cartoon Network during the last 'Bring your kids to work day' and no-one had changed it back to CNN. *The Flintstones* and *Wacky Races* played away silently, gathering a secret following during each morning repeat.

Some of the Brown Shoes in London complained about losing their offices, as if being robbed of medieval grazing rights, but there was now an atmosphere of industry. Greenwich felt like a time warp in comparison.

The different layouts were a curious reflection of the men in charge of the offices. London's humming team-mentality atmosphere had Braveheart stamped all over it. Braveheart, obviously Scottish, was the global head of the whole department. He was only a few years older than I was. He was raised in a Glasgow orphanage and started his professional life as a nightclub bouncer, with the razor scars on his forearms to prove it. He also retained that hard bastard edge that worked as well in an investment bank as it did outside Bonker's nightclub.

Braveheart was leading the charge to keep our department in the investment bank. He'd argued the toss with the Americans in the first place and he now kicked arse to make sure every move we made had chicken written all over it.

Meanwhile, every move Flatcap made had quarter-pounder with cheese written all over it. Flatcap was in charge of the Greenwich office, sent by Braveheart as a steady hand to steer us through the choppy waters of change.

But our choppy waters included a headcount cut worthy of a charge on the Russian guns and a move from Downtown Manhattan to Greenwich. If he wanted an easy life before retirement, Flatcap had picked the wrong office, although he never let it get him down. The only thing that did get him down was Sheffield Wednesday's poor form. Flatcap had been a football referee in England and he still had a gamesmastery way about him. Whenever we talked I felt he was resisting a grope in his chest pocket and every event would put him in mind of a refereeing anecdote. His heroes had names like Chopper Smith of Hackney Marshes or Nobby Noakes of Wanstead Flats. They were Sunday morning warriors, hailed as if from the Somme.

Back in London Braveheart's sidekick, and the third of my four bosses, was Energizer Bunny, named after the character in the US battery adverts. While Braveheart was the brains, Energizer Bunny would bang the galley drum and whip any laggards. But he wasn't a tyrant. Indeed, he was probably the most popular guy in the department. This was because his weapon of choice was enthusiasm. He could get so excited in a meeting you'd think he was about to prematurely ejaculate.

His physique suited his temperament. He was a small man who looked like a cute character out of *Wind in the Willows*. Despite this, he was very successful with women. Virtually all the women in the department said he had 'something' and he had five kids from two marriages to prove it.

But his underpants were also the main depository for his technical knowledge. His background appeared to have involved drinking copious amounts of lager in small West Country towns rather than anything relevant to our department. But he didn't need to be technical. The department was full of egghead time-servers who needed a rocket up their arse, and this man was some rocket. Many of the department's great successes were down to his drive and he'd been put in charge of Energy as his reward – it would have been difficult to think of a more suitable title for him.

My final boss was the leader of the Receivables team, which came under the Energy umbrella. He was a Dutchman, called Rip Van Winkle by many. Indeed his real name was so unpronounceable that the Credit Approval department decided to call him Dave.

Rip Van Winkle was the fruit of my first task when joining the bank. Energizer Bunny was in the process of developing the Receivables team and I was charged with finding the head. I'd met Rip Van Winkle a few times and he was always up to something wacky in the emerging markets. If there was a Third World company that looked a nightmare on paper you could bet this Dutchman had found some clever way of handing it cash. At the time this was what we needed. It also did me no small favour that Rip Van Winkle owed me his job.

But having four bosses was never going to be easy, especially as these four had completely different outlooks on the business. Braveheart wanted to do ground-breaking deals that would impress our new masters. Energizer Bunny wanted to make lots of money and didn't care how it was done. Rip Van Winkle wanted to find clever ways of doing things. And Flatcap just wanted to make sure we didn't fuck up.

I had to find four, often opposing, reasons to do anything and feed the appropriate line to the appropriate boss. Conference calls involving more than one were especially tricky and, far from becoming a maestro at this skill, I developed a habit of giving the wrong reason to the wrong boss. As a consequence they all thought me a dimwit.

Hammy Hamster sniffs the air

There was no sign of the orgy, at least not for me. Maybe other men in New York were being shagged senseless by great hordes of randy women, but I wasn't seeing any.

Sure, New York women were friendly and liked the accent. And I was building up a healthy collection of phone numbers. But I'd yet to be dragged back to an apartment for rampant sex sessions with the chorus line from *Cabaret*. I'd yet to be dragged anywhere by anyone. And those phone numbers meant little. People hand out their numbers willy-nilly in this town. 'Call me,' they say, but they don't mean it. If you called they'd assume you were a sad loser with no friends. Much better to keep your dignity and, of course, remain a sad loser with no friends.

In the meantime Zoe became my regular date and my best bet for a début shag, yet she was such a sweet girl I didn't like to push things too hard. I expected events would happen naturally. Actually I didn't expect events would happen naturally at all. I knew enough about women to know that most restrict themselves to helpful signals. My problem was reading the signals. I'd look for glaring green lights but see only faint amber, and the rare occasions when the signal was unmistakably green made me so nervous I'd fumble about while the woman tapped her foot with impatience. So any expectation of events happening naturally was really a vain hope that Zoe would make the move. What I should have said was that I hoped Zoe would jump on me. But she didn't, of course. Instead she talked, mainly about her work. She was employed by the City of New York to place endangered children into foster homes. This occasionally meant snatching a child from some fourteen-year-old mother living in a crack den in the South Bronx, a move that involved piling in with police, guns at the ready.

It was a difficult scene to picture. Zoe looked like she would be more at home skipping through flower meadows on the opening credits of *Little House on the Prairie*. She didn't look capable of bursting into a squat shouting, 'Freeze, motherfucker, or I'll waste ya.'

It sounded so exciting. I imagined her noisy bedlam of an office with phones ringing, shouted arguments, and Stavros being sent out for more coffee.

I couldn't bare to talk about my work. What was I going to tell her – I had a dying plant and a dodgy printer? She tried her best because she was a warm, kind person and she wanted to be interested. But her mind would wander back to little Leroy who she'd rescued that day from an HIV-positive junky in Harlem. I simply couldn't compete.

And Zoe wasn't only warm and kind. She was sexy. She had a great body and was a fantastic dancer. She even turned me on to hip-hop. Since coming to New York I'd become frustrated with nightclub music. It was either trippy techno shite or aggressive rapping with weird beats. Dancing to hip-hop looked difficult and unrewarding. It involved a sort of gorilla stomp for retards with lots of those 'respect motherfucker' pointy arm movements that I hated.

Yet Zoe showed me how it was done. She jigged her hips and shook her shoulders at different times – the hips to the beat and her shoulders to the downbeat. Meanwhile she moved her torso up and down, using my body as her guide. The whole time her eyes never left mine. It was amazing. It was like I was Zoe's giant dildo. I was a complete and utter convert and my massive erection voted enthusiastically for more.

But our evenings never ended in sex. She stayed at mine just once. We danced in the living room but it felt awkward without the press of other bodies, and we only ended up in bed because it was decided she was staying. We kissed and started to undress each other but there was no real passion. It didn't feel right. And we were down to our undies before I realized I was wearing my dodgy Asda boxers – the ones where the fly buttons wouldn't stay fastened.

As things progressed I could feel my todger stiffen up and then poke out. And I mean poke out. We weren't talking tent-poles here; we were talking Hammy Hamster sniffing the air.

I was in big trouble. I tried to lean back, so it wouldn't press into her, but she saw this as an invite to roll on top.

It was then she noticed. She pulled back slightly and glanced down. Mr Previous waved back.

'I think we'd better stop,' she said. 'Before we do something we'll regret.'

'Oh come on,' I wanted to shout. 'Let's do something we'll regret.'

But Perky had blown it. All I could do was kiss her forehead, pretend to sleep and wait for the bastard that was supposed to be in my boxers to realize he was getting no supper.

Zoe must have wondered about me after that. I don't think she thought it an accident. I think she assumed men had better control over their bodies, or at least over their boxers. Anyway, I couldn't help wondering about her. Was she just prick-teasing?

I doubted it. I think she was a sweet all-American girl who wanted to feel comfortable and I think she thought me a flighty Brit, only after a shag. She was bang on, of course, but I felt I'd served my apprenticeship rather well.

In fact much of this apprenticeship had been served helping her find a new apartment. She eventually settled on a place in the Park Slope district of Brooklyn, a bohemian quarter and lesbian enclave. Once installed, Zoe seemed much less stressed but became physically and mentally more distant. I noticed the first person to be invited round was Luke, her ex-boyfriend. And I also noted that old charmy-pants Luke had bought her a big bunch of flowers as a house-warming gift – something Pig-Ignorant Twat here had forgotten, even though she'd bought me flowers on our first date.

I feared the relationship was unravelling, but thought it worth one more go. I needed to be more American, I thought. My English awkwardness was all very engaging but it didn't make for wild sex. I had to be more direct, although I'd have thought an erect penis sticking out of my boxers was about as direct as you can get.

I decided I needed to press Zoe's buttons. I started on

a New York bus of all places, while on a Saturday shop. We sat on the back row while I played the fool. I'd tease her and push her around until she'd playfully hit me or push me away. And in order to give her a further excuse for violence I rummaged through her handbag. I found one of those posh Jean-Pierre hairbrushes – the sort used by Sloaney types in England – and started to brush her hair. At first I was gentle but Zoe reacted positively so I pressed harder and brushed the full length of her long blond hair. Soon I moved my free hand down her hair in a follow-up stroke. The free hand then changed tack, staying where it was around the back of her skull, gently massaging her head while the brush glided through her hair.

Zoe closed her eyes and pushed her head onto my hand. She even quietly moaned with pleasure. My hand then started playing with her ear, lightly running a finger round the rim. By now her body was leaning into me, her eyes tight shut.

I was so encouraged I kissed her neck, very gently brushing my lips on her skin as I clasped her hair in my hand. This time she let out an audible moan. Her back pressed into my body and her nails pinched my thigh.

It was amazing. Foreplay on a packed New York bus.

It was a shame it had to end, but our stop in Greenwich Village approached. Zoe stood up a little un-easily, although I was the self-conscious one standing up, I can tell you.

'Maybe we should stay on,' she whispered.

Of course dimwit here should have said, 'Maybe we should go back to mine and shag like bunnies.'

But I didn't. I just stood with my trousers hanging awkwardly and waited to get off the bus.

We walked to Hudson Street to visit Myers of Keswick.

This is a weird shop to find in the middle of Manhattan. It's an old-fashioned English grocery store packed full of goodies such as Hobnobs, Horlicks, HP Sauce, Ribena, Lucozade, Colman's Mustard, Robertson's Jam, Jammy Dodgers and a million other things from Blighty that are unheard of in an American supermarket.

The store was dotted with obviously British shoppers making themselves homesick. Occasionally there'd be a cry such as 'Mmm, Angel Delight', or 'Wow, Jelly Babies'.

Zoe was fascinated but we couldn't linger. She had to catch an afternoon train to Albany in Upstate New York. We took a cab to Penn Station so she could reserve a seat and we could eat a late picnic lunch. I intended introducing her to the finest of British cuisine.

The redeveloped Penn Station no longer deserves to be immortalized in Glenn Miller's 'Chattanooga Choo Choo'. Crouched beneath Madison Square Garden, the station is a low-ceilinged shopping complex that happens to have some railway lines in the basement. In the seating area for passengers, Zoe and I sat and shared Scotch eggs and Branston Pickle, which she adored. As she took each mouthful she squirmed with excitement and then moaned loudly with pleasure. She claimed she'd never tasted anything so scrummy. It made me proud to be British.

After lunch we parted with a romantic goodbye kiss on the platform. It was a nice kiss but I sensed the relationship was going nowhere and that this Luke bloke was lurking about in the background.

An old black guard shouted, 'Albany, Albany, all *aboaaarrrddd*', blew his whistle and the train left Pennsylvania Station 'bout a quarter to four.

And on Monday I received my first Dear John e-mail.

'Robert, I've been putting a lot of thought into our relationship and I realize that I am not emotionally free of Luke and if I can't have him I would rather be alone. I am sorry to tell you this.

'My form in Drip stated I was looking for someone emotionally available. But in the end I was the one who was emotionally unavailable.

Look after yourself (and get some new boxer shorts). Zoe.'

Amanda – I gotta have suction

I'm no dental-phobe, oh no. I spent a large part of my childhood at the mercy of a big ginger-haired Irish dentist and I'd learnt that the pain is never as bad as imagined. He had bad breath and fat fingers and my terror centred on these features rather than any injury he could inflict on my mouth. So when I found myself in need of a dentist in the US I saw it as an irritation, nothing more. I'm a lot wiser now.

At a farewell drink for a colleague in Pier 92 I used a finger to prize the gooey lump of popcorn from a right-side molar. Part of my tooth came out with it. Flatcap nodded wisely. 'Son,' he said, 'you're going to need a crown.'

He didn't tell me I'd also be going to hell for my trouble.

The physical and mental cost can be summarized thus:
Visits to twee medical centre concealing sadistic torture camp: 7.

Number of injections: 12 (I kid you not).

Number of different faces staring quizzically into my gaping mouth: 8.

Average age of faces staring quizzically into my gaping mouth: 20 (generous estimate).

Hours in the dentist's chair: 7½ so far (again, IKYN).

Number of hours I was prepared to swap places with

the shot-down Gulf War Tornado pilots: 7½ (they won a book deal and a lecture tour).

Number of hours thinking the dental nurse fancied me: ½.

Number of hours convinced that the dental nurse was a lesbian feminist hell-bitch determined to inflict maximum pain and discomfort on all men: 7½.

Number of snide comments about the fact that my cheeks were too tense or my tongue was in the way, even though I was struggling with a mouth full of more equipment than required to complete the Jubilee Line extension: 47 (guess).

Blessings counted in an effort to remain positive:
1) at some point they will let me go, and
2) thank God it was nothing serious.

Number of times I cursed my luck, mentally crying 'Why me?': 120 (rough estimate).

Promises made in exchange for getting out alive:
1) to eat less sugar,
2) to eat no popcorn,
3) to eat more vitamin B, or D, or zinc, or calcium,
4) to find out which nutrient aids dental health,
5) to be faithful to Mandy (I'd crossed my fingers).

Cost of treatment: crown $1,190, x-rays $62, root canal $950. Total: $2,202.

So how does it compare with old Murphy round the back of Debenhams? Well if you want to be treated like the dying extra in *ER* then American dentists are for you. It's very exciting: shouted commands in Serbo-Croatian, ever more ridiculous-looking instruments, dentists being brow-mopped by assistants, and urgent phrases like 'OK, ready with the formaldehyde' or 'We're losing it' or 'Gimme suction – Amanda I gotta have suction'.

I even had 'This is a complete mess, we're gonna have to start over.'

All of which encourages you to pay attention.

And American dentists like to keep you informed. Occasionally they projected a video of my tooth onto a TV screen. Magnified by a thousand times, it's a depressing sight to see a slight chip turn into a complete landslide – especially after the sixteen-year-old has had her go.

But is it better? How does my mouth feel?

It feels like a fucking train crash, that's how it feels. And no it isn't better. In the US the British have a reputation for bad teeth. But I'll have old Murphy's beer breath and dandruff any day. I'll also have his 1950s' surgery, his twelve-year-old *Yachting Monthlies*, his single bendy metal pick instrument and his calm smile. And I'll especially have the bit where the tarty receptionist with the lipstick says, 'That'll be ten pounds, please.'

Jim, John and Jayne try and have an orgy

The Receivables product could make it as chicken. It certainly had the right ingredients. But we committed two major sins. We didn't lend somebody else's money, we lent our own, and we charged next to nothing for the privilege. In fact we created the second problem ourselves. Our risky borrower in a crap country had his loan paid back by the good guy in the West. It reduced the risk and reduced the amount we could charge for lending the cash.

This raises eyebrows at an investment bank. 'OK, so run it by me one more time,' they'd say. 'These guys come to us begging for money and you invent ways we can charge them less, like we're a fucking charity or somethin'. Like we give a fuck. Are you guys nuts?'

We were breaking the golden rules of investment

banking and it was my job to get us back on side. And this didn't mean poncing around doing silly soya bean deals with Brazil. This meant doing serious deals that earned serious dosh. It meant doing deals that were sexy.

Now sex isn't something that springs to mind when thinking about banking. Sex turns you on, makes your hormones go wild and generally keeps you awake at night. Banking involves maths, or math as they say here, lots of verbal acrobatics with lawyers, and nothing likely to have you concerned about the uncomfortable bulge in your trousers.

That's unless you're an investment banker. Investment bankers get turned on by banking. They love it so much they talk about banking as if it were sex. In fact they mix up sex and banking to the point where a marketing meeting for the third quarter can sound like a gang of sexual deviants on an outing.

'OK, it's time to put our balls on the table,' someone will say.

At this point everyone else in the room nods and thinks about our offer to the client. Meanwhile I'm wrestling with the image of a conference room of men pulling down their trousers to rest their testicles on the desk.

'We've got this guy by the balls,' someone else will say.

Again, the room smiles in satisfaction that we seem to have the client where we want him. Not me, oh no. I'm watching our client's testicles being tightly grasped while he pays close attention.

'We're gonna fuck this guy up the arse,' says a third man.

Yep, you bet. I'm not thinking about all the money we're going to make. I'm imagining the poor client leaning over the desk and bracing himself for a good buggering.

And Rip Van Winkle had given me the task of

prostituting myself with the guys upstairs in the hope that one of them would smell money, want to grab me by the balls and fuck me up the arse. I couldn't wait.

By the guys upstairs I mean our trading floor. Even in heavenly little Greenwich the trading floor is one hell of a place. Outside, sailing boats gently bob in the late-summer breeze. Inside, the Third World War's about to break out.

The first impression is of noise. It just hits you as you walk in. Phones ring and people shout. Most are shouting into the phones, but some are shouting at colleagues a foot away. Many do both – shouting 'TAKE TEN, TEN, TEN', at someone in the room and 'OK, we'll take nine and three-quarters', into the phone. And everyone ignores the loudspeakers, which broadcast distorted messages about the potato industry employment figures or something equally off the wall.

The second impression is of confinement. No-one has more than three square feet of desk space and the desks are no more than shelves for stacks of computer monitors. Each desk has around six, many flashing the same tables of impenetrable numbers. TVs hanging from the ceiling show a sharp-looking woman mouthing in silence from the floor of the New York Stock Exchange while a band of gobbledegook rolls by at the base of the screen.

Most of the traders are millionaires in their thirties with matching egos. In this world inflated egos are vital. They're needed to carve out empires and go hunting for more.

And my aim was to manipulate these egos. I wanted them competing against each other to try and get hold of our portfolio of Receivables loans.

At first the strategy worked. They were all over me. I would wander up to the trading floor and be greeted like Jayne Mansfield walking by a naval yard. Two traders

95

called John and Jim were particularly aroused. John was a huge bear of a man. He was very fat and very American, with a picture of his very fat and very American kids stuck to his trading screen. Jim was a small guy who used the word fuck as a prefix to every noun.

John and Jim did something very similar to Receivables. They had all the 'As' and 'Bs' and they could draw a damn fine impression of the London Underground when describing a deal. But John and Jim's world was sex. In fact it was such an orgy it made Receivables look like an early night with a cup of cocoa. That's because they took loads of Receivables deals and bundled them up for the bond market. They had 'As' and 'Bs' swarming all over the shop, but they'd ram them all into one jar and use them as security for other people – usually US insurance companies or pension funds – to lend against. It goes without saying that John and Jim charged a fortune for the privilege. And their 'As' weren't cash-strapped dodgy companies in crap countries, oh no. They were fuck-off blue-chip US corporates. And the 'Bs' were individual Americans, paying their bills. The 'As' just couldn't be bothered to wait for this cash.

John and Jim didn't worry that some of these individuals wouldn't pay. They assumed as much and added far more 'Bs' into the pot than was needed to pay back the lenders. Sometimes twenty in every hundred 'Bs' could tell 'A' to take a hike and there would still be enough cash to pay off the loan. This was called over-collateralization, because bankers like long words. Selling future-income backed loans like this was called securitization. And our portfolio of Receivables deals was securitizable. We had the necessary 'As' and 'Bs', and we had a range of loans that would provide the pension funds and insurance companies with what they were looking for – which was a nice steady income over time.

John and Jim loved our stuff – not Russia, not now –

but the rest, oh yes. Middle East, fucking great. Asia, at the right fucking price. Africa, why fucking not? And they liked our structures. No fucking money going back to these crappy fucking countries. They just ship the fucking oil, do they? To this big fucking Western company, do they? The fuck-off company then pays the fucking money to the fucking bank, does it? That fucking money pays back the fucking loan, does it? Fucking great.

So what could go wrong? Fucking egos, that's what. The Securitization team in Greenwich had a sister team in London. And our Receivables deals had been originated out of the London office. This led the London Securitization team to insist they were the guys to go around fucking the market up the arse – never mind that all the investors' money would be in US dollars and would come from aunties in Wisconsin and not grannies in Hastings. What's more, the London Securitization head was able to grab the top guy in the whole bank by the balls as he was still in London trying to get the place straight after the merger. The top guy then grabbed Braveheart by the balls. Braveheart then issued a memo saying only London could talk about the Securitization of our portfolio, and could he now have his balls back, please.

John and Jim stopped returning my calls. They looked shifty and uncomfortable when I met them in the cafe and instead of greeting me like Jayne Mansfield I was treated more like a hideously ugly double-bagger with leprosy.

Luckily John and Jim weren't my only hope of having a role in the sexy stuff. There was also the US Private Placement market for borrowers who wanted discreet loans from discreet lenders, and who didn't want to have their name shouted all over Wall Street by guys in red suspenders saying 'fuck' a lot.

But the Private Placement market isn't as sexy as the Public market. Our Private Placement function was run by an old woman, although one with such a fearsome reputation she point-blank refused to move to Greenwich with the rest of the bank. She had a corner office with a fine view of the Brooklyn Bridge and she wasn't about to end up in some parochial bunker.

And, yes, her corner office was large, and, indeed, the Brooklyn Bridge spanned the blue expanse of the East River beyond the window. But behind this desk sat a small grey-haired granny with granny glasses, a granny mop hairstyle and a granny cardigan. If investment banking was pure sex, this was getting a little perverted.

She didn't look up as I entered. She carried on reading some boring-looking document rather than acknowledge my presence in her room. I thought this odd. The secretary had summoned me after a fifteen-minute wait so she must have been ready to see me. But, no, she continued to read.

As she looked like a granny I wondered if her senses had dulled with age and she had yet to notice me, so I took two steps forward.

'What do you want?' she barked at the papers. There wasn't even a flicker of a look my way.

'Er, I've come to talk about securitizing Receivables,' I said.

She made a note in the margin of her document and turned the page.

Oh really Robert, how nice. Do come in and sit down. Would you like a coffee? Is it still raining? What about those Yankees, hey? How's things in Greenwich? Nothing. Not a word. Not a look. I was scum and she was going to make damn sure I knew it.

'Where?' she asked eventually, turning another page.

'Well, Russia and—'

'Forget it,' she snapped.

Then she pressed a button on her phone, shouted 'Moody's' and finally looked at me.

'Forget it,' she repeated.

She picked up the receiver and spun round to face the window. All I could see was the back of a large leather chair blocking the Gothic arches of Brooklyn Bridge.

No chance of getting my balls on the table with this woman.

OCTOBER

I guess he scored last night

Bridget. Her name was Bridget. She reminded me of this in a patronizing voice, half joking, half hurt.

'Oh that's right,' I replied, lifting my eyes to the sky in a 'silly me' sort of way.

But she could have said she was Godzilla and I'd have lifted my eyes to the sky in a 'silly-me' sort of way. She just happened to be in my bed. And it just happened to be morning – well, around midday on Sunday. When I woke, she was there.

'What's my name?' was the first thing she asked – a slightly unfair question as she could have just parachuted through the ceiling for all the recollection I had.

'Er, did we, er—?'

'You?' she laughed. 'You were incapable of anything.'

Oh dear. The reason for such a memory lapse is New York's licencing hours. The bars shut at 4 a.m. And while most people go out around midnight, the Brits, used to the 11 p.m. swill, go out at eight-thirty. We have a few beers somewhere relaxed and then move on to the Martinis or seabreezes by ten – usually in a trendier bar Downtown. After that the slippery slope beckons. By midnight we're rolling drunk and acting like knobs, and by 2 a.m. anyone we meet is placed in a black hole that

100

accepts no recall in the morning – hence waking up beside a complete stranger.

Bridget was a friendly, spiky-haired fashion designer from Oregon (an Oregano?) who thought it fun to wake up next to a pissed Brit. After the morning introductions we had breakfast in my local diner and wandered around Central Park. She was still in her evening dress so I expect passers-by must have thought, 'Hey, I guess he scored last night.'

And I guess I had. It was the closest I'd come to a one-night stand since coming to New York. I just wish I knew how I'd done it.

I had no problem communicating with women. But I talked to a woman the way I talked to a mate – with about the same level of sexual intensity. I'd no idea how to lead things down a seductive path. I'm convinced it only happened with Mandy because she was a West Ham supporter, a bit of a miracle find and one unlikely to be repeated in New York. But I'd Braveheart's orders to obey so I was going to have to improve.

Trevor had promised to help. Trevor was Fiona's husband and Fiona, as an old college house-mate, was my best friend in New York. She was over here to set up a New York office for her internet company. Trevor played a supporting role, indulging in a spot of sailing on the side. His main pastime, however, was drinking. He could drink for England and had a bar manner that was everything I wished for. He was good-looking and as cheeky as a cockney whelk-seller. He could approach any woman and within minutes the two of them would be flirting outrageously. In fact he was so good that he wasn't the ideal pulling partner. When I joined him I came across as his goon of a mate, playing Andy Ridgeley to his George Michael. Often I'd just stand and apologetically smile as he held the floor and the women did everything short of unhooking their bras.

My problem was the fear of rejection. I assumed women didn't fancy me and I didn't want to invite a decline. But Trevor said that was bollocks. Rejection, he said, was the key to pulling success. It was a vital part of the process. It meant nothing. It meant she was frigid, or knew you were too good for her, or that she was up her own arse. It certainly didn't mean you were an ugly arsehole.

Confidence and arrogance were vital, said Trevor. Women find nervous men a turn-off. They need to be nervous of you because you're the greatest fucking thing on the planet.

Trevor's practical route for getting round the fear of rejection was to: 'Get your first rejection in early. It's like jumping straight in at the deep end. It's a shock but you're immediately acclimatized – much better than the inch-by-inch wade.

'Go straight up to the most fanciable woman in the bar and say she's gorgeous and you spotted her immediately,' he said. 'She'll reject you and you're off. But you've no more fear of rejection. And you never know . . .'

It was a revelation. Women were no longer frightening creatures waiting to crush my self-esteem. After all, they were standing in a young singles bar with their friends and they weren't there to talk to each other. They were there to talk to men, although the men would have to make the move. Most women knew this and were sympathetic – encouraging, even. The occasional bitch prepared to exploit her advantage and turn your ego to jelly was just pointing out her own shortcomings.

I loved Trevor for that. I also loved the fact we weren't in competition. He'd engineer it so I'd meet the pretty, single one – despite her obvious interest in Trevor. He didn't mind – he was staggering home to the wife anyway.

Trevor was a million miles from Nat in this respect. Nat was the first of Fiona's London employees to join the New York venture. And he faced an early problem – his London girlfriend Jill. She'd wanted to join him in New York, but Nat was reluctant. On his recce visits he'd seen a city full of fantastic-looking women hungry for torrid sex with British men so he'd ditched Jill, but now he was regretting it. Jill had recovered from this mortal blow and quickly found a new boyfriend. This was not in Nat's script, especially as New York's twenty-four-hour orgy had yet to materialize.

The thought of Jill now made Nat morose, which didn't improve his chances with women. On one occasion a woman broke from talking to him to approach me. I was busily engaging her friend in some Trevor-inspired chat. 'Tell your friend he's a nice guy,' she said, 'but tell him to shut up about his stupid ex.'

It was a shame. Nat was tall and handsome with come-to-bed eyes. But when his eyes said 'pity me' as he droned on about Jill he had the sex appeal of a maggot.

Nat and I would often be the last two out, propping up some nameless wank-off trendy bar in SoHo or the Lower East Side. Nat would bang on but at that point I didn't care. The seabreezes coursed through my veins and I'd drunkenly scan the room.

The scene would have a dream-like quality. Nat's Jill monologue would echo round my head as if detached from reality, like an announcement at a railway station. I'd half listen, nod, occasionally say, 'Yeah, shit mate,' and watch the young crowd having intense conversations while trying to look like movie stars. I'd watch people half dancing to the DJ's blend of ambient vibes, and I'd watch two girls approach the bar and stand right next to us, looking for a way through to be served.

And this is where Nat and I would become rivals. The woman designated as mine would immediately become more attractive to Nat. He could be talking to Cameron Diaz while I chatted to a Vietnamese pot-bellied pig and he'd still want to swap, assuming mine was better looking because she was talking to me.

But this time the cards fell in my favour. Melanie and Ellie were from Miami and in New York on a weekend shop'n' snog break. Nat started talking to Melanie, the one I fancied. She had dark hair, soppy eyes and a heavenly body. Meanwhile I talked to Ellie, who was too skinny and boyish for my taste.

Inevitably Nat started to muscle in on what he thought was my territory. He made general comments to us all, then just to Ellie. He became flirty with Ellie, giving her his best lines and his best eyes. And soon enough we were subtly adjusting positions so I was left with his reject.

Great – Melanie and I stood alone. Shit – usual panic about what to say. Except now a little Trevor appeared on my shoulder. 'Look into her eyes,' he'd say.

I stared madly at her. She stared back. We both wore silly grins.

'Don't just stare,' said Trevor. 'She'll think you're a nutter. Say something. But don't be neutral – make it flirty.'

'You're gorgeous and I spotted you immediately,' I said.

'Resist the urge to puke,' said Trevor. 'She's loving it.'

'She's hating it,' I said to Trevor. 'It's such a corny line.'

'That's such a corny line,' said Melanie. 'I love it.'

'Told you,' said Trevor. 'Women love that sort of shit.'

'But she's an architecture student,' I said. 'Shouldn't I impress her with my critique of Frank Lloyd Wright?'

'Save it,' said Trevor. 'She gets that at college. She's not here for that – she's here to cop off. Look at that dress.'

'That's a fantastic dress,' I said to Melanie. 'You look amazing in it.'

'Oh, those lines,' said Melanie.

'She hates them,' I said to Trevor, the panic returning.

'So what if she does?' said Trevor. 'You won't score telling her that Frankie's loads are white.'

'Hmmm, keep them coming,' said Melanie.

She fell towards me in a mock faint.

'Told you,' said Trevor. 'Touch her.'

'What?'

'Touch her. Touch her arm.'

I touched her arm.

'That was crap,' said Trevor. 'Touch it again and then slide your hand down to hers. Then let go.'

I touched her arm, slid my hand down to hers and her fingers closed around mine. Fucking hell. I . . . fucking hell.

'Stroke her face.'

I was no longer arguing.

She smiled as the back of my hand brushed her cheek. And when stroking her face it seemed right to kiss her forehead, to kiss her cheek, to kiss her lips, to kiss her lips again, to brush my lips against hers and linger, to gently prize her lips apart with mine.

Trevor was gone. Job done.

I noticed Nat's jealous regard – yet another event that wasn't in the script.

You're all set

What is it with America and technology? At once it's fantastically advanced and blindingly stupid. At first I thought it was me. I've never been very patient with technology and my preferred solution to any problem is to throw the thing out the window. And I always assume everyone knows more about technology than me, especially if their job title has the word technical in it.

And that's precisely what Tom had. He was the *Technical* Vice-President, or something. He was also as fat as a house, wore band-tour T-shirts, geeky glasses and didn't have the faintest idea what to do with his mop of blond hair. Perfectly qualified, you'd think, to sort out the transfer of my email from London to Greenwich. Just transfer it over – no probs.

Probs. People in London swore blind they'd sent me emails. They'd tried my new email address. Nothing. They'd tried my old email address. Nothing. And they'd tried to press reply when I sent them an email. Nothing.

Every time I called Tom. He'd stand puffing at my desk, press a few buttons and say, 'Yep, I think that's fixed her. You're all set.'

Americans have this annoying habit of saying 'You're all set' in response to everything. They serve you dinner – 'You're all set'. They come and take your plate – 'Are you all set?' They give you the cheque – 'You're all set'. They put a bag over your head and throw you into quick-drying concrete, 'You're all set'.

And the chances are that you're a long way from 'all set'. It means I've had enough of dealing with your problem so I'm going to press a couple of buttons, hum and ha a bit, say 'You're all set', and bugger off back to my game of computer Solitaire.

Tom would try anything to convince me my email was all set but he was no sooner back to his card game than someone in London was accusing me of never replying to their emails. I started to develop a complex. Eventually loveable Tom was rumbled and his replacement had yet another Tom story to add to his collection.

But US technology is, indeed, designed to give you a complex. Take the phones. Calling any large organization

106

is like playing a computer at chess. You have to second-guess the mind of a machine and you're left with a deep feeling of inadequacy. I have yet to ring a single company that employs more than fifty people and not face test by tone entry.

The choices never end: 'Press one for English – pause – press one for billing, two for non-working apparatus, three for change in your waist measurement, four for everything else – pause – enter account number – pause – sorry, I did not understand, please re-enter your account number – pause – sorry, you are a jerk, go straight to jail and do not pass go.'

Say you don't have an account number. In fact you're trying to get an account number but can't because no-one will answer the fucking phone.

I agree this is becoming a frustrating part of life the world over. But it has reached new dimensions in the US. For instance, with directory assistance, the dalek will insist you give a town and a listing. It will then give you a number that is almost certain to be incorrect. I mean not just wrong but, blimey. A request for the Lincoln Center, New York, will become the York Center, New Lincoln for sure. This is because the dalek is searching based on word recognition. It has zero intelligence.

The only way to get the right number is to get hold of a human, who will also, alas, have zero intelligence. So when the dalek asks 'What city?' do not say New York, or any vaguely sensible place. Say 'Shagsville, Venus.'

Then, when it asks 'What listing?' blow a long raspberry into the phone.

A human will come on line. But this is no ordinary human. This is a human that gives the impression of having been woken from a deep sleep. 'Whhhaaat?'

You can hear her fumble for the light as she sits up and looks for her slippers.

At least she attempts to find a solution. Try getting help from a human at a large company and it's a whole new ball game. This is because most Americans have learnt that human contact is possible by repeatedly pressing 'star-zero-pound' – the three bottom digits on the keypad. In this case, though, the human is likely to sound like you've interrupted a seduction.

'Wat?' they'll shout.

And don't worry, you won't get any help. The humans at the end of this route love nothing more than to blankly state 'No, you cannot do that. I cannot help you.'

No new number, no alternative channel, no possible recourse – just a cul-de-sac that says 'You lose, busta – now scram.'

If this level of telephonic endeavour frustrates you, don't get a mobile phone.

The US has its own electricity system so appliances from abroad don't work here. It also has its own pint measures, shoe sizes, dress sizes, paper sizes etc. etc. Yet all this US uniqueness has dim and distant origins. The pilgrims somehow developed smaller drink containers and larger feet while crossing the pond on the *Mayflower*. Not so mobile phones. How the Americans managed to take 1990s' technology and create a system utterly useless outside of the US is a complete mystery.

And it's mostly useless inside the US. When handed a mobile phone I was told of a fantastic new feature. It was called roaming. This meant I could use the phone in both Connecticut and New York. When I crossed the border all I had to do was press these two buttons and then press Set, or Store, or something. Then I'd only to remember to reverse it when I crossed back. Wasn't that clever?

Not to a man used to turning up in a new country and

seeing his phone display automatically change to RussCom or FrogTel it wasn't. And when I asked if I could call abroad I swear the woman looked at me as if to ask 'Where's that?'

The sun sets on The Empire (snog)

Forget *Sleepless in Seattle*, the Empire State Building must be one of the least romantic spots on Earth. It's crap, crowded and cold. Fellow tourists leave you smug about your own worldliness and taste, and the sheer press of people makes the experience resemble a bad commute rather than a spot where marriage proposals are irresistible. But Melanie and Ellie wanted more than just a bar snog to remember New York by. They called Nat on his mobile (I was having trouble with mine) and we were soon hailing a cab for a late-afternoon rendezvous at the Rockefeller Center before a trip to the top of New York's most famous building.

We were to meet the girls at the piazza restaurant by the gaudy gold statue of Prometheus. As we arrived Melanie and Ellie stopped eating. 'Come on, girls,' said the camp waiter. 'Don't leave your food now the boys have arrived.'

But Melanie couldn't play the doughy-eyed sex goddess while tucking into steak and fries so she sat back in her chair and glanced guiltily at the food. The steak glared truculently back, reminding the world that, indeed, elegant ladies do stuff their faces.

Still, it didn't bother me. I merrily finished off the steak while Nat fiddled with Ellie's abandoned salad – it was easy to see why Melanie had the curves. But Melanie's sexuality didn't end there. Every fibre of her being played the temptress.

'Did you miss me last night?' she asked, staring hard at me with her pupils dilated.

'Of course,' I said. 'I thought about you all night. I could hardly sleep.'

'What were your thoughts?' She tilted her head and opened her mouth.

'I couldn't possibly say,' I said, looking down as if shamed by the recollection.

'Were they rude?' she asked.

'Oh they were rude alright,' I said. I laughed to break the tension.

'Was I good?' she asked, her brazen eyes ablaze.

'Oh, very good,' I said.

It was a game, of course, and Melanie loved playing it. So while Nat and Ellie chatted across the table I had to maintain this sexual banter. I felt trapped in Trevor's persona and almost jealous of the normality with which Nat and Ellie talked. In the end I became grateful for the lengthening shadows and the need to catch the sunset from the top of the Empire State Building.

The Empire State stands out as the city's favourite emblem far more than the marooned Liberty. This is due partly to its size and partly to its shape, but mainly to its position. It squats bang in the centre of Manhattan and acts as the island's pivot. If God wanted to tear Manhattan from the Earth, he'd use the Empire State as his lever.

Indeed, the planners must have searched for Manhattan's core – a spiritual as much as a geographic calculation – and settled on Fifth and 34th. The Empire State stares Downtown over the gruff Lower Manhattan districts, but stands guard at the entrance of Midtown. Its position makes the building visible from nearly all of New York, helping to orientate emerging subway riders. The building is also New York's sundial. Its pointing shadow casts an accusing finger across the city as the sun sweeps west. In the morning it's telling the West Side to get out of bed and by evening it's swung round to scold the East Side for its greed.

Yet for all its stature, first timers can't help but notice the Empire State's ugliness. It's a monolithic obelisk compared to the slender elegance or baroque finery on offer elsewhere. Indeed, it's impossible not to feel a tinge of regret that the Chrysler doesn't occupy such a site. Like a small-time celebrity in a posh restaurant, the Chrysler has been shunted off to an awkward side table with a view obscured by the fat bastard Pan Am Building. Meanwhile, the megastar Empire State is treated to a table right in the heart of the action and with the best view of the stage.

But emotions are torn. Sure it's ugly but that simple shape is an unmistakable feature of the New York skyline. The building's profile is a potent symbol for the city. Like a vast hypodermic needle, it's a powerful branding for the licentious New York of lore.

The shape loses none of its dynamism on approach. It almost overpowers its surroundings, stooping over the anonymous tat around it like a curious gardener inspecting the insects in the grass. By 30th Street it peaks through every gap in the buildings, filling the sky with its presence and forcing the eyes up in respect for its size.

But the conflict continues. Up close it appears such a functional place, at least below the 86th floor. You get the impression the architect said, 'OK guys, just make this baby tall, and quick. Once we're up in the clouds we'll think about the fancy stuff.'

And he left the choice of external decor to the accountants. The windows have a mean look and the featureless grey limestone hurtles skyward, only stopping for the odd apologetic art deco motif in the window panels.

It all adds to the air of faded glory, especially as the

building's scars are noticeable close up. Painful gashes run the height of the building, exposing the rusting steel reinforcement beneath. The tower looks in a sorry state, like a favourite uncle turned senile or a movie actor found drunk in the street.

The ugliness and shabbiness of the building, however, are nothing compared to the grotesque images inside. Sure the tainted exterior has given way to the marble floors and ornate bronze panelling of the lobby, but the queues of tourists run the show in here and US tourists ain't a pretty sight. Suburban America lines up in an excited, snaking mass in vastly inflated lurid sports coats and the worst array of ill-conceived baseball hats ever assembled in one space. Fat Pennsylvanian families queue with Michigan grannies and the occasional gang of Hispanics. Lumpen America is all around and any hope of a stimulating experience on the Observation Deck evaporates: it's going to be a battle for space with Martha, Marvin and the kids.

They crowd into the lift, making no attempt to observe elevator etiquette as they chatter on with their blindingly obvious commentary. 'Geez, it's a long way up,' one will say during the ascent, or 'I hear the view from the top is awesome.'

But they're right. It is a long way up and, yes, the view is awesome. Nothing quite prepares you for the sight of Manhattan beneath your feet. The height seems exaggerated – sure the Empire State looks tall, but this is closer to flying. Some primeval instinct tells you this is wrong. Surely we are breaking the rules of nature – we cannot float above the cluttered streets without being sucked back by the pull of gravity. No wonder there's a cage. The streets beg you to join them. No need to line up with the crap families. Go the quick way. The grannies seem tempted – white-knuckle tourism for the over seventies.

But it's worth the 'Jeez, it's a long way down' comments. Beyond the cage is the most recognizable urban landscape on the planet. The city sprawls off in all directions, belying any official figures about New York's size. The urban zone that is greater New York stretches as far as the eye can see – only halted in the south by the ocean and in all other directions by the horizon or fingers of water.

The sky fires red and orange streaks above the belching chimneys of New Jersey. Lights already twinkle along suburban streets – the dead-straight lines merging into a distant perspective and making the whole scene resemble a vast electronic circuit board. To the north, strings of curved lights hang like bunting as suspension bridges cross New York's complex of wide waterways. Most reach across to Long Island, a broad landscape of patchwork light that points towards the encircling dark.

But it's the closer view that people want to see. It's the feeling of levitation above the immediate streets as the traffic silently glides along the avenues. From up here the Empire State's central position is obvious. If Manhattan's a ship we are standing on the bridge. In front of us is the bow with the World Trade Center the foremost mast – the lazy red blink of its roof-top lights pointing the ship seaward. Around us is the ship's machinery and behind us the dark forbidding cargo hold of Central Park.

I pointed all this out to Melanie, as she snuggled into my shoulder to hide from the biting wind. I thought she'd be impressed by my powers of observation and creative imagination. Instead she said, 'You're weird', but moved in for a snog all the same. In fact Melanie seemed content to shuffle round with the crap tourists and gave me a lingering kiss in front of each new vista. 'Oh look at the sunset over New Jersey', I'd say (snog). 'Ah, Midtown – that's the Rockefeller with GE written on it', (snog). 'And this is Long Island – there's Brooklyn', (snog). 'Isn't Downtown a long way off?' (snog). She was living her romantic fantasy and some pseudo-intellectual gobshite wasn't going to spoil it.

Finally she became curious. 'What's that?' she asked.

'What's what?' I'd forgotten the tour and was now concentrating on nibbling her ear, assuming such behaviour was expected.

'That,' she pulled me off to point at a wedge-shaped building about ten blocks to the south. 'It's cute.'

'It's the Flatiron Building,' I said. 'It was New York's first skyscraper.'

It looked no more than a stump from up here.

'It's a strange shape,' said Melanie.

'That's because of the way Broadway cuts across Fifth Avenue at an angle . . .' (snog).

Having got her answer Melanie drew the lecture to a close. But my attention remained. The diagonal line of Broadway sliced across the anal grid of Manhattan like the winning line in a noughts and crosses game. It was as if the town draftsman was busy at his drawing board, biting his tongue as he lined up yet another straight north-south avenue with his ruler, when a chum slapped him on the back. 'Hey Cas, watsup?' Whoosh went Cas's pen across the plan. 'Shit man, look what you made me do – and if you think I'm gonna start over . . .'

Despite the obvious insult to Manhattan's sense of symmetry, Broadway creates some of the city's most interesting features. As the name suggests, the acute angle of the Flatiron encourages comparison with common objects, although it's a name that diminishes a sleek chunk of stone brooding arrogantly at the junction of New York's two most celebrated streets. The point of the Flatiron appears to slice through the southbound traffic like a rotating woodsaw through lumber. It's such a sharp angle you wonder what it must be like inside.

114

'Here's your office, John,' says the owner. 'No room for a desk I'm afraid, but take a look at that view.'

Indeed, as Broadway's errant path meets each avenue, an hourglass-shaped opening is created to break up the tight canyons. Times Square – Broadway's junction with Seventh – is one such opening. Times Square is surely the most exciting stretch of street in the world. Nowhere else is the eye so assaulted, the ear so abused, the sheer drama of a city street so thrown in your face. It's the most vertically chaotic scene imaginable, every inch yelling for your attention.

The bedlam towers above you in great electronic hoardings that destroy the office-block conformity of the rest of Midtown. Vast faces grin down on the traffic, giant words glitter and fade in cascades of lights – Canon, Suntory, Samsung. Electronic newsreel rolls by high up on façades – 'earthquake: many dead . . dollar up . . Dow down . . Mets lose . . rain later'.

As the world swirls above in ticker-tape lights you realize that this is the planet's beating heart. Your pulse can't help but race, your adrenalin must flow. Feet move faster, tempers fray, senses sharpen. Every scruffy piece of this junction oozes the seedy atmosphere of the city. If you could bottle New York, here would be your spring.

The Big Sleazy

New Orleans is Bad Behaviour, USA. It's a delinquent's Disneyland – a metropolis built on the very notion of being out of control. This is despite the city's efforts to reinvent itself as a family tourist destination. Promotional flyers show pictures of Mississippi paddle-steamers and the aquarium. 'A charming town for a visit, and don't forget the kids'. Sure.

Try as they might, New Orleans is New Orleans. It's a great big non-stop piss-up – as well as a suitable venue for my next rendezvous with Mandy.

Six weeks apart and a complete failure at infidelity had left me in the mood for some serious sex. She said she was going to bring leather boots and a nurse's uniform. I said I was going to bring a furtive imagination and a major erection.

But first, the booze. New Orleans is the only US city where drunken behaviour is positively encouraged. Pissed-up gangs stagger round the French Quarter from midday until 6a.m. They lurch from one bar to the next, laughing like lottery winners. In fact Bourbon Street is a bar. Street counters hand out margaritas the way New York sells hot dogs.

Bourbon Street's architecture is designed for drunks. Every bar has a balcony and vast mobs lean over and bay at the crowd below. Men shout at women to show their tits – the reward for such a favour being a plastic-bead necklace. And while they shout at every passing female it's quickly obvious where the attention should go – to the women with quick-lift tops and a zillion bead necklaces. Some women reciprocate and demand a willy-flash for the same payment. As expected, the ratio of payers to players is suddenly reversed, with all the men happy to reveal their todgers but with few paying customers.

But you soon tire of the tits and willies and the limited conversation this creates. It's then time to head indoors and listen to some New Orleans music. Ageing rock bands bash out classics to wrecked holidaymakers, while even older jazz quartets play one last number to the hushed and sober crowd in the serious jazz halls.

The most famous of these jazz joints is Preservation Hall, and an apparent must for any visitor. I wouldn't bother. You are expected to stand in silence and listen to the music in awe. Drinking is considered disrespectful and there are very few chairs and no tables. I couldn't see a thing except some white American's back and I could do no more than quietly tap my feet.

Trust the puritan white Americans. There was I thinking jazz was a musical invention intended to rise above the hubbub of a smoky speakeasy. But no, I'm supposed to listen to jazz like it's a bloody opera. What bollocks. The very word means fuck, for fuck's sake. The music is sex. You're supposed to seduce a woman or shoot a rival, not stay mute and clap politely at the end.

And there's no need to go to these sanctums. Just about every bar has some form of live music. My favourite was a dingy tumbledown shack on the quiet edge of the French Quarter. It always had some old bugger ragging the piano for all he was worth. He sat there getting bombed on bourbon and the occasional smoke in the backyard. The place was lit by the dimmest of candles and the gloom added to the ancient ambience.

As we absorbed the mood a rat shot by, causing the shack cat to scramble from his slumber and electrifying the bar with drama. I loved it. In such a place you could grow old a contented man, reliving tales of Tennessee Williams drinking the place dry or Louis Armstrong busking on the corner.

In fact, some of the best jazz musicians *are* busking on the corner, although they have to compete with the tap-dancing kids. These crop-haired black children begging with a tap-dance summed up the Deep South to me. It looked like a scene from a past era when paddle steamers berthed laden with cotton, and women in ballooning dresses paraded in their lacy finery.

Yet the town has a bawdy air like no other. One rock bar on Bourbon decided to liven up a Thursday night with a 'Best Butt Contest' for any ladies who fancied a go. This began as an orderly dance competition, really looking for the best wiggle. But as things heated up the dancers became more adventurous. Soon it was strictly g-strings as arse after arse ground away like crazy. And as it got down to the final two – with absolutely no prize offered – the dancing became the most evocative fuck-me-now display I've ever seen. Best butt was all but forgotten as stripping, props and suggestive hand and mouth movements all came into play. The loser stormed off the stage while the winner hugged the bar owner. Both must have spent the next day wearing sunglasses and a big hat.

Such revelry had quite an impact on Mandy. We were shagging for England for the few hours a night we weren't drinking. At one point she took out Perky in the street and led him home, walking him through the hotel and into the lift. We were so fired up we never made it to the room, utilizing an armchair in the lobby on our floor instead.

In the room we were even more depraved. We had two great sessions with the nurse's uniform, one where she tied me up, in a strange mix of sexual perversities, and the other where I wore the uniform.

Indeed, New Orleans has a weird effect on your concept of the sexually normal. The tail end of Bourbon Street is the gay area, signalled by rainbow flags hanging outside the bars. Having got this far on our bar crawl it seemed a logical place for Mandy and I to end the evening. Of course we were a bit pissed from the crawl, so Mandy soon started challenging the men to be photographed with their knobs out. Not one man in the place refused her. Meanwhile I sat at the bar and watched two young studs prance on top of the counter. They wore nothing but walking boots and Calvin Klein underwear pulled down to reveal their bum cheeks.

I fell into conversation with Kelley, a blond guy from Pittsburgh. He was good-looking, married with two kids and as bent as a nine-bob note. His wife had become reconciled to his orientation as long as he was discreet. Just as he said this he broke off and called over one of the prancing underwear boys. The boy crouched down and kissed Kelley full on the mouth. Kelley casually placed his hand inside the boy's boxers and started to gently wank him. After a while the boy stood up and strolled on, the bulge in his pants looking considerably more purposeful.

New Orleans sure is one heady brew – and one that attracts America's most anarchic elements. While star-struck graduates must head for Los Angeles and the money-grabbers for New York, New Orleans' annual intake of college kids consists of those thrown out for drug abuse or for setting light to the senior principal's car during rag week. They certainly all have the look of rebellion about them.

And these don't-give-a-shit kids mix with the general stupor of the sleepy South to create the worst restaurant service known to man. You'll be shown to a filthy table and wait a week to be served. When the food finally arrives it's poorly cooked and wasn't what you ordered. While complaints are dealt with, confusions soon pile up and replacement food is likely to have that I-just-spat-in-your-omelette look to it.

The service is worst at breakfast, when New Orleans is waking up regretting the night before. One meal came looking like it had been found in yesterday's bin bag. Their appeal was that the chef had turned up drunk and promptly fallen asleep. The overnight chef stayed on but was now in the mood to fight all comers. The waitress told me she'd happily report my complaint but knew he'd want to see me in person – he was that kind of guy. I shut up and picked my way around the meal.

New Orleans' air of menace is capped by its voodoo obsession. Voodoo shops are a common sight and contain a scary assortment of objects and potions intended to take out your enemy. Advertisements brandish pictures of voodoo dolls with pins in them, accompanied by lines such as 'Keep up with your ex-lovers'.

This is a far cry from the Voodoo Museum, which points out that voodoo is a legitimate religion and not about evil spells and trancey dances at all. They claim it is unfairly attacked as witchcraft by Christians, annoyed about their use of the crucifix in ceremony – which voodooists believe represents the crossroads of life where wisdom meets fortune – and isn't heresy. The museum also shows a video of worshippers going about their faith. Unfortunately this seems almost entirely made up of people conjuring evil spells and performing trancey dances. And those crosses don't half look like they've been nicked from St Peter's round the corner.

I couldn't work out any order to the museum as beads, skulls and grotesque masks mixed with the inevitable dolls and crucifixes in a complete jumble. Meanwhile, disturbing African music rumbled in the background. Mandy soon had the willies and wanted to leave (she'd had enough of willies). I agreed – New York may have its eccentricities but New Orleans was off its bleeding rocker.

Bad karma

New York's ethnic and cultural groupings fascinated me. It seemed that every nationality had a little enclave of the city to call its own. Every nationality, that is, except the Brits. We refused to concentrate in a single area because we used to own the whole town and we'd yet to come to terms with our eviction.

It's hard to think of the Brits crowded into a few streets high up on the Upper East Side. I just couldn't imagine an intense zone of Tescos, Rose & Crowns and Taj Mahals. We're not ones to fly Union flags from car aerials and tenement windows like the Puerto Ricans and Dominicans. And I doubt they'd let us have a parade down Fifth Avenue. Indeed, a lot of the festivals seemed to celebrate our departure rather than arrival. I'd have squirmed at our attempts at a parade.

But there's one cultural grouping that quickly wound me up. And this lot aren't confined to a few streets – they're everywhere. They're also branded 100 per cent New York. The place wouldn't be the same without them – although personally I wouldn't regret the loss. And no, I don't care about any political correctness when it comes to this lot. They're a pain – fuck 'em. I wish them dead.

In fact I shouldn't have to wait too long because I'm talking about the bent double, little old grannies. There are thousands of them bashing around Manhattan and especially the Upper West Side with their stupid upright wire shopping carts. They use these carts as a walking aid-cum-battering ram. Many's the day I've been tempted to lift one of these pests into their cart and set them off down Columbus Avenue. They'd cling on for dear life as they careered past the yuppies eating brunch alfresco at Isabella's or the Ocean Grill.

Speed, or the lack of it, is a major problem with this lot. You can forget the hustle of New York if you get stuck behind one of these old bags. They're as slow as a mule train, and about as polite. They particularly like to hang out at narrow points on the sidewalk and their fascination with supermarket goods at key bottlenecks knows no bounds.

Lecturing is major problem number two. They delight in chiding anyone within earshot, as well as a few who make a passable impression of being out of range. Store owners, dog walkers, security guards, joggers and crazies

121

all get it in the neck about their shortcomings. But their favourite pastime is berating doormen. Now these poor guys have a hard enough time as it is. For a start they are forced to stand in the street dressed as 1970s' cinema ushers, complete with purple caps and Iraqi moustaches. They are employed to make residential buildings look posh and the tenants look rich. Their job description, therefore, centres on opening doors, hailing cabs, petting dogs and generally fawning about like a eunuch at the Sultan's palace.

However, the doorman's troubles really begin when he misses the beat on a particular grovel. Busy hustling one old bag into a cab he may miss a door-opening demand from another just landed in the lobby. I witnessed such an event on Park Avenue, world epicentre of brown-nosing doormen. Old bag number two, rather than use her seemingly capable and luggage-free arms to push open the door, stood and kicked it repeatedly until Saddam got to her. Venom poured from the dragon's mouth and continued in a seamless stream. Through all this, the doorman is forced to remain polite and deferential – rather than push the old cow's face into the potted tree next to the awning.

And such behaviour is not reserved for the in-house flunky. Barney's on Madison has its own doormen, employed as cab-grabbers. Now getting a cab in Manhattan is as easy as sticking your hand in the air. In Midtown just flicking your wrist to check the time usually results in a screech of brakes as yellow cabs compete for your trade. But our unique brand of New Yorker sees lifting a finger to halt one of these cabs as beneath her.

'Where *is* the doorman?' I heard one exasperated old bag shout outside Barney's.

She had no shopping and, again, perfectly functioning limbs. But was she going to stop a cab and, horror, open the bloody door herself? Does the Pope eat bagels?

I suppose I have to admit my prejudice here – my landlady. What a witch. She's a classic example of a New York granny – a hard-as-nails psycho masquerading as a sweet, frail old lady. This old bag had completely turned me over in terms of the apartment. I was paying a ridiculous rent, even by New York's standards, and I was living in a dump. Just about everything in the apartment was crap.

Let's start with the terrace – or lack of it. I arrived home every day in the expectation of some progress towards its completion, and every day I was disappointed. Very occasionally I'd arrive home to find the two brick-pier supports raised by one brick course. But most days – in fact almost always – there was nothing. And even the one-brick course days made me seethe with anger. This meant Serge had turned up, laid a total of eight bricks and promptly buggered off. Jesus Christ – in Britain four men in a Cortina could have finished the whole thing in one day.

By October all progress had come to a halt. I rang the old bag and complained.

'Oh, poor Serge,' she said. 'He's had pneumonia. He's been very ill.'

'But Serge isn't the only builder in New York,' I retorted.

She ignored this statement and just repeated, 'Poor Serge.'

She even managed to turn my failure to accept this as a reasonable excuse for three months of no progress into a propaganda victory. The next time I saw Serge – on a Saturday morning when I wasn't looking or feeling my best – he put on a creaky voice and told me about his illness. His eyes then narrowed.

'You no believe. I know.'

I'd taken to removing $500 from my rent cheque each month in protest. I said I was placing it in escrow until the bloody thing was finished. This had no effect. So I then refused to pay a penny, which coincided with a miraculous recovery by Serge who started to appear everyday.

But the terrace was just an irritation, a monument to my naivety. It was everything else that really got to me. Take the heating. The apartment had two old-fashioned ribbed radiators that added to the character of the place and looked very capable. I'd also been told New York apartments are so overheated that most tenants spend the winter with the windows flung open. And, yes, my radiators clanked to life in October as expected. Boy did they clank up. When on, my apartment sounded like the engine room of the *Titanic*. An engine room, what's more, that employed an army of midgets to squat in the basement and bang the pipes with spanners.

Meanwhile, steam hissed into the apartment. Each radiator had a valve that looked and acted like the steam whistle on a ship. Within minutes of coming on the apartment stank like a Chinese laundry and the air felt so humid I could hardly breath. In the end the only way to stop the steam was to tightly suffocate the whistles with tea towels, although this only dulled the hiss and delayed the steam.

But that wasn't all. The radiators had no on-off switch or valve and the whole system appeared to be without any form of temperature control. The radiators were either rapidly heating, with the midgets banging away like demented rock stars, or rapidly cooling, causing the floors to creak as they contracted.

The witch told me the radiators operated on a thermostat, relating to the outside temperature. In this case I had no idea New York was such a unique city. It's the only place on Earth where the temperatures rise at night and lower during the day. How else can I explain the radiators' prompt shut-down at 6p.m. – after a full day of steaming up the empty flat?

I'd arrive home to catch the dying embers of warmth and by eight the place was freezing and remained so until four in the morning when the midgets came on-shift. Not that sleep was possible anyway. As the steam filled the room I was soon gasping for air and my body chose lack of sleep over asphyxiation.

The heating went on the 'Get it sorted or you get no fucking rent' list and by some miracle New York's weather began to move in synch with the rest of the planet. At last the radiators stayed on – or rather constantly warmed and cooled – all night.

But this didn't warm the apartment, oh no. The two French doors to the non-existent terrace had been completed a while before I moved in. Yet Serge had learnt his building skills in the west – the Wild West. One door stuck at the bottom but had daylight visible at the top. But this was better than the door that didn't stick. A skinny couple could shake hands through the gap in that door – assuming of course there was something to support somebody standing outside, which, of course, there wasn't.

Eventually I bought a hardware store's entire stock of insulation tape and sealed the doors and even the wood panelling. My wonderful shag-palace of an apartment, with such lovely period features, ended up looking like a playpen for senile *Blue Peter* presenters.

The next problem was noise. New York is a noisy city but I thought I'd planned well to avoid the worst. I had a rear-facing flat in as quiet a residential area as Manhattan can offer. There's little traffic and the whoo-whoo of the sirens was dulled as my apartment faced a series of back gardens.

Great, except I hadn't planned for some idiot hanging

up giant bamboo wind chimes in an effort to induce good karma.

Karma my arse. I was frantic.

These huge hollow trees boomed out mad tunes to the slightest breeze. It sounded like a hyperactive five-year old playing the glockenspiel through an amplifier. You try sleeping through that. I certainly couldn't – especially once the weather became more tempestuous. And I couldn't complain because I didn't know where they were. I couldn't see the things, no matter how hard I looked. Eventually I realized they must be hanging from a roof garden above me but I felt too foolish to knock up every apartment and ask them if they owned the wind chimes and, if so, could they please turn the volume down.

The internal noise was little better. The wall at the head of my bed seemed to have a kitchen the other side with the work counters no more than inches from where I slept. Every cup, spoon, knife and plate placed on a counter echoed round my bedroom. I knew when my neighbours cooked, when they washed up and when they made coffee. One night they were trying to cook rice. How do I know? Because they split the pack and it spilt all over the floor. I shot out of bed convinced the ceiling was falling in.

As if the noise wasn't enough, I had to contend with the plumbing. The shower tap developed a habit of producing water only after three minutes of gurgling like a child trying to spew. Although making plenty of noise, not a drop would come out. Every morning it did this, to the point where the first thing I'd do on rising was turn on the tap. I'd then have to occupy myself for a few minutes before it spluttered into life.

And the plughole was just as bad. It took more and more time for the water to drain until one day it decided it couldn't be bothered anymore. I returned from work to find my morning shower water still there, although now a revolting rust colour.

I'd had enough. I rang our absentee superintendent. His name was Sam, not that I ever spoke to him. Instead I was always greeted by a patronizing message that said in an emergency I could page him but, 'please, only in the case of a *real* emergency.'

I took to leaving messages that said, 'In my view this is a *real* emergency and I'll ring you once an hour until it's *really* sorted.'

It wasn't sorted by my efforts, though. Keith and Liz had similar problems next door. In fact they were so pissed off they were close to burning effigies of the land-lady, and I noticed their flat now contained a worrying voodooish shrine. But while they waited for the magic to work they rang their lawyers. He got the superintendent round in no time. Rent strikes and lawyers, it's the only language these old bags understand.

Get outta my face, motherfucker

I never thought I'd get used to the skyscrapers, but I did. At some point I strolled among the Midtown canyons and a little compartment in my brain didn't whisper 'Wow'. At around the same time I walked by the Empire State Building and didn't look up. And eventually even the World Trade Center began to look more like two upright toothpaste boxes than the thrusting feat of engineering I once thought them to be.

But it didn't mean I was bored with New York. Far from it. It meant I'd realized New York isn't special because of the skyscrapers. Any old town can throw up oversized chunks of glass and steel. It's the little things that give New York its flavour, not the monoliths.

My favourite zone became the area between City Hall and 23rd Street. This is the home of New York's soul. From a distance, this two-mile stretch looks like Manhattan's pause between the dual New York business centres of Midtown and the Financial District. But up close it's the New York with all the spice. This low-rise band of neighbourhoods was the original New York melting pot. It housed all the ethnic enclaves: the East European Jews of the Lower East, the Italians of Little Italy and the Chinese of Chinatown.

These were the people who made New York. They crammed into nineteenth-century tenement housing and moulded the image of New Yorkers we love and loathe today. But while some areas, such as Chinatown, retain their cultural feel, most have given way to the yuppies. As in London, rootless suburban whites have developed a taste for the earthy grit of the urban masses. They've moved in, dressed down and hung out. And they've smoothed the very rough edges they craved. The well hard New York of old is still there but it now sits cheek by jowl with beatnik coffee bars and oh-so-radical clothes stores.

Yet the faddish restaurants can't hide the ragged Victorian-boom buildings overhead. And they wouldn't want to obscure the black Zs of the iron fire escapes scaling every building like ladders up a board game. The escapes make *West Side Story* come alive.

The billboards bring you back to modern New York. They cover every bare tenements' side wall but underline, rather than mask, the shabby buildings. Giant models flaunt their decadence and sneer at the pathetic mortals on the street below. They are DKNY gods with hands the size of trees and shirt buttons as big as a pizza.

The tenements are capped with flat roofs supporting raised water towers. These squat cylinders with cone tops are a symbol of old New York. They look like cartoon space rockets as they sit on stilts primed for take-off. Tintin and Snowy should be climbing the short ladder while Thomson and Thompson fret near by. The towers litter the view like windmills across a prairie. They *are* a sign: 'New York No Miles.' You've made it, grab a coffee and soak up the atmosphere.

And old New York has atmosphere oozing from every crevice – it even comes out the drains. Swirls of white vapour pour from the manholes creating curtains of thick air that linger in the streets. Yellow cabs emerge through the mist like models on a catwalk or dancers in a nightclub. It's as if Manhattan is sitting on a stirring volcano or a bubbling cauldron. In winter, clouds of steam belch from orange pipes like a giant's breath and rise in fingers to flicker at the buildings. But even in summer the manholes simmer away with wisps licking at the passing wheels. To walk the streets and kick through a steam cloud is to know you're in the coolest city on the planet (this town's so hip it even has its own dry-ice machines).

The street furniture adds to the effect and falls in with the beat. Take the yellow pedestrian crossings. DONT WALK. WALK. *WOW!* First-time visitors to the city get their initial buzz of excitement when they see those signs. As soon as the orange DONT WALK turns to the white WALK they cross with a swaggering, 'Hey, I'm a New Yorker – get outta my face, motherfucker.'

And the fire hydrants. They are a classic bit of New York ironmongery. They sit like manly squat knobs halfway along every street. In fact they look like miniature firemen, their dome tops mimicking the yellow helmets. Then there's the red emergency-call posts, with buttons for the police or fire department. They look like mantelpiece clocks, are covered in about a thousand layers of paint and drip with nostalgia. You can see Officer Dibble chasing Top Cat down an alley or Officer Krupke confronting the feuding Jets and Sharks. I almost want to be mugged so I can stagger to the post and breathe 'They got me,' before collapsing in the gutter. A crowd will gather as Kojak arrives through swirling lights. Some crazy bitch saw it all happen but hell, the Limey son-ofabitch had it comin'.

NOVEMBER

Village idiots

New Yorkers are well into their neighbourhoods. They claim every district has its own flavour and is a distinct community within the city. Locals are fiercely loyal to their few blocks and love nothing more than a good bitch about everywhere else.

Of course, all this bitching is a complete load of bollocks. It's just New Yorkers doing what they do best – hanging about up their own arses. For a start, all the districts look the same. Both Gramercy and Chelsea are urban areas made up of straight streets, residential terraces and apartment blocks. Both are a mix of delis, Starbucks, Gaps and duane reades. But you wouldn't know that to listen to the debates. You'd think Chelsea was an alpine resort and Gramercy a Cornish fishing village.

And the people are pretty much the same mix of young professionals, old grannies and ethnic families. Sure, the ethnic flavour may change, but they're not the ones banging on about their neighbourhoods. They want to save up enough money to move to the suburbs, leaving the white yuppies to argue over which area's the most bohemian.

Such snobbery can occur on a minute scale. I had the

following conversation with an attractive woman in a bar.

'Where do you live?' she asked.

'On the Upper West Side.'

'Hey, so do I – whereabouts?'

'On 88th Street.'

'Oh,' downward crease of mouth. 'That's a little high. I never go above 86th Street.'

'Why, are you scared of heights?' I asked.

'Er, no,' she looked at me quizzically.

'Oh, well what about the cold?' I said. 'Too far north for you is it? Those two blocks make for a shorter summer?'

'Er, no,' her quizzical look deepened.

'Sorry, it's just that I thought you may have a logical reason.'

'I just think it a little far up, that's all. 88th and what?'

'88th and Central Park West.'

'Oh,' now she was smiling, 'that's pretty. And right by the park. I thought you meant 88th and Amsterdam.' (88th and Amsterdam is two blocks over.)

'Oh heavens no, I never go there – yuk.'

'No, I don't blame you.'

Oh yes, that famous American instinct for irony. Still she had big tits so I suspect she gets along fine without it.

But the crime of living too far north is nothing – a mere traffic offence – compared to the serious felony of not living in Manhattan. People who don't live in Manhattan are called the Bridge and Tunnel brigade. Nightclub and restaurant reviewers can kill an establishment by awarding them the dreaded B&T moniker, as in 'B&Ts love it at the weekend'. Cabaret hosts can condemn a leaving party by shouting 'Take the bridge, it's safer' to the delight of those staying late because they obviously live in Manhattan. And any hint that you're a

B&Ter has you out of a conversation with a Manhattanite immediately.

One clear hint that you're a B&Ter is a genuine New York accent. Few native New Yorkers live in Manhattan, happy to swap the high rents for a garden. Meanwhile the 'urban' snobs that insult them are recent New York immigrants, brought up in Wantaway, Ohio or Squarepeg, Pennsylvania.

Back in Manhattan the neighbourhood nonsense has been extended to the naming of areas. Now New York has a problem with district names which is mainly due to its youth. London's districts – such as Fulham or Camden – have genuine names reaching back into the dark ages when one geezer and his geese decided to start a hamlet. Manhattan, meanwhile, was a rocky island full of gullible savage nomads. There were no ready-made names other than Manahatta for the whole island.

Yet from early on New York was planned as a large metropolis. Some poor bugger wandered the whole island with a tape measure and pegged out one mother of a city. And when he plotted the New York grid, our surveyor wasn't saying, 'I know, I'm wearing blue today, let's call these fifteen blocks Chelsea.'

To him they were simply West 14th to 30th Street. So at some point in the history of West 14th to 30th Street someone had to say, 'I'm fed up with calling this area West 14th to 30th Street, I'm gonna think of a better name. Hmmm, Chelsea. Yeah, that sounds nice. Chelsea it is.' In fact it was probably a real-estate agent wanting to put 10 per cent on the value of the tiny apartments he was selling – and he wasn't thinking of Stamford Bridge.

Realtors can be the only explanation for much of the silly district naming that goes on here, especially the newish fad of creating compound names. This is where bits of street names or district names are added to compass points or other indicators to produce a name for an area that hadn't previously felt the need. SoHo is the most famous and a name I can understand. It's the area SOuth of HOuston Street (pronounced House-ton). It also follows that people who live north of Houston aren't going to wait for a catchy name to drop from the sky. They'll say, 'That's a clever idea. Hey everyone, we now live in NoHo.'

I can also, at a stretch, live with Tribeca – or TriBeCa. This means the TRIangle BElow CAnal – the triangle created by the Hudson River cutting in towards the bow of Manhattan. But it still suggests a few people are talking up a bit of a scruffy area.

It's after Tribeca that things get silly. One new area is Nolita – NOrth of Little ITAly. I'm told this name is about three years old. It's a clear signal the hipsters are moving in: setting up bars, opening art galleries and generally being chic while waiting for daddy's monthly cheque.

And the creation of Nolita has opened the asylum doors. A recent invention is Dumbo: Down Under Manhattan Bridge Overpass. Lots of hairy-arsed artists in oversized sweaters now do arty things in Dumbo, previously a post-industrial smashed-up zone not worthy of a name. Then someone told me about Grampus – GRAMercy Prior to Union Square. Now get a grip, man. This is about two blocks in size. Actually I reckon this was something my storyteller thought of while popping out for coffee. He's since told everyone he's met in order to try and make his mark on New York.

Well, bugger it. If he can name districts then so can I. I've invented Lesbian – Lower East Side Between little Italy And Norfolk street; Evil Deaddd – East VILlage Due EAst of the Di and Dodi Deli (it does exist) on Second Avenue; and BeNoSo – BEtween NOho and SOho. This is the central reservation on Houston Street.

And that, lads, is how you humiliate your boss

November brought a stroke of luck – a free trip home. A departmental get-together, an 'Offsite', was to be held at a converted Surrey abbey, starting Sunday evening. It'd be good to meet some of the old gang: Karl, an anal German who was so direct you'd think he was trying to get you sacked; Kevin, a Mancunian by birth but now living in Chelmsford, poor lad; Rhys, a Welshman, and a major rival for Mandy; and, of course, Rip Van Winkle and Energizer Bunny.

Braveheart had split the department into teams. Kevin and Flatcap were in with other Northerners and named the Flatcaps, to the delight of Flatcap himself. Karl, Rip Van Winkle and assorted Spaniards and Italians became Eurotrash, and Rhys, as well as any Scots and Irish, became the Celts. Other teams were selected using less flattering criteria. The Southern Softies was a thinly disguised jibe at the public-school boys in the department, the Bankers were the old, grey commercial bankers (no cockney rhyming slang reference intended, I think) and Energizer Bunny and myself were in the Wide Boys – again to the delight of Flatcap.

The first day started well enough, with Barry, the laid-back Aussie, receiving all the early flak for oversleeping. No allowance was made for the fact that an 8 a.m. start in Surrey was 3 a.m. in New York and we were virtually just off the plane. Barry's team was deducted ten points and he was in the doghouse.

I lasted until lunch with no slip-ups and as the afternoon session was to be run by a team-building guru – here to infuse a sense of common purpose among the troops – I relaxed. Oh how I wish I had stopped there.

Braveheart came and sat near the Wide Boys as the

guru launched into his talk about team leadership by showing film clips which demonstrated either good or bad practice. For the good we saw *Apollo 13*, where teams in Mission Control were trying to build model solutions to the capsule's problems. We also had the scene from *Henry V* where our 'Arry tells the nervous English soldiery what glory awaits them for fighting the Frogs at Agincourt.

For the bad he showed the 1970s' film *Kes*, about a Yorkshire lad's obsession with a kestrel. The scene was a school football match on a frozen pitch in mid-winter. A conceited PE instructor was the ref as well as the centre forward for one of the teams. He kicked off but the opposition soon dispossessed him and were attacking. Through being ref he regained control for his side, awarded himself a penalty and ordered it retaken after the snot-ridden goalie saved it. This time he scored and turned to his team in triumph, shouting, 'And that, lads, is how you take a penalty.'

I couldn't help it. I'd played too many five-a-side matches with Braveheart. Too many times Braveheart had decided he'd been fouled or goals had been disallowed for obscure reasons and others allowed, although patently illegal.

'Is that Braveheart playing five-a-side or what?' I said to the room.

They all laughed. Oh yes, they laughed and laughed until the guru became curious. He wanted to share the joke. Braveheart's face reddened and he stumbled his words. Shit, I'd embarrassed the managing director. I should have realized that Braveheart desperately wanted to be seen as the Houston Mission Controller or Henry V – not the vain ref in *Kes*.

Braveheart made a deathly pledge of revenge.

The guru next introduced a film on a trainer who'd hardened the Scottish women's crown-green bowls team by asking us to think of a conservative sport in a conservative country.

We all guessed away and my pseudo-bloody-intellectualism just had to come to the fore.

'Archery in Bhutan,' I suggested.

In fact it was so noisy no-one heard, except Braveheart.

'Archery in Bhutan,' Braveheart repeated with cruelty in his voice. 'This one here has suggested archery in Bhutan.'

This was the cue for the room to collapse laughing. OK, one-all.

But Braveheart didn't settle for draws, oh no. The clips moved on. The next film focused on an athlete who'd lost his reputation over a drugs scandal. No matter what he did, said the guru, this man was never going to win back his reputation. I felt a kick and looked to see a glinting Braveheart.

'Are you listening to this?' he said.

Christ, I really had offended him.

Things were not about to improve.

The session ended with pre-dinner drinks. An excitable mood now pervaded the gathering, which, with the free-flowing red wine with dinner, soon had me drunk. I lost track of time. It must have been ten at the latest when we returned to the bar, although still only five in New York. The beer just kept coming. Some of the old drinking gang were absent – no Braveheart, no Energizer Bunny. Then Rip Van Winkle disappeared. These hardened party animals all seemed to go to bed remarkably early, although I was told it was one-thirty.

Eventually a hardcore remained. By this time I was so pissed I started pointing at individuals and telling them whether I thought them sexy or not. This was the men.

I'm told it was around four when we gave up. And I'm told I asked Barry to make sure I was up by eight – not a wise move, given his track record.

The telephone finally shook me awake. I fumbled for the handset and it fell to the floor. As I retrieved it I could already hear swearing.

'It's gone fucking eight,' shouted Energizer Bunny. 'Get your fucking arse down here now.'

Oh fuck, I felt terrible.

I crawled to the bathroom.

Oh fuck, I looked terrible.

I stumbled into some clothes and staggered down the hall: unshaven, unwashed, hair sticking up, face like Frank Bruno after a trip to Vegas.

I sneaked into the meeting room hoping not to be spotted but a chorus of sarcastic moans rang out – my 'hey I'm OK about this' grin looking very unconvincing. The scoreboard already had minus ten chalked by the Wide Boys.

'Twat,' said Energizer Bunny as I sat down.

I looked around hoping some of my fellow drunks had also failed to make it. No such luck.

Boy I felt like shit. By lunch I was a physical and emotional wreck. I'd sat silently through the sessions and contributed zero to the team exercises. Kevin and Barry were also feeling pretty bad and the three of us sat quietly scoffing food in the dining room.

'I only made it down at one minute to eight,' said Kevin, trying to console me.

A minute that may have saved your career, mate.

Barry didn't have the vaguest memory of being reminded to wake me.

To our horror, Braveheart joined us.

'Flatcap was talking to me this morning,' said Braveheart. 'And Bob, he's sorely disappointed with your performance. Especially after we paid for your flight.'

By the end of the session – and with a surprise Eurotrash victory – I was consumed with guilt and felt I'd better carry out some damage limitation.

138

I shuffled up to Flatcap and looked at the ground. 'Braveheart tells me you're pretty angry about my performance today,' I said. 'I'm sorry – I feel I've let you down.'

Christ, I felt like a little boy.

'I haven't said a bloody word to him about it,' he said. He gave me a broad smile. 'Son, I think you've been wound up.'

I turned to see Braveheart chuckling. Victory was his.

Don't rate yours much

Overall, Braveheart's message was positive. Many of our old commercial bank ways were disappearing, normally coinciding with the disappearance of the old commercial bankers. We were becoming more Red Suspenders and less Brown Shoes. We weren't yet chicken but we were no longer obvious burgers, and the Americans were pleased with our progress.

The key to this change in perception was our view of risk. In the old days we'd hand out money and just hope to get it back. We'd stick a finger in the air, put an ear to the ground, squint, and say, 'Yep, we'll get it back.'

But that was no longer good enough. Now we had to work out the odds of some bugger running off with the cash. I mean really – mathematically – what were the chances of a default?

Real investment bankers always look at risk this way because those odds determine the price an investor will pay to buy a loan or bond in the capital markets. As the risk changes so the price changes, allowing you to always calculate the real value of the loans you hold at any given moment. Bond and loan valuations are the opposite of stocks and shares in this respect. Share prices reflect the potential future earnings of a company. With bonds and loans the earnings are known – it's the interest rate. So the market price reflects the likelihood of the borrower not repaying.

Such calculations are way beyond your average investment banker so the banks employ a series of companies – called ratings agencies – to look at loan and bond issues and rate the risk. Of course the whole ratings exercise is shrouded in gobbledegook, only understandable to the initiated. Yet, as ever, it's really remarkably simple.

The most commonly used gobbledegook is Standard & Poor's, the largest of the ratings agencies. They use a series of letters and symbols to rate the creditworthiness of a borrower. The least risky are rated AAA, 'triple-A' in the gobbledegook. A triple-A borrower is like, say, the US or UK government – certain to pay on the nose. Next down is double-A plus, then double-A, double-A minus, single A plus and so on.

Most big companies are safely in the double-As and ranked as low risk. The real risk starts when the rating falls below 'triple-B minus'. This is when ratings stop being titled Investment Grade, or unlikely to default, and become Speculative Grade, or junk. Junk bonds have high returns but the risk to match. If you don't know what you're doing in the junk market you could wave off your cash at the dockside only to watch it sink in the harbour.

But Braveheart was keen to show the Americans we knew what we were doing. He declared that any deal involving the use of the bank's money could rank no lower than a single-A. We'd calculate this by first taking the S&P rating for the borrower. Then we'd knock it up a few notches if we managed to improve the risk through our box and arrow structures.

Single-A was tough. Our Receivables structures came up against an S&P rule that said no borrower could be rated above the country where it was located. S&P rated Russia double-B minus and Brazil triple-B minus. Both well below our threshold. We could draw all the boxes and arrows we liked, we still had a Brazilian borrower, and that meant a triple-B minus rating, tops.

Every deal I'd done as a banker was underwater. I was going to have to completely reinvent myself or drown.

Of course these ratings had a second, informal, use in the office. They were a ranking system for members of the opposite sex. No scoring story was complete without a rating, which we'd all assume had been enhanced a few notches. If someone came in Monday morning claiming to have bagged a triple-B minus you knew we were really in major junk territory and any self-respecting guy would have rather shagged a hot dog.

Most claimed to play only in the double-A bracket but I'd seen this lot in action too many times for such claims to be believable. They'd go for junk women every time. In fact many had adopted 'Go ugly early' as their slogan for pulling success. They only seemed to win the double-As when they were on their own. Funny, that. And, yes, I'd been keeping a mental note of my near conquests in New York.

	Rating	Considerations
Bernadette	AA (honest)	Porsched-up power keg with big ex
Zoe	A+	Liked my pickle, less sure about Perky
Bridget	BBB–	Oregano with dodgy rating
Melanie	A–	Loved my lines but visiting from Miami.

I was about to meet a triple-A.

Who dares wins

Nat and I stood in Prohibition, an Upper West Side high-light only four blocks from my apartment. While most New York bars were really restaurants, Prohibition was really a bar – it just happened to serve food. Soul bands played most nights and it was usually packed with single women.

It was a perfect place to bring Ricky, the latest of Fiona's boys over from London. Ricky was an exotic-looking man with long dark hair woven into a pigtail, olive skin and black-rimmed Chris Evans glasses. He was a great lad, with a big smile and a loud laugh.

Ricky had quickly developed the euphoria of the English male in New York. Stunning women wet their knickers at the way he spoke and he couldn't get enough of it. He was out every night trawling the bars and trying out his English accent on any woman who'd listen. And he was soon off into the crowd at Prohibition.

'I'm awfully sorry,' I could hear him saying as he cut through the crowd. 'Will you excuse me please. Thank you very much indeed. So kind.'

He was casting lines into abundant waters.

Nat and I regarded him like old fishermen watching the boy. We stood at the bar knocking back Tanqueray and tonics as we talked about the Miami girls, Melanie and Ellie. The trip up the Empire State had ended with a session back at my place. But while Melanie had been content to kiss and cuddle and swap sexual banter, Nat had shagged Ellie on my sofa. He was planning a trip to Miami and they emailed each other constantly. Great.

As we talked, three women made their way through the crowd to get to the bar. The one trying to order the drinks had to lean across me to catch the barman. I moved to give her room.

'Thank you,' she said.

'You're very welcome,' I said, pressing the English toff button.

'Hey, where you from?' she asked.

'I'm from the Upper West Side,' I retorted. 'This is my local.'

'Well it's certainly got posh round here,' she said.

My accent was obviously improving – most Americans assume the British are Australians unless they sound like Prince Charles straining on the bog.

She was called Brandi and was the least attractive of the three, although still a single-A. Her friend was Krystal. She was a stunner, a triple-A if ever there was one. I couldn't take my eyes off her. She clumsily tripped through the crowd blocking out the third woman, Kerry (AA – leggy blonde but with a stern face). They were all Upper West Siders, although originally from Atlanta.

Krystal said something inaudible to Brandi and they turned to me.

'We think you've got a great fanny,' said Brandi.

Nat and I collapsed laughing.

'I have a great fanny?'

'Yes,' she confirmed. 'At least Krystal and I think so.'

She patted my Levi's on the bum.

'That's a fanny?' I asked, patting her bum.

'That's a fanny,' she responded, again patting my bum.

We were getting on fine.

'That's not a fanny in Britain,' I said.

'Oh, what's a fanny in Britain?' Brandi asked.

I thought about patting it, I really did. But we weren't getting on *that* well.

'Well only women have them,' I said.

'Oh gee.' She pretended to be shocked but she loved it

– Trevor's theory of mentioning sex in the first two minutes proving to be spot on.

'What d'you call that?' she asked, after a further pat.

'Bum. Tell me I've got a great bum.'

'Well Robert,' she winked. 'We think you've got a great bum.'

This was followed by another pat, well more of a grope, of my arse.

By now Nat was talking to Krystal and Ricky had spotted the opportunity and joined us, no doubt practising a few 'awfully awfullys' on the way over.

But it was such a tight corner the six of us couldn't stand together. We immediately became three pairs, with Brandi and I hemmed in by the bar. We chatted about Atlanta, although I couldn't concentrate. I was infatuated with Krystal. She talked with Nat, although she kept exchanging glances with me.

Christ, she was cute. She was small, she had a lovely face, she had dark hair and she had a shapely figure. She ticked all my boxes – Standard & Poor's would definitely give her top rating. And she was itching to swap places with Brandi. Finally she abandoned Nat and clambered across, offering him no excuse or link. Nat didn't seem bothered. I expect he thought Brandi the attractive one anyway. After all, she'd been talking to me.

After a while Brandi suggested a move to a West Village bar called Automatic Slims.

The West Village is the cutesy side of Greenwich Village with cobblestone streets and small red-brick houses. The south end of the West Village is the quiet residential end, although there was nothing quiet about Automatic Slims. It was brimming with people and in full party mode. It was one sweaty huddle as club anthems belted out. People danced on the chairs, on the tables and even on the bar. The place felt full of promise.

And when they played Will Smith's *Gettin' Jiggy Wit It*, Automatic Slims seemed fit to burst. This was New York's favourite summer hit and Krystal and I wriggled away frantically. Then we stopped dead and had a lovely, lingering kiss. It was almost a friendly 'you're mine but let's carry on partying' snog. We were cool. Nothing heavy. She was absolutely fucking gorgeous.

Four a.m. approached. Unwilling to let the night die, Brandi asked the bouncer where we could go to beat closing time. He knew somewhere and poured us into a cab, leaving Nat and Kerry to go home separately. We ended up in a basement bar God knows where. It had no sign outside but one mother of a bouncer on the door. Having no sign normally means the bar is hyper-trendy. But this place wasn't trendy. It was a Mafia hangout full of seriously mean Italian-Americans wearing baggy suits. The men looked like they were relaxing after a day spent shooting their relations and handing out horses' heads.

I was too drunk for this place. I became overexcited.

'We're hangin' wit da Mob,' I shouted. 'I'm gonna make ya an offer ya cannot refuse. Salut.'

I was trying to be Al Pacino, Robert de Niro and Marlon Brando all in one. Mind you, so were most of the guys in the place.

I wanted to go and speak to a mobster. I thought it'd be great. But, as Ricky pointed out, I was very pissed and might end up in the backyard trash or bobbing down the Hudson with no face. I satisfied myself with staring at a gangster's moll. She had a particularly low neckline barely hiding the most gargantuan breasts. I pointed them out to Brandi and Krystal.

'They're not real,' insisted Brandi. 'They can't be.'

'They're real big,' said Krystal, 'but they could be genuine.'

'They're fake I'm telling you. They're too pert. If

they were real they'd be down to her knees.'

'It may be a good bra,' said Krystal.

'I know,' I suggested. 'I'll give one of you a dare.'

This changed everything.

'No, no, no,' they both shouted, jumping up and down in excitement.

'Her, her, her,' they both pointed at each other. 'Not me, her. Her, her, her.'

Neither refused to do it. They just wanted me to choose the other one. I had total power.

'OK, two dares,' I said. 'One asks her and I'll think of something else for the other.'

'Her, her, her,' they shouted, jumping up and down in front of me.

It was enough to give me a hard-on, which may explain why I was prepared to play Russian roulette in a bar that looked like a scene out of *GoodFellas*.

'I'll flip a coin,' I suggested.

'Heads, heads, heads,' they shouted in unison.

Krystal gave me a sensual kiss.

'Heads,' she said.

'She's heads,' I agreed.

I flipped. 'Tails, sorry.'

Krystal steeled herself and went over to the woman while we stood well back. The woman's boyfriend looked seriously menacing. I didn't envy Krystal, although she seemed to be getting on OK. The three of them chatted away for a minute or so before they all exploded with laughter.

Krystal came back.

'What did you say?' we asked.

'Well I was very polite 'n' all and said that I was no lesbian but we jus' couldn't help admiring her. I said we liked her dress and that she had beautiful hair. I then kinda jus' looked at her bust and said, gee, are those for real?'

146

'And what did she say?' I asked.

Krystal put on a deep macho voice.

'Real enough, baby,' she said. 'Real enough.' It seemed mean to point out that the question hadn't been answered.

'My turn, my turn,' Brandi jumped up like a dog begging for a biscuit.

'OK,' I said. 'Go up to that guy and give him a sloppy kiss on the lips.'

'Tongues?'

'Tongues.'

Brandi took a big slug of her vodka and moved in. He wasn't a bad-looking lad – a young Italian stud with that arrogant bored look. He leaned casually against a wall. Brandi stood in front of him for about a second. He coolly regarded her, not budging an inch. Then she planted her lips on his and opened her mouth. I could see a flash of tongue.

He was great. He didn't move. He accepted the kiss as if strange women were always coming up to him and shoving their tongues down his throat.

She returned in triumph.

'My turn, my turn,' said Krystal.

It took time to think of the next one. We were standing in an area near the door, by a wall dotted with small, ornate pictures. They had deep wooden frames and looked pretty valuable.

'OK Krystal,' I said. 'Steal one of the paintings.'

'Oh my God,' they both screamed. 'Oh my God.'

We spent a few minutes studying the pictures. We checked for hooks and catches, knocked them to see if they were secure and generally mooched around like thieves before a heist. Then Krystal took a painting off the wall, put it under her coat, put her coat under her arm, linked her arm in mine and strolled out with a cheery 'Goodnight' to the bouncer. We walked onto the street, hailed a cab, bundled in and shot off. Once we were beyond the corner we collapsed in delight.

What a woman.

We dropped Ricky off home and headed north for the Upper West Side. I paid off the cab at their place and they invited me up. After cracking open a few beers we played around with the painting. Eventually a nail was drunkenly banged in with the heel of a shoe and their trophy was mounted.

After a while Brandi yawned, said something about walking the dog in the morning and slipped off to bed. Krystal gave me a cuddle.

'Come on,' she said. 'Come up and tuck me in.'

Her room was tiny – really just an entrance hall from a roof garden. She put on some music and we lay on the bed and kissed. She was beautiful, and what a girl.

'I'm gonna get ready for bed,' she said and undressed in front of me. She cleaned her teeth in the adjacent bathroom and said I could do the same.

When I came back she was fast asleep.

Muffin the mule

I woke with Krystal in my arms. It wasn't a romantic awakening. My ear was resting by the phone when it rang.

'Jesus Christ,' I said, starting violently.

Krystal answered it.

'Hmmm?'

Pause.

'Urr huuu.'

There was a long pause.

She was lying on her front with a white sheet clinging to her body. She looked like a sculpture – her revealed

148

back taut and firm, her neck so slender, her wrapped bum a curved delight. Make that an angel.

'Jeez, mom,' she exploded with impatience. 'It's eight in the morning. I love ya 'n' all, but can't you ring me later and tell me about ya darn vacation.'

And with that she put the phone down.

'Uhhh,' she turned to me. 'My mom. She thinks we're in bed at ten and up at dawn, like her.'

She lay her head on my chest, brushing my stomach with her hand. Then she started to kiss my nipple, very gently at first but then quite hard – almost biting it. All the time her hand brushed my stomach, moving lower and lower with every sweep.

Of course old Perky didn't have a hangover. He was wide awake, raring to go. He climbed up to meet her hand, panting away like an over-keen puppy.

Whoops, I thought – not again. But Krystal was different. She just took it in her palm and began to gently wank me. She continued these strokes and kissed my ear, biting the lobe. She kissed my neck, then my shoulder. She kissed my chest, went back to my nipples, down to my stomach – oh my God.

Her long hair brushed my abdomen like a veil, preventing the full view. Behind, her head rocked up and down on my knob.

The screen was just as well. If I could've seen what I felt I'd have exploded there and then. And that wasn't the plan, oh no. This was where I showed her what I could do, oh yes. I cupped her face and moved to kiss her lips. Perky protested at the interruption but his turn would come. First, I had to work.

I moved her onto her back and began to massage her as we kissed, rubbing her thighs, her calves, her feet. I moved to kiss her ears, then her neck, then her chest. I used my tongue to surround her tiny erect nipples, avoiding full contact, using my breath, pretending to bite. I kissed her stomach, I kissed her sides, I kissed her thighs. She opened her legs and sighed with pleasure. She wanted it and she was going to get it. But first I'd tease her to hell and back.

Then she did a delightful thing. As I kissed her toes and rubbed her inner thigh, her hand moved down and gently rubbed her clit – wow. Forget the teasing, we were going in. My mouth joined her hand and together we massaged her vagina. I forced my nose hard on her button, my tongue darting into the crease of fragrant flesh. She ground against my face, forcing herself to a loud, crushing climax.

'Ohhh, ohhh, *ohhhhhh*,' she screamed.

She was so loud Brandi must have thought we had intruders – and intruders that gave damn fine head. Certainly the dog started to bark, which broke the spell. Krystal relaxed.

'Wait,' she said and went to her bathroom, my eyes following her cute little bum as it wiggled about. She scratched around in a cupboard and came back with a condom: yes, yes, yes – *YEEESSS*.

Krystal tried to put it on but fumbled it so my knob ended up looking more like a jester's balloon than a sex weapon primed for action. So I took it off and applied it myself before moving on top of her.

She was tiny, a little rose beneath me as I slowly moved in and out. I increased the pace very steadily as she smiled up and delicately rubbed my back. I kissed every part of her face, my breath more urgent with the quickening strokes.

Fucking urgent, as it happened. The booze the night before had left me seriously knackered and I was beginning to lose the rhythm. I slowed again. I put my body very close to hers and cautiously moved in and out, trying to recover. Yet she bucked her behind to speed me up. She wanted a hard fuck and I was being told to get a move on. I began to feel like a mule being whipped up a hill.

But she was the one on the hill. She was considering a second orgasm and wanted it hard and fast – something Muffin here was having serious trouble delivering. I ground away like a slave in the sun.

'Yeah, yeah,' she said to encourage me. 'Yeah, yeah.'

Buck, buck.

Any notion of romance was over. This was pure porno filth fucking. She wanted to come and rent-a-dick here had to sort it. Pant, pant, pant as I slowly pushed her up the hill – it felt like I was pushing a car up the fucking thing.

'Yeah, yeah . . . ohh, yeah, ohh yeah . . . yeahhhhhhh . . .' buck, buck.

'Pant, pant . . . ohh fuck, ohh fuck . . . pant, pant . . .'

'Yeahhhh, yeah . . . ohhhhh, ohhh, *OHHHH* . . .'

'Rough, rough, rough,' the dog started on cue.

'*Fuuuucccck.*' I collapsed.

There was no prospect of me coming – the dog stood more chance than I did. Just stopping felt like an orgasm.

Krystal didn't hang around for the soppy post-shag chat. She announced she had to work. She was a part-time hostess in a trendy restaurant and she had ten minutes to get ready. As she faffed in the bathroom I fell asleep, the condom still hanging from my droopy willy.

It felt like she was gone hours as I lapsed into a deep coma. But she returned soon enough, wearing a knock-out sarong. I must have looked like shit but she was back in full angel mode – you'd have thought she'd gone to bed the same time as her mother.

I quickly dressed and we walked down to the street. In the few months I'd lived in New York I'd never seen the city at this time on a Sunday morning, although it was around ten. It looked lovely. The sun shone, the air felt

151

clean and dogs had shiny coats. Joggers looked like they were enjoying themselves, people smiled and said 'Good morning' to each other and Jimmy Stewart walked by whistling. Everything seemed marvellous. Either that or I'd just made love to the woman of my dreams.

We arranged a mid-week dinner and parted. And as I walked the ten blocks north I thought about where to take her. It would have to be somewhere romantic, somewhere I could find out everything about her, somewhere I could stare in her eyes and imagine what the kids would look like.

I walked on air all week. I felt so confident. I flirted with all the women at work. I could have you, oh yes. You'd be mine if I wanted, for sure. I'm such a catch – just look at the babe I'm dating.

Such was my sexual prowess I decided to do something a bit naughty. I emailed Tina, a girl I'd met with Nat in Prohibition the week before. Nat had been paired up with her friend. I keyed in Tina@platinumbooks.com and sent her a message. Nothing provocative – well not at first, anyway.

'Remember me? I'm the guy you abandoned outside Prohibition. After such a good chat as well.'

About two hours later I received a reply.

'I remember everything. I remember leaving you. You poor lamb, left on your own. Sorry, but I had to make sure my friend got home safely. She was very drunk.'

I left it an hour.

'How is your friend? Did Nat ever call her? But also, how are you? Surprised to hear from me? Pleased?'

We were now down to forty minutes between replies.

'My friend's fine. Nat didn't call. No chemistry. Surprised to hear from you? Of course not, men always want more of me, ha, ha. Pleased? Of course.'

Twenty minutes later I wrote back.

152

'Chemistry?'

Ten minutes.

'Chemistry.'

Tina was on the hook.

Mine for the landing, oh yes.

Worth a fuck, oh yes.

Then I'd dump her, oh yes.

What a bastard, oh yes.

But I wouldn't be a bastard to Krystal, oh no. She'd get the best.

For our date I'd chosen Restaurant Row. This is 46th Street in Midtown and it's known for its romantic eateries. I picked Barbetta because the *Zagat's Guide* made it sound especially slushy.

And it was. I sat on a stool and anticipated her arrival in a perfect scene. A piano player tinkled soft tunes in the cocktail area of plush sofas. A smooth barman fixed me a Martini with two olives and talked of his Ukrainian home.

Forty minutes, and two Martinis, later I was still anticipating Krystal's arrival. I'd exhausted the comparison of Dynamo Kiev and Manchester United with the barman and the manager kept looking at his watch and then me. My exuberant mood had turned to concern. Did she get the name of the restaurant? Did I say the wrong street? Should I leg it and get drunk in an Irish bar?

I couldn't. I'd spent all week showing off about this date – she had to come.

Finally she entered, amidst a flurry of bags and apologies. 'Raabert, I'm *sooo* sorry. I had this friend and she'd just split with her man and she was upset 'n' all and na-de-dah-de-dah.'

She actually said the last bit. She was so endearing.

As soon as she appeared I melted. She gave me a big kiss and clumsily pulled herself up on the adjacent stool.

'And then,' she continued, 'I decided I hated what I was wearing. I wanted to go home and change for you, but because of my friend I had no time. So I went to Gap.'

She'd been shopping in Gap? The Ukrainian and the manager had marked me down as a no-show and were getting the whiskies ready while Krystal was in Gap?

'I knew I'd be late,' she said. 'But I thought, does he want me on time or does he want me to be cute? And I thought, cute.'

Oh, how right she was: cute, cute, cute – *CUTE*.

After a happy drink at the bar – I was now on my third Martini and starting to feel well-oiled – we strolled in for dinner. The barman and the manager beamed, clearly impressed I'd pulled such a babe. I ordered a bottle of Burgundy at sixty bucks a throw, and sat in her radiance while we ignored the menu and mucked about.

We talked of New York living and its contrast with home. It turned out that New York was far more of a culture shock for Krystal than me, wat wiv me bein' a well-'ard Londoner 'n' all. Her pet hate was the noise. She was woken every morning by restoration work on the San Remo building, an historic Upper West Side landmark with its Gothic twin towers overlooking the park. At one point, she said, she pleaded with one of the workmen to allow her a lie-in.

'I'm jus' a lil' ol' southern country gal,' she shouted from her roof terrace. 'An' this noise is drivin' me crazy.'

He stopped, of course. I bet he comes by every morning to try and catch a glimpse of this lil' ol' southern country gal.

She was so beguiling. She'd put her hair up, then down, then up again. Each time she'd look at me to make sure I'd noticed. When it was down she'd look at me sideways through the fringe. When it was up she'd throw back her head and pout. I just sat and panted. I couldn't go to the loo – the urinals would have to be on the ceiling.

'How's your mother?' I asked.

I was trying to calm things down so I could have a slash.

'Oh, she's fine,' she said. 'She'd just come back from London when she rang. But I didn't tell her I was about to make love to an Englishman.'

Roarrrr – keep those urinals bolted to the ceiling.

'I bet she's very beautiful,' I said.

It was a cheesy, smoochy line but I didn't care.

'No she's not,' said Krystal innocently. 'I get my looks from my father.'

I sat silently for a minute, smirking. Finally she absorbed what she'd said.

'Douhhh,' she hit my arm. 'Now you've gone and made me be all immodest 'n' all.'

She ran to the bathroom to regain her composure.

I don't remember the food. I didn't care. I didn't care when the bill came. I didn't even look. I just slipped in my card and signed with a flamboyant swirl and a generous tip, oh yes.

She sat flushed from the wine, all giggles and the occasional hiccup.

'I've gotta lil' buzz,' she said.

I could have sat there forever. I didn't want it to end. I kept asking her questions: about her life in Atlanta, her ambitions, her likes, dislikes, ideal weekends, whether looks mattered but shouldn't – that sort of thing.

'So where did you work before joining *New York* magazine?' I asked.

'Oh, a little publisher called Platinum Books,' she said. 'I did a similar thing there.'

Nooo. Stop the clock. Don't say it. Say something else. Anything.

I said it.

'Oh, d'you know someone called Tina?'

'Tina Goldblat?' she perked up, jumping in her seat with excitement.

'You know Tina?' she said. 'I can't believe you know her.'

'Oh, I met her in Prohibition—'

'Have you two made out?' she said abruptly.

I'd learnt that making out in America means to snog and not, as I used to think, a full-on shag – that line in 'Summer Nights' always shocked me.

'No, no,' I said hastily. 'Nat was trying to snog her friend.'

'Snogged,' she giggled. 'You cute lil' Englishman with your cute lil' accent. *Hic*.'

She put her hand to her mouth.

'I think I need to go home,' she said.

The youngest one in curls

The cheesy image of the American family has a firm grounding in reality, especially in places like Greenwich, Connecticut. US families aspire to a wholesomeness that leaves most Europeans grasping for the puke bucket.

Dad is tall, calm and authoritative. He is a rock, a moral pillar, an immovable object with a flat stomach. Mum, or Mom, is blonde, pretty and trim. She is an understanding pool of kindness and tolerance, a practical homebuilder and a whiz in the kitchen. The kids are well-behaved and well-rounded. They are sporty, enthusiastic, talented and ambitious. Only the dog is eccentric – and possibly old Grandpa Adams with his salty sea-dog tales to scare the youngsters at Thanksgiving.

There's no shouting in this world and stress is absent. Problems are solved through dialogue and reason. Sure, parents fret about their children, but that deep well of love, combined with large helpings of clear thinking, always results in a happy ending and a final joke involving the crazy dog.

It looks lovely, although American friends say it's a façade. They say Dad is a drink-driver who tries to fuck his secretary. They say Mom is a neurotic Prozac fiend who cries in front of the mirror, the son has impregnated the Mexican maid, and the daughter has pierced nipples and thinks she's a lesbian.

I'm not so sure, although they sound like a lot of fun. I've watched fucked-up mothers in Asda on the Isle of Dogs and it doesn't look like a scene from *The Brady Bunch* or *Happy Days* to me. Fucked-up families wear shit, look like shit, eat shit and shout at their kids in public.

'Darren will you fucking well behave,' is about as reasonable as it gets in Asda, as Darren is smacked into the Pot Noodle display.

It wouldn't happen here. Here the whole world comes to a halt while parent and child have a reasoned discussion on the child's misbehaviour.

I witnessed such a discussion in Central Park.

'Tommy, why did you do that?' asked the mother calmly. 'Why did you kick that poor dog?'

'I don't know Mommy,' says Tommy, no older than five. 'I kinda just wanted to, I guess.'

'Well you must have had a reason. You wouldn't hurt a dog for no reason would you?'

'Nooo,' he said.

Of course Tommy would, but he got caught this time.

'So why?'

'He got in my way.'

'Tommy.' Sincere voice. 'Do you kick everything that gets in your way?'

'No.'

157

'So why the dog?'

'I don't know.'

'Was it because the dog is smaller than you?'

'I guess.'

'Well, you're smaller than me. Would you like it if I kicked you because you were in my way?'

'No.'

'So what do you say to the dog?'

'Sorry, I guess.'

'You only guess.'

'No, I'm sorry dog.'

Of course the dog didn't give a shit. He'd already forgotten he'd been hit and was busy wagging his tail and sniffing some poo. But what a great mom. Tommy learnt a lot in that exchange. Darren's only lesson was that being smacked into the Pot Noodles hurts.

And it isn't just on punishment that Tommy gets a better ride than Darren. Tommy's year is punctuated with great holidays and festivals. I first noticed this at Halloween. Forget the pathetic apple-bobbing your mum organized in the kitchen, or the later British version of trick-or-treating – which rapidly developed a menacing 'Look after your car, mister' undertone – Halloween in the States is a huge festival of the macabre. Every kid puts on the most outrageous horror costumes and goes to a party after days spent trick-or-treating for real candy and real toys. It looks great, especially when the trim blonde moms dress up in catsuit outfits and go to the party as well.

Then there's Thanksgiving. Obviously us Brits don't have this holiday because we've always managed to bring in the harvest without the aid of the Indians (we didn't shoot them afterwards either) but boy, are we missing out. The holiday is really all about food and families. It's the biggest family get-together of the year – a chance to fall out with your cousins all over again.

Thanksgiving in New York is especially good to kids because of the Thanksgiving Day Parade. It runs from the Upper West Side down to Macy's on 34th Street. The parade features vast balloons depicting cartoon characters like Winnie the Pooh and Mickey Mouse. These are inflated near the Museum of Natural History the night before and parents bring their kids to watch.

Given that most American kids are spoilt rotten it's amazing they're not all completely fucked in the head. But they're not. Most adolescents I overhear on the train talk about college degrees and sensible careers. Now these kids are on their way to a Rangers or Yankees game so there's a direct link to my own youth, spent largely on trains heading for Wednesday night League Cup replays against Cardiff City or Oldham Athletic. But as a spotty Essex adolescent I don't remember one conversation about colleges or careers. Our conversation revolved around West Ham taking the Shed End or Tottenham steaming the North Bank – not whether Harvard was better than Yale or JP Morgan preferable to Merrill Lynch.

But American kids can compare investment banks all day and still come across as idiots, because they talk like idiots. Their speech is no more than a series of clichés linked to form sentences. And the clichés are limited in number.

'It's like, yanno, totally amazing man,' is the most common statement from a white American teenager. Substitute amazing with weird, gross, far out or *happnin* and you've almost covered their entire vocabulary.

In fact their diction's so poor they're returning the language to its Neolithic roots of groans and grunts. I overheard one girl say, 'It's, like, yanno, totally *eeggh*.' Then she jerked her face forward in an expression of revolt. Her word range didn't even stretch to 'gross'.

Don't get me wrong, I don't subscribe to the 'all Yanks

are thick' theory. Any country that can invent the Internet, Viagra and fat-free frozen yoghurt is pretty bright, although fuck knows why they put a man on the moon. American kids sound dim in order to fit in with their peers. Any American teenager caught talking like a Victorian professor will soon be thrown under one of those yellow Charlie Brown school buses.

American teenagers also drink beer in order to fit in with their peers. On the Thursday night train, gangs of kids head for an evening spent wandering Times Square. They walk the train like packs of prairie dogs, wearing over-baggy clothes and rebellious headgear. And they carry a can or bottle of beer – held as a symbol of their revolt – hidden in the ubiquitous brown paper bag.

Brown bags or not, the teenagers are breaking the law. Americans can't legally drink before they're twenty-one. I find this amazing. How can anyone go through college without copious amounts of alcohol? And forget trying your luck in the pubs. Bars in the US ask for ID from just about everyone. The day I don't have to produce evidence of my age to enter a bar or a club will be the day I know I should settle in a country village with my own pewter jug behind the bar of the inn. There are people I know who are closer to retirement than the legal drinking age and yet still have to produce ID.

'Born 1945, in you come.'

But it's typical of this country to protect its children just that little bit more. Take drugs. Since the Reagan administration, drugs have been so demonized kids now view any illegal substance as a certain route to degradation and eventual death.

All common sense has been abandoned. The state of Michigan, for instance, enforces a mandatory life sentence for the possession of marijuana, and a man in Oklahoma is serving ninety-three years for growing pot in his basement. Meanwhile his neighbour – a wife-beater with a drink problem – can legally own enough artillery to take out a small republic and his pubescent children can kill people on the road after the same degree of instruction given to someone buying a mobile phone.

This country has got to be on something.

DECEMBER

Companions for life?

I have often wondered how stupid I am. No, I mean really – what kind of dimwit has my body got as a life partner? By this I don't mean A-levels and IQ tests. Some of the thickest people I know could paper their bedroom walls with qualifications. I mean life – how stupid am I at life?

There should be a test. It should be based on real situations and with three possible outcomes: clever, expected, dimwit.

Here's an example. Your date tells you she used to work at the same company as another woman you've been trying to shag – how do you react?

Clever: 'Oh, I know that company, they're a small publisher of children's books and learning manuals. Yes, I have some shares in them.'

Expected: 'Oh, sorry, never heard of them.'

Dimwit: 'Oh, do you know Tina?'

The certificate arrived with a late night phone call.

'Raabert, it's Krystal.' She sounded a bit tipsy. 'Hey, guess what? I've just spoken to Tina and she says we should all go out.'

'Great,' I said warily.

'Yep. And she said she'll bring her new English boyfriend.'

My heart leapt in the air. Krystal giggled a little and then quickly made her excuses.

Was that what I thought it was? Had all been revealed and was Krystal just taking the piss? Or could it be that Tina was seeing another English bloke, having acquired the taste?

My concern deepened the next day at work. I'd maintained radio silence with Tina since dinner with Krystal, just in case. But this didn't prevent Tina emailing me.

'By the way,' she tagged onto her last message, 'do you know Krystal Baker?' She signed it, 'Curious George.'

What could I do? Things were unravelling fast. I decided to come clean with Tina.

'Sure I know Krystal. We've had a couple of dates. She's fun. She said she worked at Platinum Books so I asked if she knew you. Curiosity satisfied?'

Tina came back immediately. No need for deliberate pausing now.

'Curiosity satisfied. And curiosity killed the cat.'

That was the last I heard from Tina.

And Krystal became evasive. Her caller-ID pad must have listed my name in long columns I rang so often, but she never took it.

Eventually she did call back but she was busy. She reeled off great lists of things she had to do, all more important than seeing me. This included walking the dog.

But this dimwit still didn't get it.

'Oh, I'd like a walk in the park,' I said. 'I'll walk the dog with you.'

'Actually it's a jog with the dog and it's over to the Eastside to see a friend,' she said. 'And we have to go shopping first.'

'Oh, shopping . . .'

For God's sake, work it out.

But I did manage to persuade Krystal to come out

again. Trevor and Fiona were having a party at their apartment and I invited Krystal and Brandi by email – that way she'd at least read it. Krystal replied that she'd come.

On the Saturday of the party I just happened to cycle by the trendy restaurant where Krystal was a hostess and thought I'd pop in, on a whim, to confirm she was coming. Krystal greeted me with a kiss on the cheek, and a 'Hello darling'.

She even described me as a 'cute Englishman living in the neighbourhood', on a customer survey the restaurant was conducting (this being New York, restaurant surveys involve their opinion of the customers rather than the other way round). Perhaps I'd been paranoid about the Tina thing after all. Perhaps that dog really did need a fuck of a lot of exercise.

I agreed to come round at nine and we'd walk the few extra blocks to Trevor and Fiona's. I went home and lay in the bath for an hour, vowing never to be so stupid again.

But as I soaked the phone rang.

It was Krystal calling from a payphone.

'Raabert. I'm in SoHo. I'm getting my hair done. I'm gonna be late. I'll meet you at the party.'

'No, no – I'll wait here,' I said. 'Call me when you're ready.'

'No I don't want you waiting,' she said. 'I'll see you at the party. I mean it. What's the address?'

I knew it was a ruse. I'd been blown out again.

I waited in the apartment until nearly ten. She didn't call. I'd given her the address but, come on, this lil' ol' southern country gal wasn't about to remember an address verbally given to her on a phone stand in the street. I walked to the party a beaten man.

It was dead. Only a handful of people had turned up and Trevor and Fiona were suitably embarrassed. They were relieved that Krystal and Brandi hadn't come. It would have looked a bit sad.

Anger was more my emotion. 'Fuck women,' I said, swinging a bottle of Sam Adams about.

The only other single Englishman in the room had been in New York six months and had yet to have a date. I gave him the benefit of my experience.

'Date?' I ranted. 'You want a date? You can get a date in this town like that.'

I clicked my fingers while holding the Sam Adams and some beer dropped onto the rug.

'But they'll just fuck you around,' I continued. 'One minute hot, the next cold. And another thing. The women in this town are only interested in the size of your wallet.'

I spent half an hour in this sort of mood, rapidly knocking back the beer. I became louder and louder until I was swinging round the room shouting, 'bitches and whores. They're all bitches and whores.'

Only the buzzer stopped me.

Trevor released the door, went into the lobby and leaned over the banisters.

'You know those two birds you invited, Bob?' he shouted. 'Well they're on their way up.'

My mood had to do a rapid turnaround.

The trouble was I was pissed and my emotion valve was stuck. I decided my best policy was to keep quiet and smile. As they came in I just stood grinning like a farm-hand.

Everyone else stared at them as if they were the prize items at an auction. And you couldn't blame them. Krystal looked fantastic. Her hair had a 1960s' Mary Quant look and she wore a tight oriental dress.

My jaw dropped.

Krystal didn't notice. The two of them were excitedly telling of their earlier encounter with Steve Martin. He'd

165

rang the restaurant and asked for a delivery to his San Remo apartment. They didn't do delivery, they snorted, but made a special exception in his case. Krystal was sent and she'd called Brandi, who'd tagged along for the ride. Steve had given a $30 tip and they'd been invited into his apartment.

As they relayed the tale I tried to sober up and improve my humour. Of course, everyone else in the room had heard my earlier rant against women and my credibility was taking a bit of a battering, to say the least.

After Nat arrived Trevor and Fiona suggested a move to a bar, or anywhere that didn't reveal our poor level of integration into the happening New York scene.

We strolled to the Evelyn Lounge on Columbus.

During the walk I watched Krystal for her mood. I just couldn't tell – she was friendly enough – but I noticed I was getting more from Brandi. And once in the bar, Nat and Krystal chatted happily while I was cornered on a couch with Brandi.

I couldn't seem to alter the alignment no matter how hard I tried. I'd ask Krystal questions – only to receive monosyllabic answers. I'd make space on the couch – to be told she was happy standing. And I'd offer to buy the drinks, but Krystal was fine, thanks – although Brandi, Trevor, Fiona, Nat, Mary, Mungo and Midge would all like Martinis.

Eventually Nat went to the bathroom and I pounced.

'Your hair looks nice,' I said.

'Thank you,' she said.

She offered nothing more. She smiled at the room.

'I'm glad you came,' I said, trying to smile directly at her.

She wouldn't hold my look.

'I told you I would,' she said firmly. 'If I say I'll come, I come.'

She looked away – hoping Nat would rescue her.

We sunk into silence. I started to retreat into misogynist mode: fuck her. Her earlier behaviour in the restaurant must have been an act for the benefit of her chic colleagues.

'Hello darling, *moi, moi*. Cute Englishman, *moi, moi*. Just off to Steve's, *moi, moi*.'

Bitch. I offered nothing.

'Look Raabert,' she said finally. 'I'm angry with you over Tina. I thought it was seedy and sleazy. I can't believe you did it.'

'Is that what the call was about?'

'Yesss, silly,' she smiled. 'I was just teasing you.'

'I was the English boyfriend?'

'Yeees.'

'Oh no,' I looked down, embarrassed. 'I haven't had a date with her—'

'Raabert it's OK, really. I'm not angry anymore. I just wanted to tell you.'

'But I can explain.'

She didn't want an explanation. I didn't have one anyway. I was going to use the 'would I be so stupid' defence, but of course I knew. Yes, I would be so stupid.

I was a certified dimwit.

Hey Fatso, ya wanna cawfee?

Necessity is the mother of invention. It's a proverb. I looked it up. I assumed it was Shakespeare but it turned out to be one of Will's rivals, a bloke called George Chapman. I'd never heard of Chapman. Forced to guess I'd have said George Chapman was a small-time East End villain in a porkpie hat, maybe a cohort of the Krays – with a middle name like The Gent or Crusher – not a contemporary of the Bard.

Chapman's most famous play was *The Blind Beggar of Alexandria*. And while an appropriate title for a cohort of the Krays, it has to be ranked as a flop. Who's ever heard of it? Its West End run didn't break all records, did it? Those Broadway lights aren't exactly flashing 'Chapman's thriller – 400th great year', are they? Chapman himself is hardly a household name – the guy's a nobody, an historical footnote – no more.

And my career was heading Chapman's way. In the history of banking I'd be a footnote at best.

* Came to US, spent year lamenting state of markets and lack of employer's interest in anything he was any good at. Rumbled soon after and sacked.

** Was also crap at chasing women.

And Rip Van Winkle didn't exactly cheer me up. He was spending his days knocking up a lifeboat for himself and the London Receivables team and all the seats had been reserved. They'd forgotten about me across the pond.

'Isn't it the case that clever and inventive you will have to be,' was his only advice.

But any invention was going to fall on the sword of perception. This isn't another Chapman proverb but was the gist of the Receivables team's problem. Sure, we could claim we were just like Securitization – using future revenues as security for loans. But we weren't. They made a fortune lending someone else's money to good borrowers. We handed out the bank's money at giveaway rates to dodgy borrowers in even dodgier countries.

And Securitization was sexy. Even the borrowers loved it. They could large it on Wall Street fucking people up the arse. Receivables wasn't sexy at all. It was for borrowers at the bottom of the heap. They were so shit, or in such a shit country, they had to rely on their customers to pay off their loans. Who in their right mind, and with the right rating, was going to volunteer for that?

Who indeed? I started asking round the office. After all, I had nothing else to do. I talked to anybody who'd spare the time. I'd bug them for a meeting and then furiously draw boxes and arrows on their whiteboards in the hope that Receivables was the very thing their lives lacked. After a few weeks, virtually every whiteboard in Greenwich sported my scruffy little diagrams.

Most people were at least polite. 'Hmmm, ahhh, oh yes,' they'd say with a hard look of concentration, probably thinking, 'What the fuck has this got to do with me?'

But as soon as they could they'd say, 'Robert, that was absolutely fascinating. Thank you.' And I'd be hustled out the office so they could crack on with some real work or get back to the *New York Times* crossword. It seemed hopeless.

Eventually I spoke to an affable American called Kent. This guy had that healthy and happy glow that said he'd never been whacked into the Pot Noodles display as a kid and he wouldn't dream of doing such a thing to his own children. I'd bet his house had one of those wood-panelled station wagons on the drive and a netball hoop above the garage.

Kent studied the diagram as if trying to solve a difficult clue in the morning's crossword. He concentrated especially hard on the dotted line cutting the diagram in half. It had 'good country' written on one side and 'crap country' on the other.

'Hmmm,' he said. 'I think I see your problem. We view your Company A as a bad company. That's why we get your Company B to repay the loan. But Company A could be a great company and he'd still need Company B to repay his loan because he's in, excuse me, a crap country.'

'Yep,' I said. 'It's the sovereign ceiling – you're only as good as the country you're in.'

'And we no longer want to do deals in risky countries – even with these structures.'

'Nope,' I said.

'And if Company A was in a good country he'd have to be, excuse me, a crap company to need a Company B to pay off his loan.'

'Yep.' I was impressed. At last, someone understood my dilemma.

'So you need to find Company As in good countries but who are not, excuse me, crap companies.'

That's exactly what we needed.

'Companies, say, that have a good name in their chosen field but are branching out into a new, risky, industry. So the dotted line that separates the As and Bs in your structure could say "good industry" or "old industry" on one side and, "new industry" or, excuse me, "crap industry" on the other – rather than "good country", excuse me, "crap country". They are entering a new world and it will be as risky as a Russia or Brazil, however good their reputation in the old world.'

Blimey, Kent was on to something. I just wish he'd learn to swear. He should spend some time on the trading floor.

'Companies may well want to keep the new industry part of their business separate from the old industry part. Indeed government regulation may force them to separate in order to protect the customers in their old business. Once separated you've got a new company – your Company A. It's a good name because of its old industry parent, but it has to borrow independently for the first time. It has no track record and is in a new industry with no track record. He'd definitely need these sorts of structures to entice lenders to lend to him.'

I was excited now. This guy had a complete understanding of how my product could be applied in the US – maybe my death row reprieve had arrived.

'What is it, what is it?' I shouted like an excited child at a pantomime.

'Power,' he said. 'The US electricity industry.'

In turned out that the power industry was in a right pickle. It was no longer the pipe and slippers business it seems when passing those stripy chimneys. The government had decided that the friendly power companies – who'd been knocking out electricity for generations and carrying it to every home in America – had too much, well, power. They were a monopoly, generating and selling power within a carved-out territory and without any competition. Under new pro-competition rules this had to change. From now on, anyone could generate power and sell it to the distributors – the power companies who delivered it and whose name appeared on the bill. And, in a given territory, the generators shouldn't be the distributors and the distributors shouldn't be the generators. They should be separate companies able to shop around for suppliers or buyers.

All this shopping around was supposed to lead to cheaper power and more choice for the consumer – at least that was the theory. In fact it was the same theory as the UK's own power privatization in the 1980s. National Power and PowerGen make the stuff and sell it to the LEB or Norweb. The LEB doesn't generate. PowerGen doesn't distribute.

But in the US they'd taken it a stage further. Power had become a tradeable commodity just like gold, or oil, or packaged-up Receivables loans in the bond market. Power workers no longer wore silly plastic suits with plastic bags on their shoes and shower caps on their head. They wore red suspenders and had little Mexicans shine their shoes. And they wouldn't spend all day looking at obscure dials and writing numbers on a clipboard. They'd hang out in fuck-off trading rooms and shout into phones.

171

'Mrs fucking Kowalski of Staten fucking Island has put the fucking coffee on,' they'd shout. 'Who'll sell me forty fucking watts?'

Of course, it wasn't like that. They bought great big chunks of electricity and they didn't care about Mrs Kowalski of Staten Island. They were buying and selling power in the hope of correctly guessing movements in the power price. Their aim was to buy low and sell high and if that was the wrong way round they'd be in trouble. In fact, to use the technical terminology of the industry, they'd be fucked.

Mrs Kowalski needed protecting from all this volatility so some states were forcing the power companies to form separate subsidiaries for their trading operations. And these separate trading companies, while still with the old company's name, had to raise their own cash.

So we had good companies in a new industry.

Yet this was one bugger's muddle of a new industry, largely due to around one hundred and fifty trading companies who had got in on the act. They had quickly realized that trading power isn't like trading oil or gold. It doesn't exist in any tangible form. You can't point at it or drop it on your foot. When traders buy power, they're really buying a power station's output at a particular point in time. And time can't be stored. It comes, it goes. And if they haven't sold their power when the moment arrives to buy it, they're back to using the industry's technical terminology. Either that or they're going to have to find some fucking big batteries to store the stuff in.

Rather than buy batteries, the power traders dealt with this by reversing the buy-sell principle of the market. They'd sell the power first and worry about where they'd buy it from nearer the time. Sometimes much nearer the time. Sometimes just as the adverts were coming on and Mrs Kowalski was turning to her husband

and saying, 'Hey Fatso, ya wanna *cawfee*?'

As she slumps off to the kitchen the trader is busy buying his power from the generator so he can fulfil his contract to Mrs Kowalski's distributor. Our trader is gambling that the power station hasn't sold all its capacity and will be keen to get whatever they can for the spare stuff. It's like buying theatre tickets from that booth in Leicester Square or the TKTS place in Times Square. It's on the day, so it must be half price. And it's almost certain you'll get to see the show. After all, theatres aren't often sold out, are they? And power stations can always meet the demand for power, can't they?

Well actually, no. An unexpected June heatwave had every bugger turning on their air conditioning while the power stations were preparing for a July-August peak by sprucing themselves up at half capacity. There was suddenly much more demand for power than was available to supply, causing the price of any spare power to rocket from $30 per megawatt to $7,000. That's one hell of a price hike – especially as Mrs Kowalski's distributors could wave a contract at the trader specifying a fixed price of $30.01.

'Holy shit,' says the trader, 'I'm going to have to refer to some of the industry's technical terminology.'

The trader goes under and Mrs Kowalski is left wondering why the red light on her coffee maker won't come on and the lights have gone out. And Fatso is shouting from the living room that the TV has gone off.

It happened in June 1998, just as I was innocently watching Graeme Le Saux let his Chelsea team mate through to score for Romania. Petrescu hit the back of the net, England went two-one down and half of America went dark. Very quickly one hundred and fifty power traders became around thirty.

The survivors were mostly the trading arms of the old power companies, plus a few big oil and gas names who'd decided to join the jamboree. But they were all good names in an industry with a bad reputation. Every time I mentioned it people would say, 'Whooo buddy, didn't that whole business get all fucked up last June?'

Yep, they were good companies in a crap industry – I had it. Now all I had to do was get in front of the right people.

Deli hyperbole

British supermarkets are infatuated with the New York deli. They see it as a great marketing tool for pushing all manner of processed substances they label food. It seems that every pungent meat slice or smelly savoury is awarded the New York deli prefix. 'New York deli pastrami', 'New York deli pretzels', 'New York deli pizzas', 'New York deli dim sum choc-chip cheesecake' – they can't get enough of it.

The New York deli, it seems, reeks of cosmopolitan pizazz and in-your-face flavour. The packaging even sports a picture of Liberty surrounded by a few skyscrapers and maybe one of those yellow cabs with the chequered band that you never see in New York. These foods are cool. They are the rock stars of the cold meat counters, the supermodels of the ready meals. They are little explosive bundles of taste sitting on Sainsbury's shelves and selling like 'New York deli hot cakes'.

But any thrill-seeking British food shoppers, so moved by Tesco's 'New York deli clam chowder Waldorf bagel' they simply have to visit the real thing, are in for a shock. I'm afraid the New York deli falls short of its billing.

In reality the New York deli is no more than the local convenience store, like those found on every street corner in every urban area in Britain. And just as I'd be sceptical coming across 'Birmingham Corner Shop Mushy Peas' or 'Glasgow Chippy Deep-Fried Mars Bars' in US supermarkets, I expect New Yorkers treat the New York deli label with a degree of caution. They'd read it like a health warning: 'Beware: contains badly prepared food that tastes like shit'.

Many New York delis sell no fresh food and the majority of those that do go no further than a 'cold cuts' counter containing one oblong of ham, one block of cheddar cheese, a slab of processed turkey and maybe a tub of tuna. And while these counters are usually geared for knocking up sandwiches, anything more complex than a bread roll will produce blank stares from the bored sandwich-makers.

Certainly don't ask for a granary bap, one of my first linguistic mistakes in New York. 'A grainy bat?' said the incredulous assistant to his imaginary co-worker. 'This guy's at a lunch counter and he wants a grainy bat?'

Imaginary co-workers are rarely required. Most deli owners can be found with a phone tucked under their chin and they make only the most minuscule face and head movements to indicate what you, the customer, should do in order to hand over your money and keep their families alive for the next week. And these are the polite ones. Delis are the temples of the great New York trait of being able to render your very existence questionable. No-one's being rude, it's just that there's normally a great debate in progress and it's a damn sight more important than your shopping. It's so crucial it seems to last for days and involves the same participants – the owner and a gang of dubious semi-permanents who hang around the place and look unlikely to ever buy anything.

The debate is in an impenetrable foreign language, often Urdu or Korean, and while a minor effort is made at cashing up your purchases, it's of lowly significance compared to the dispute. And progress can come to a complete halt if things become particularly animated. You're left suspended until they've made their point, which may take some time, especially if the friend – lurking somewhere at the back of the store – has a valid response.

The argument can become so emotional I've been tempted to butt in. 'What?' I've wanted to ask. 'What is it? How long have we got?'

Yet I know if they were shouting in English I'd be hearing, 'I've told him before – you put the chicken in the green container: green, green. Not the yellow container – that's for the flour. He's such a chump.'

As well as the odd sandwich most delis can manage a coffee, or at least the caffeinated scoopings from the bottom of the Hudson River that New York delis try and pass off as coffee. But it's a sludge New Yorkers take great pride in, so much so they serve it in one of the city's great icons: the naff blue and white 'We Are Happy to Serve You' cups. The wording on these cups is in pseudo-Greek-style lettering and the cup is decorated with white figurines and classical bordering. They are everywhere and have become a celebrated part of kitsch New York iconography – Andy Warhol would have been proud.

In fact Warhol would have found much to inspire him in a modern New York deli. These days it wouldn't be the Campbell's soup cans he'd notice, it would be the Snapple. Lined up like stout glass soldiers, they dominate the lines of fridges that occupy one wall of a deli. Snapple amazes me. I've yet to witness anyone buying a bottle of the stuff. The delis appear to be great Snapple dumping grounds, with the different-coloured bottles parading their unwanted wacky flavours like fat pink girls at a pageant. 'Oh, there's the Dixie Peach, I've never tried that one.' 'Hmm, Mango Madness, I think I'll give it a miss.' 'Ah, Bali Blast – maybe not.'

But the artistic possibilities of the Snapple bottles are nothing compared to the deli's other great product indulgence – breakfast cereals. The only meal New Yorkers would even contemplate preparing themselves is breakfast. Consequently the shelves groan under the weight of cereal packages. The boxes line the tight aisles from floor to ceiling. They are cardboard alleys of Americana: loud, colourful, tasteless, almost hallucinogenic images. Cartoon characters leer, words scream, strange combinations of logos and cereal shapes mix in a lurid dance that leaves the head spinning.

It really is a trip gone haywire in the cereal zone. Out in the Midwest wheat belt some seriously stoned people have taken over General Mills. The lunatics are running around having board meetings and marketing conferences. And they don't vote themselves wage rises, oh no. They pass round the LSD and think up the next batch of deranged cereals to freak out the townies back east.

They especially get off on the names, although this being America I detect a few rules. First the name must suggest the process by which the cereal came to life: roasted, toasted, crusted, frosted. Then we need a taste: cinnamon, honey, cocoa, nut. Third there's the shape of the cereal lumps inside: clusters, nuggets, puffs, Os. Finally there's the drug-induced whizzy bit that sells the stuff: Grahams, Cheerios, Chex, Kix.

The guy that came up with Grahams must have been especially bombed – naming a cereal after a middle-aged bloke in a cardy. And what about Cheerios – a shouted parting to a vicar's wife? Some cereals seem to have woken up on the bathroom floor and decided to try and get their head together. They've been given names like Basic 4, Common Sense and even Product 19. But these are a small minority. The drugfest continues unabated as boxes of Froot Loops, Boo Berry and Graham OH!S sneer at the clean-cut dullards in the corner.

The whole cereal freak show is especially intense in the New York deli because space is so limited. The boxes literally lean over you as if mimicking the Manhattan streets. Indeed there's so little room in most delis that the food density is almost overpowering. You end up being grateful for the robustness of packaging. Any terrorist group wanting to wipe out New York should invent a packaging vaporizer – one beam over Manhattan and half the city would drown in a Snapple, cereal and coffee goo.

A fat tail on my forward curve

Starting a new business isn't easy. Starting a new business in a new country was going to be terrifying. I had no idea what I was talking about and there was no-one to ask. Kent had been a great help but his contribution was his awareness of the new trading environment in the power industry – he didn't know anyone who did it. So, just as I had done with Receivables, I was going to have to pick up the phone and cold call my way into the market.

The guys to talk to were obviously the traders. But these guys were too busy shouting into their phones to talk to a boring banker trying to sell them a concept for a loan. Most didn't want to know and a couple said something like, 'Hey buddy I'm tradin' here. Get off the line', but this was rare. This wasn't New York. Many of the traders were in Houston, Texas. They were equally adamant that I shouldn't waste their time but they were much politer about it. They all had mighty fine accents 'n' all, but they were 'mighty busy right now, so if yooo don't mind I'd kinda like to put the phone down on yooo. Y'all have a nice day.'

Eventually one guy did stop and talk. His name was Skip and, although I imagined a scruffy kid playing baseball in a dusty yard, he thought what I had to say was mighty interesting.

'I don't need yooo,' he said, 'cos my daddy'll look after meee.'

He meant the parent company had enough money to back the trading operation and didn't mind the risk – although maybe the baseball kid was threatening to set his father on the guy with a strange accent. But he wasn't in a hurry, so I carried on.

'I can see a lot of application for this pro-duct,' said Skip. 'But we ain't the company for yooo. Y'all best talk to Hardon. Those boys been doin' Receivables for a while now. And not just power neither. They're what you might call energy traders. Those boys been using it on gas and oil and jus' 'bout anything else they can get their hands on.'

It couldn't have been better. First, we weren't first. Banks never want to be first. Sure the management always say 'Oh we're innovators, financial pioneers, we boldly go where no bank has been before', but the Credit Approval departments soon stop that. They always assume first means all the other banks have rejected it for a reason we've yet to discover. Second, it was Hardon – what a company. Hardon was one of the bank's best clients.

Power trading was a sideline for Hardon, which spent most of its time producing oil and gas. This meant the bank's relationship with Hardon was run from our Houston office. Indeed, our Houston office was only there to run the relationships with the big energy companies. They schmoozed the directors and made sure they got what they wanted. And what they wanted was usually a round of golf, a nice dinner and a visit to a local strip club. The energy industry in the US is a man's world, and they expect their bankers to have large expense accounts and a good knowledge of the local exotic nightlife.

And our key man in the Houston office had one of the largest expense accounts and a great knowledge of the local exotic nightlife. Like Flatcap he was a northern Englishman. Unlike Flatcap he was a party animal. He was famous throughout the bank for his sense of fun and his addiction to pretty women. In fact, some worried he was a lawsuit waiting to happen, although that was to underestimate one of the world's natural charmers. It was impossible to dislike him and even the most brass-balled feminist found his humour hard to resist. Nonetheless, he was better off in good ol' Texas than in uptight New York.

He called himself the Main Man, as in 'I'm the Main Man. I'm just fucking brilliant. Absolutely fucking brilliant.'

'Wey, hey, Big Boy,' was always how he greeted my calls. 'How's Mandy?'

He'd noticed Mandy's chest on his last visit to the London office and she was now firmly on the Main Man's radar.

'How are your boys?'

This was always the next question. It wasn't another reference to Mandy's anatomy. He meant West Ham. He was an ardent Manchester United fan and saw being located five thousand miles from Old Trafford as no barrier to his passion – like most Manchester United fans, in fact.

'So, Big Boy, what can I do for you?'

'Power trading Receivables finance,' I said. 'We should get into it.'

'We should,' said the Main Man. 'We most definitely should.'

He didn't have a clue what I was talking about.

The Main Man is what's known as a relationship manager. Relationship managers know everything there is to know about the clients, but next to nothing about banking. They are the link between the client and the geeky rocket scientists in the office. The geeks know everything there is to know about banking, but next to nothing about the clients. Together they form the core of any bank.

'Hardon,' I said, knowing that the mention of his favourite client would firm up his interest. 'They're one of the biggest power traders in the US.'

'You're not wrong, Big Boy. You're not wrong.'

'We want to offer them Receivables financing against their energy marketing contracts,' I said.

'Fucking hell, Big Boy,' he said. 'That's awesome.'

He always spoke on the speakerphone rather than into the handset. This meant he could do things like clap his hands in excitement or wander round the building. As a result his voice would sometimes boom into my ear and sometimes sound like he was making himself a coffee in the kitchen across the hall. I could find myself chatting away for ages only to find him in his assistant's room when I paused for a response.

'Fucking great, Big Boy,' would be the distant reply once the silence became expectant enough to reach him. 'That sounds fucking great.'

'Can you get me to the right guys at Hardon?' I asked.

'Hardon fucking love me,' he said. 'They just fucking love me. I've just been invited to their skiing weekend. Leave it with me, Big Boy.'

And if there was one thing the Main Man could deliver, it was the right man. A few days later he called back to announce he'd arranged a dinner, not only with the

181

power trading people but with Eric, the very man responsible for their efforts at raising finance against the power trading contracts. I had to fly down to Houston the next night.

Hardon is one of the most aggressive companies in the energy sector and their employees are worked hard and paid well. Eric was working fucking hard, and the Porsche in the restaurant car park suggested the fucking also applied to his pay. But he looked terrible. He had puffy eyes, pale skin and crumpled clothes. He'd come straight from the office and could only spare an hour.

Eric was working like crazy because the rating agencies were considering a downgrade for Hardon. They were raising an eyebrow at the company's level of debt as well as its concentration of credit risk on fewer and fewer names – due to the number of bankruptcies in power trading. Eric had seen a way out by bundling all the remaining power trading contracts and securitizing them. First, he'd sell the contracts to a special company, which meant the credit risk was no longer Hardon's. Then the special company would raise a loan using these contracts as security. Finally, the special company would pass the money raised to Hardon – as a forward payment for the contracts. Hardon would use the cash to pay off some debt.

If Eric pulled it off, their triple-B plus rating would be safe and he'd be a hero. And if we could get involved in a securitization, so would I.

Eric's mind was so frazzled with his task he could speak about little else. This would have been fine if either the Main Man or I had any idea what he was talking about.

'The volatilities of the power assets restrict the tenor and leave a fat tail on their forward curve,' said Eric.

Most tenors I'd seen certainly had a fat tail, but on their forward curve? It sounded uncomfortable.

'You have to swap out that fat tail or bolt on a wrap – which is expensive.'

Forget discomfort, this sounded painful.

'So Hardon swaps out the price risk for the counterparty. But if the asset is in a standalone we pick up a residual risk through the hedge.'

Picking up a risk through a hedge sounded like the sort of thing I used to do in other people's back gardens as a kid. I wouldn't recommend it.

'This residual is at the standalone's rating and can hit our bottom line hard.'

As I say, not recommended.

'And our rating makes Hardon an expensive swap party.'

In fact Eric looked like he'd been at an expensive swap party all week. It may also have explained the fat tail on his forward curve.

'So we need a bank to be the swap party. To stand in the middle between us and the standalone.'

Great, it sounded like we were being invited – although if we were in the middle I'd like to know who was behind me.

While Eric spoke, we said nothing. We occasionally nodded enthusiastically, when we thought Eric might appreciate an enthusiastic nod, but otherwise we kept quiet. And the Main Man occasionally shot me a look that said, 'I hope you understand this because I'm fucked if I do.'

I didn't have a clue.

At around midnight poor Eric went back to the office and the Main Man and I stood in a Houston car park. I wondered what our next move should be. The Main Man suggested some of the local exotic nightlife.

Please, just hand over the money

Eric had until year end to work out how to get around $1 billion of debt off Hardon's balance sheet. It was already mid-December. Christmas for Eric had been cancelled and if I wanted in I should make no plans to buy a turkey, especially as I had so much to learn.

When trying to get into a new business the main problem is the jargon. Insiders talk a different language. It's the quickest way to spot and dismiss the outsiders as well as keep your bosses off your back. But luckily we had a translator. Blake was our swaps guy and a man fluent in Hardon Eric-speak.

I tried to sketch Blake an outline. It wasn't easy. It was like reading a Greek newspaper and then trying to relate the story of the politician and the topless dancer – in Greek. But, to my amazement, Blake understood enough to want to hear more. So I arranged a conference call between Eric in Houston and Blake and myself in Greenwich.

'This is great, Barb,' Blake said afterwards (he was from Virginia). 'It's exactly the sort of business we want to do.'

Eric called the deal Powerball, not because it was a complete lottery but because he wanted to cheer himself up.

'We'll make a million on Powerball,' said Blake, after he looked at the figures. 'We'll split it fifty-fifty but I'll put it all on my book.'

Blimey, half a million and his department were putting up all the cash. Braveheart would have to like this. And boy, did I need a deal. My last transaction was the Brazilian soya bean fiasco and we now had Brazilian risk coming out of our ears, thanks to me. My only positive response would be to come up with a new deal that didn't use any balance sheet, that wasn't in a crap country, that earned us a packet and had wings and those flabby red bits on its head. Blake and Eric were my only hope.

I now had to present the deal to our department's internal transaction Forum. The Forum is crucial. It acts as a safety valve, allowing everyone in the department to pick a transaction apart before letting outsiders see it. The Forum acts as a monkey filter, checking for primate ancestry while it can still be covered up. But Braveheart couldn't resist using the Forum as a means of public humiliation for those not in favour. And since the referee in *Kes* comment, I was not in favour. I needed to think strategically.

The trouble is that thinking strategically requires a bigger brain than mine. Every strategy I've ever concocted has turned sour. This is because I've always been hopeless at working out how people react. The very people I'd bet to react a certain way reacted differently the minute my money was down. If I knew someone always said white, they'd suddenly say black – left was suddenly right, salt pepper, yes no and hero arse. Never put me in charge of a battle. We'd be running up the white flag in no time.

Given this, I assumed my strategy of bringing Blake to the Forum would backfire. My strategic brain said the Forum would have to be polite because Blake was a guest. They couldn't put on their normal act of behaving like a pack of dogs at Braveheart's heel. But my non-strategic brain said that anyone who brought an outsider to our gang meeting was likely to get his head kicked in.

I knew that pack of dogs and they loved nothing more than tearing into a deal. And I guessed I'd soon be torn apart. Meanwhile, Blake would hold their stare and talk a gentle gobbledegook. Their eyes would glaze, they'd settle in the corner and they'd go to sleep. Better that and the beating, I thought, than being revealed as a monkey.

And it worked. Braveheart was deferential and the dogs snoozed by his feet. Blake talked gobbledegook into the speakerphone as eyes glazed over on both sides of the Atlantic. No-one asked any questions and our proposed deal was waved through with hardly a murmur. I decided to spend the evening reviewing Wellington's battle plan for Waterloo. I'm sure I could spot a few refinements.

But one battle does not win a war (proverb: unknown origin – possible confusion with swallows). We had a week until Christmas and Eric's nerves were worse than a turkey's. Blake's view of the deal wasn't based on the bank's positive perception of Hardon, as I'd expected, but on the bank's negative view of power marketing. All he could see were Graeme Le Saux price hikes and companies going down like a bad morning in Ypres, which meant he wanted to charge Eric a fortune.

To prevent his deal sinking like a lead balloon, Eric started chucking things out of the basket. Out went all the contracts with low-rated power companies, to be replaced by nice buoyant stuff like gas sales contracts with no nasty price spikes hidden in the cupboard. Powerball had become Gasball, yet our price was still way over what Eric was willing to pay. He developed the gritted-teeth voice of a man peering into the abyss while his only potential saviours prevaricate.

'Yes I'm being treated well,' he'd say. 'Please, just hand over the money.'

Occasionally his alter ego kidnapper would grab the phone.

'Come on,' he'd shout. 'Give me the fucking money.'

But we just couldn't do it.

Eric stopped returning our calls. He could have done a runner, we mused – Jesus, I would've – or he could have been in a stress-induced coma beneath his desk. Then again, he may have talked to a bank that said, 'This is a great deal and we're gonna make a mint. Let's go for it.'

After three days with no call, Blake began to mutter about Eric. He thought it bad manners not to call back. I just thought about the turkeys.

The elf's erection

Christmas in the States starts late. Not for them the four-month build up. Seasonal biscuit tins and tinsel aren't choking US supermarket aisles from September onwards. Crap liqueur ads aren't splashed across their screens from the moment the clocks go back. In fact, Christmas only really gets going once the plates have been cleared from the Thanksgiving turkey dinner at the end of November.

But when Christmas begins, boy, how it begins. The day after Thanksgiving is known as Black Friday. This is no memorial to all those dead turkeys but the opening day of the Christmas shopping season. And from Black Friday to Christmas Eve absolutely everything is geared towards this one holiday.

Throughout December the population of a small country jostles for space along Fifth Avenue in Midtown. Some come to see the lights at the Rockefeller Center, but most are trying to shop for the spoilt brats, creating a one-block-an-hour human chain across the width of the sidewalk. The whole scene is a living hell and often results in shouted arguments and insult exchanges – usually involving the mothers talking about fucking each other.

'Hey motherfucker wat you doin' shovin' me?'

'Fuck you motherfucker, you're in my motherfucking way.'

'I'm in *your* motherfucking way, motherfucker. No motherfucking way. Fuck, motherfucker, you're in *my* motherfucking way. Now git.'

This rarely degenerates into a full-blown brawl. Sure, there are enough cops stationed on Fifth Avenue to put down a minor coup but they're too busy being fat and lazy to stop any fighting. No, Americans have this ability to shout at each other without ever threatening violence. It's the one advantage of liberal gun laws – you never know what's in their pocket.

But I've quickly developed a hatred of Fifth Avenue. There's nothing to be said for it. Sure, New Yorkers are proud of their main shopping drag. They boast that it's Manhattan's best address. All the chic New York posters depict the Plaza Hotel or Bergdorf Goodman, both on Fifth, and there's even a perfume called Fifth Avenue, which presumably smells of hot dogs or roasting peanuts. Yet the only sense I get when walking down Fifth is that there are too many people on the planet. Within minutes my claustrophobia buttons are pressed and I'm running down a side street shouting 'Get away from me, get away from me.'

Why put up with that if you don't have to? The trouble is, I had to. Every visitor from Blighty wants a trip down Fifth with excursions to 34th Street for Macy's and Lex for Bloomingdale's. It's pointless pointing out that Fifth isn't New York or that it's a replica of every main shopping district in every large US city.

The real flavour of New York is found in shops like Strand Books. Connoisseurs claim this East Village book outlet oozes atmosphere with its 'eight miles' of books and its earthy credibility. Staff members are usually scruffy and have loud, involved conversations while ignoring your attempts to solicit their help. The place is also a disorderly mess, with handwritten signs directing you to the wrong place and long lines at the cash registers. Scruffy, rude, chaotic, self-obsessed and with a line at every exit – what else could you want from a New York store?

How about lunacy? That's where Kiehl's comes in. This is an East Village cosmetics shop and a motorbike museum. No, I'm not joking. It's a very popular store where one half is given over to home brand lotions and potions, and the other half is dedicated to a line of Harley Davidson motorcycles, obviously collected by Mr Kiehl after he went off his rocker. Cucumber facecream, tea tree oil shampoo and, oh yes, a rack of fuck-off Harley Ds – nice one.

But Jerry Ohlinger's Movie Material Store in Chelsea is my favourite shop. This is the fucked-up New York shopping experience. It looks like Jerry banged the place together over the weekend and got his dyslexic brother to knock up the sign. It's filthy and covered in rubbish. Jerry, meanwhile, looks hung-over. He's all stubble, stained vest and beer gut. At least I think that's Jerry. The place is staffed by people who all think they're in charge. Occasionally one will say to another, 'Hey you, sweep the floor willya?' and is inevitably ignored. What does it sell? Oh, er, photos of movie stars. And when I say sell . . .

But Christmas in New York isn't just about shopping. It's about getting excited. And by mid-December I was getting excited, especially after I saw the erection of an enormous inflatable elf on Columbus Avenue. He remained buoyant by the constant injection of new air up his bum and his jolly smile and outstretched hands made me laugh every time I whizzed by on my bike.

The elf advertised Christmas trees for sale. He needn't. The Upper West Side sidewalks spent Christmas doing a reasonable impression of Vermont after a hurricane. Columbus Avenue was a fir alley from 88th Street down to the Museum of Natural History on 79th, with the all-night delis working especially hard towards the goal of a deforested Northern Hemisphere.

But they obviously know their market. Americans spare few blushes when it comes to Christmas decorations. New York apartment windows sported the most unashamed displays, although this was nothing compared to the good citizens of Greenwich. Here, many residents must have spent last year's bonus on flashing fairy lights for the house, lawn, roof and a sizeable chunk of the night sky. Every garden was filled with fairy-light reindeers that lit up like, well, like daft-looking fairy-light reindeers.

Overnight, discreet suburbs became a winter wonderland, and a complete nightmare for any humbugger preferring a few modest bulbs on the conifer. In fact our US Scrooge must have emigrated by now. He stands no chance of a modest existence when it comes to seasonal house decor. Each few months brings a new neighbourly competition. July's stars and stripes stagger on to be lowered in favour of Halloween's jagged pumpkin lamps. At Thanksgiving these are replaced by a still-life harvest creation, including the remainder of the pumpkins. Having witnessed no-one eating pumpkin I'm beginning to suspect a plot by the Pumpkin Marketing Board.

I was keen to see the displays for spring, as well as how much more of the bonus would have to be spent on making the house look ridiculous. I was hoping for neon crucifixions at Easter, with fairy-light bunnies on the lawn.

One Christmas tradition that spans the Atlantic is the office Christmas party. And, boy, did we have a weird one. In England most of the parties I've attended involve a buffet, a dance floor and a ton of alcohol. The food is incidental and the dance floor no more than a place for drunks to reel around while trying to regain their balance. If there are speeches they're kept general and kept to a minimum. Not in America, oh no. By the time the speeches were finished most people were ready to go home. The top boys had even flown in from London to give each other presents, slap each other on the back and drone on for over an hour. And while all the Brits made 'boring' eye movements to each other, the Americans loved it. Any particularly cheesy bit was greeted with whoops of delight and standing ovations. I thought someone was going to run up and kiss our American masters, I really did. These guys were their heroes. They stood there clutching their presents like Oscar winners, while thanking Auntie Maureen and Blondie the dog.

Anyway, the dinosaurs came and went, man evolved from a tadpole-like thing into a land creature that stood up straight, the Ice Age happened and great white tribes moved across the Eurasian steppes and settled, eventually conquering the Americas. And the Americans finally stopped talking and I got to eat my cold baked salmon.

Dessert was forgotten as the band started knocking out murdered versions of 1970s' classics. Indeed, the band themselves had the look of murdered versions of 1970s' classics. They'd witnessed their career slide in an alcoholic haze. Madison Square Garden and Carnegie Hall to university campuses and finally a suburban party for a financial boutique – perhaps they expected us to wear hot pants. Still, after a few Heinekens they sounded pretty reasonable and the dance floor filled.

I started sniffing round for women, most of whom looked lovely. Again, the Heinekens helped but it's amazing how fantastic some women can look when scrubbed up and in a nice dress. When they padded around the office in jeans and sweatshirts I hardly noticed them. But here, in flowing cocktail dresses showing slender shoulders and smooth legs, they looked magnificent. It was a pity they stuck to the men they knew.

There weren't even that many women around. Our Christmas bash had a reputation for laddish behaviour and apparently some women avoided the event as a result.

American women don't appreciate laddish behaviour, unlike their British counterparts who find it amusing in an 'aren't they pathetic' sort of way. Mind you, American lads don't behave in an 'aren't they pathetic' sort of way. American lads are more cigars than lager and more lap dancing than cheeky chat-up lines. The atmosphere's clubby, it excludes women and it isn't self-deprecating – quite the reverse.

It was a pity so many women stayed away, because it didn't seem that bad to me. Sure there was a lot of cigar smoke, sure there was a lot of guffawing in a very hetero-sexual male-bonding kind of way, but I saw no really boorish behaviour. Perhaps the men were on probation this year, hoping the women would return the next.

But I was in no mood for cigars and guffawing. I walked outside to the line of limos and slumped onto a back seat.

'West 88th Street, please. In Manhattan,' I said.

'Where you from?' asked the driver.

'England,' I said.

'Hey, I'm from Argentina. What about that game?'

'Yep, best game of the World Cup.'

'By far,' he said.

'And we'd have won if it wasn't for Beckham,' I said.

'No way.'

And I sat back for the most rewarding exchange of the evening – I even got to mention Maradona's handball.

JANUARY

Fantasy dating

My confidence with women had evaporated. I was back in my shell, fearing rejection. But it was the New Year and I had to get back on my bike. I needed Trevor and I needed Peter's Bar.

Peter's Bar on the Upper West Side is notorious. It's a typical New York corridor bar with a fancy restaurant attached. The bar's a squeeze, which makes it an excellent pick-up joint.

'Remember,' said Trevor as we scanned the bar, 'if you're wondering if she fancies you – she does. Women don't give ambiguous signals in a bar like this.'

We tried our usual trick of ordering drinks from the very point of the bar that lodged two likely women.

'Sorry, excuse me.'

The next trick is to over-order the drinks. Get talking to the bar staff – about ice or the brand of vodka. That way the women hear the accent.

'Are you Australian?' asked one.

Not again – I wish they'd work it out.

'No,' I said. 'I'm English.'

'I thought that's what I heard,' she said. 'But the Englishmen I meet are usually unattractive.'

No wondering here. She may have insulted my

193

countrymen but she'd been pretty clear about me – so bollocks to all you ugly losers. I went straight for the cheesy lines.

'You have amazing eyes,' I said.

She smiled as if to say, 'I know.'

And she did. From the first held glance she switched them on, luring me into her trap like a black widow spider – the long black hair and pale skin helped. Her name was Lauren and she was with her friend, er, Thingy. She was from New Jersey and I gave it the usual chat about coming from Essex, London's equivalent. We were getting on fine. Those eyes helped.

'Oh I like this song,' she said, jigging her body to the music. 'It's the Watzit Boys isn't it?'

'Er, it's Bob Marley I think,' I said. I knew – there's no mistaking Bob.

'No, no, it's definitely the Watzit Boys,' she insisted.

She smiled defiantly and held my gaze.

We were in a crowded bar surrounded by noise, yet we became an island of silence. I could feel the energy coming from her body. I could sense the rise of her breasts, the curve of her hips, those legs beneath her short tight skirt. She was cute. She was dark. Her eyes sent signals to my trousers. I wanted to climb back on my bike.

'I'll bet it's Bob Marley,' I said finally.

The silence had to end. We were locked in a holding pattern and I was impatient to land.

'What's the bet?' she asked, a daring zest creeping into those eyes.

'Dinner.'

'Dinner,' she agreed.

The juke box confirmed it – selection 3010, *Bob Marley: Legend*. She turned to me with a smile.

'Dinner it is,' she said.

'Dinner it is,' I confirmed. 'Dinner with . . .' oh bugger, I'd forgotten her name.

'You've forgotten my name,' she said. 'I'm buying you dinner and you've forgotten my name.'

'No I haven't,' I said hastily.

'Well?'

'I bet you I haven't,' I said.

I knew it was in there somewhere.

A doddery old man runs my memory recall system. He sits in a dusty library and fumbles for his glasses as he ponders a request.

'Hmmmm,' he thinks. 'Now I was only given this information a minute ago. So it has to be here.'

Meanwhile he's looking under piles of dusty books or through mountainous curly-papered in-trays.

'What do you bet?' she asked.

'I bet a drink after dinner,' I said.

The old boy was on his second in-tray by now, muttering to himself and shaking his head in cheerful despair. 'Seeshh, now where oh where did I put this?'

'A drink after dinner,' she agreed. 'Now what's my name?'

'Lauren,' I said. 'It's Lauren.'

It was right at the bottom of the second pile – mislaid due to alcohol.

Lauren picked the Ocean Grill right on the posh part of Columbus for our mid-week date. I arrived early, headed for the bar and checked out the menu. Blimey – she meant to impress.

The Ocean Grill is a high-ceilinged dining room with a loud but semi-formal atmosphere. As the name suggests it specializes in fish, and most of the dining groups were tucking into large plates of iced oysters.

I wore my New York pulling gear – 501s and a dark-blue cotton shirt. It was a look known in New York as 'Euro' and it said 'interesting'.

I wondered what Lauren would wear. I hoped it would be the short tight skirt and that blouse that made her

195

breasts point towards me like guns on a battleship.

But when Lauren arrived, the statutory five minutes late, she was wearing black trousers and a plain red sweater. She looked nice, but conservative.

I was beginning to detect a New York trend. Women wear short skirts on the pull in the pick-up bars. It's sexually aggressive and shouts 'come and get laid'. First-date clothing, however, shouts 'not yet'. The uniform is sexually neutral trousers and a sweater – nothing you can easily look down or get your hands up.

And I immediately detected more caution from Lauren. She no longer wore her fuck-me face and her body language was more circumspect.

We went to the table and I tried a little speech.

'Look, I appreciate the gesture—'

'No Robert, I'm paying for tonight. It's on me.'

'But it's so—'

'No buts.' She held up a finger.

She had that woman-in-charge look and I oh-so-reluctantly surrendered.

Lauren seemed a very sensible woman. She ran the accounts office for a radio station, no doubt called something impenetrable like 'WKLZ 106.1 – Non-stop Classic Hits'. She'd recently moved to Manhattan from New Jersey, now she could afford it, and had a level-headed, adult way about her. It was a million miles from the sex kitten I'd met in Peter's Bar.

She still had amazing green eyes and long, jet-black hair but in the harsh light of the dining room she'd lost that sexual aura that had attracted me to her in the first place. Sure, she could hold my stare in a sensual way, but those eyes did the work. I got the impression she wanted to switch them off.

I decided to follow Trevor's advice and keep it flirty.

'Oysters,' I said, looking at the menu. 'We should have some oysters. They're an aphrodisiac.'

She smiled a womanly smile learnt from her mother when being taught how to put down overly amorous men.

'Do you feel the need for them?' she asked.

I needed something.

Being an English lout I'd brought my beer to the table, and as she said she didn't want to drink I ordered another and tucked into that when it arrived.

'Boy you drink fast,' she said.

'No,' I retorted. 'Americans drink slow, or not at all.'

'Americans have to be in control,' she said.

'Brits have to be out of control,' I replied.

This was not good. She'd stated her intention to not drink. There'd be no slippery slope towards oblivion, no being taken advantage of. Bollocks, I thought, I hate this slut to nun routine.

When we ordered the food I switched to wine but chose a wine I was pretty sure was only available by the bottle.

'Can I have a glass of the Burgundy?' I asked.

'We only have that by the bottle,' said the waiter.

'Ohh,' I looked disappointed. 'Lauren, you will at least have a glass with your meal, won't you?'

'No,' she said firmly. 'I'm not drinking tonight.'

'Hmmm,' I stared hard at the wine list. 'So what do you do by the glass?'

He reeled off a couple of names and I turned up my nose.

'I really fancied the Burgundy,' I said.

'Well have it, then,' said Lauren, almost impatiently. 'I'll help you with one glass.'

Bingo – now she'd loosen up.

Such cautious dating really drives me mad. We both gave the impression of being relaxed when we were both as tense as hell. I wanted to break the ice by saying something like 'Oh, I'm such a romantic,' or 'Oh, I think great sex is really important,' or 'Oh, I think we should shag before you get on my nerves and I stop fancying you.'

Instead I sat in silent frustration. How I dreamt of a date involving a great act of female spontaneity. In fact I know the act – it was in a British car advert from around '96. The advert centres on what goes through a man's mind as he drives: winning races, saving children, that sort of thing. One 'thought' has him in a crowded restaurant with a woman. She climbs on the table, kneels in front of him, throws off his glasses and lands him a blooming great smacker on the lips. And she wasn't wearing sexually neutral fucking trousers. She was wearing a very short, licensed-to-kill, black dress. That's my fantasy.

But New York dates are closer to job interviews than seductions. Any spark from the night you met is extinguished by conversation as neutral as her trousers. A warning sign flashed in Lauren's mind the minute any subject became interesting: 'Danger, danger, you may reveal you're human – close all doors.'

I ended up being grateful for the waiter's cheerful visits.

We skipped dessert and I suggested a drink, the second part of her debt to me. I was beginning to regret my choice of forfeits – I should have made the second prize a big snog with her kneeling on the table. We moved to the Evelyn Lounge next door. I chose a table in a cosy corner but with dining-room chairs rather than sofas or armchairs. I had a plan that required erectness.

Immediately it was better: louder music, lower lighting, more people, closer bodies.

'Go on,' said Trevor. 'Now it's right. Talk some shit.'

I steeled myself.

'You amazed me the other night,' I started.

'How?'

'Your presence in the bar was electrifying – I felt a force between us.'

'I felt it too,' she said, finally lowering her guard. 'When we didn't talk and just—' she stopped. That fucking warning signal had gone on again.

'Stared,' I finished.

I moved towards her and then pulled back, uncertain.

'Too early, you dick,' said Trevor. 'Give it some more shit.'

'But it wasn't just your eyes,' I continued. 'When we were standing next to each other, not touching. That space between us, that air. It seemed so charged.'

She just stared back, aware of the space between us, aware of the charge within it, aware of the space disappearing.

She shut her eyes and returned the kiss, lightly. She wasn't sure. She liked it so she let it happen. She was enjoying herself but the signal was strictly amber – she wasn't about to become my car advert fantasy.

I guess she thought, 'Nice guy, lovely accent – full of shit.'

And I was full of shit, but shit worked. I couldn't understand why it had taken me so long to work it out.

'You're not equals,' Trevor would say. 'You're a hunting male and she wants to be hunted.'

And your weapon is talking shit. She twists and turns while you throw shit lines. Talking about her work isn't throwing shit lines – it's having a conversation. She'll think you don't want to trap her and she'll find a man who does. Talking about the charged space between you is throwing shit lines. She'll soon be cornered.

We finished our drinks and I suggested Prohibition because we could dance to a band and it was four blocks from my apartment.

Prohibition was packed. A band banged out soul classics and the crush of people forced us together, with me

199

leaning in for the occasional snog. She'd completely melted into me by now. She was drunk on the romance. I thought I was odds-on for a shag.

'This is so romantic,' I said, hoping some shit might move things on. 'It's one of those moments you'll remember.'

She sighed and looked deeply into my eyes. She wanted to believe I wasn't just a bullshitter, she really did. But she had to fight the sensible side of her brain – a sensible side that shouted 'he's talking crap' every time I spoke.

Around 1a.m. I suggested we leave and she happily grabbed her jacket and stepped into the street. But now it was raining – thick New York rain that runs down the avenues in sheets.

Lauren stood under the awning and sneered.

'I'll grab a cab,' I said and ran towards the line of yellow taxis, but she followed me with that sensible look back on her face.

'I'm going home,' she said. 'Thank you for a lovely evening.'

It was said as though she meant it – no ifs, no buts.

'Well thank you,' I said. 'You paid for it. The next date's on me.'

'You bet,' she said.

Victory through boredom

Commuters are grumpy the world over. At least they're grumpy both here and in the UK. Maybe in Brazil, or somewhere sunny with lots of beautiful people, commuting is just one great big barrel of laughs. Maybe there's a salsa dance party everyday, and the train's late arrival is ignored because the commuters are having such fun.

Eventually the stationmaster confiscates the band's instruments and the commuters stagger off in search of a nightclub. But in boring old London and New York there are no parties or music – just fed up commuters resenting the waste of time.

Yet the commuters on my morning train also resented me. This is because I boarded at 125th Street, the first stop out of Grand Central. Peculiarly, the seats on the Greenwich trains are in sets of five, and the Grand Central aristocracy manage to spread themselves out across all of them. Our 'reverse commute' trains offered a degree of space that the poor buggers going into the city could only dream of. But my Grand Central adversaries took a seat for their arse, a seat for a coat, a seat for a briefcase and two for the *Wall Street Journal*. Of course this left no room for the coffee and bagels, so they had to squeeze up and share with the newspapers.

So there was certainly no room for some interloping 125th Street pain in the arse. My God no: feet up, newspapers spread out, jacket carefully laid to avoid creases, briefcase open and spilling documents – nothing spare here, pal. They weren't stupid enough to believe I'd stand while they held court in a mock-up of Mussolini's office, but they thought they could intimidate me into squeezing up with someone else.

Reacting with maximum negative body language – hurrrmph, hurrrmph, scowl, scowl – they'd slowly clear their things with an attitude that said, 'OK, you get one of the five this time buddy, but I ain't happy.'

In fact the only people who seem happy are the conductors. And what makes them especially chirpy is making an announcement over the tannoy. Boy, these guys love their announcements.

'Rye, Rye, Rye,' they shout. 'This is Rye, folks. If you're detraining at Rye, make sure you have all your personal possessions with you, including your umbrella because they forecast rain for mid-morning with a high of fifty-five.'

The conductors are like a child with a new toy. 'Hey, if I press this button the whole damn train has to listen to me banging on the whole journey about shit they already know.' Eventually you learn to filter out the racket, although I'm told this takes ten years.

Although a blue-collar job, these conductors love their work for sure. They love the uniforms – especially the blue collars – they love punching a curiously large number of holes in obscure pieces of paper, and they especially love the rules and regulations. It really turns them on. Take my bike. I didn't mind having to buy a bike permit for the train. I didn't mind being told I had to store it in the 'offside' doorway. I didn't even mind them saying I could only travel in the rear two cars. But when one Nazi pulled out a leaflet entitled 'Regulations for Bicycle Use on the Metro-North Railroad' and pointed out that one of the twenty-three regulations stated I couldn't put my bike on the train during the very hours I was likely to commute, I minded.

Despite going against the traffic, every journey I'd ever made as a reverse commuter had been illegal. Great.

No American will blink at these rules. A country created to expand unhindered by the nonsense of petty regulations is drowning in the stuff. And Americans love throwing the rules in your face. I was even hauled in front of Human Resources for wearing cycling shorts in the office. It was a violation of the dress code and my walk through reception before changing into my suit was spotted and reported.

I spent ages trying to grasp how this land of liberty became so bound up in red tape. It's as if Americans loved freedom so much they passed a million and one laws to protect it. In the end there are so many laws, and America is so fucking free, no-one can move.

And if the laws don't get you, the bureaucracy will. I've filled in more forms since I arrived than during my entire life in the UK. I filled in three forms on arrival at the office, simply to get a security pass. Becoming a member of the in-office gym took three forms and a letter from a doctor I'd never met. I filled in four forms to get the wages department to pay me, while opening a bank account took six forms and an hour-long personal interview.

But this was just the beginning. It's the details that get me: my height, weight, sexually transmitted diseases, mother's maiden name, whether I've ever been a Communist or committed genocide, all recorded on forms nobody will ever read. I mean, have I ever committed genocide? Can you imagine anyone ticking 'yes'?

'Oh shit, the genocide question. Look I was young, I was a hothead – we spared the women and children.'

I had thought Americans were pretty much like us – a mixture of pragmatism and moderation in all things other than alcohol consumption. But I was wrong. They're a bunch of rabid fanatics. It defines them.

To an American, everything's a religion. Politics: religion. Commerce: religion. Sport: religion. No wonder they go completely doolally when it actually involves Jesus and God and stuff.

And like all religious nutters they love to preach. Being English I'm quite happy being crap thank you very much. I'm not asking for help and I'm certainly keen to avoid a lecture. No chance round here. I get lectures in the gym: 'Hey, you wanna take longer deeper breaths'; in the diner: 'Hey, let air in the ketchup bottle when pouring, it'll come out easier'; on my bike: 'Hey, you wanna put your feet at the front of the pedals'; and in the park: 'Hey, don't stand there. Ya gonna block a roller-blader'.

And like all Brits I say, 'Thanks,' wait for them to go away and then go back to my old, crap, way of doing things. We didn't lose an empire by listening to this bunch of zealots, oh no.

Shagging on the beach

I hated my apartment. Everything about it frustrated me. It's a frustration many New Yorkers feel and part of the reason for the success of Starbucks, those tacky coffee bars on virtually every Manhattan corner. People can't bear to spend the evenings staring at the four walls of their apartment, so they spend it staring at the four walls of Starbucks. But this is too sad a ritual for me. I'd rather get quietly pissed in a bar. So when I had to get out I'd put *The Economist* in my jacket pocket and go for a drink – or a few drinks.

I'd normally head for one of the bars on Amsterdam Avenue. While most were rough and ready hangouts for students they had the lively atmosphere I craved. On this occasion I settled on Jake's Dilemma, a spit and sawdust joint around 81st Street. I sat on a barstool and ordered a Bass.

The bar was quiet for a Thursday, although it was still early. I noticed only one woman – not that I was on the pull. She was wearing a yellow jacket that didn't suit her but she had long, dark hair and was small, always the type I notice. But she disappeared to the back of the bar and I soon forgot her. Instead, I tried to concentrate on an article about the euro.

I was soon on my second beer. It was beginning to slip down nicely. I could feel my blood thinning and my joints loosening. A trickle was making its way to my brain and creating a lucidity of thought. Yeah, maybe I could go on. I'd heard about those Latin nightclubs. They'd be full of small dark women.

'Mind if I sit here?'

Slightly startled, I looked up to see the woman in yellow. She'd climbed onto the stool next to me, although a line of empty stools stretched down the bar. She sat right by the beer tap faucet and turned to her reflection in the stainless steel surround, flicking her hair to make sure it fell on her face. Then she looked directly at me.

'How y'all doin'?' she said, in a lovely southern-belle accent.

'I'm absolutely fine, thanks awfully. And how are you, my dear?'

I'd adopted the usual accent and expected the usual response but no, she just carried on.

'I'm bored,' she said. 'My friends have gotten themselves into a pool contest leaving lil' ol' me on my lonesome.'

Lil' ol' me indeed – yet another graduate of the Penelope Pitstop school of speech.

'Well you should sit here and talk to me,' I said. 'What's your name?'

'Tiffany,' she said, turning back to look at herself in the faucet.

'Well Tiffany, I'm Robert, and it's jolly nice to meet you.'

I was really laying on the Hugh Grant. It was normally fail-safe.

'So Tiffany,' I said. 'Where you from?'

'I'm from Virginia, in the South.' In fact she said *Ver-jean-yaaa*. She seemed very proud of it.

'D'you like *Ver-jean-yaaa*?' I asked, trying a slight mock to inject some levity.

'Oh *Ver-jean-yaaa*'s so fine,' she said. She turned to me and touched the arm that held an erect *Economist* open on the euro article. 'It's *sooo* beautiful.'

She looked into my eyes. I stirred but she quickly returned to her reflection.

'So I've heard,' I said. 'But is it exciting? What's there to do at night in Virginia?'

I took a deep draught of my beer.

'Shagging,' she said.

I didn't quite spit the beer out, but the swallow went wrong and I had to put my hand to my mouth to prevent an unsightly splutter.

'I'm sorry,' I said, putting my drink down in case I'd heard her correctly the first time.

'Shagging,' she most definitely said. 'I like shagging. Especially on the beach.'

'Really,' I said.

I had such a grin on my face.

'Yessirree,' she said. 'It's such a pity they don't do shagging in New York.'

'I agree,' I said.

'Why?' She turned to me. 'Do you go shagging?'

'Er, it depends what we're talking about,' I said cautiously.

'Yunnooo, the Carolina shag,' she said. 'It's a dance 'n all.'

'Ohh, I see,' I said, slightly disappointed. 'Is it fun?'

'Oh, such fun.'

'You'll have to show me,' I said.

I wanted to tell her what shagging meant to the English but she didn't seem interested. She'd yet to acknowledge I was English, a subject that normally takes up the first ten minutes of any conversation. So I thought I'd push her in the right direction. 'Have you ever been to England?' I asked.

'No, but I'd love to go,' she said. 'France too. I'd love to go to Paris.'

Oh dear, the stock how-to-insult-an-Englishman answer.

'I've never left the United States,' she said.

I've heard this from so many Americans I'm no longer

surprised by it. Most Americans I've met don't even own a passport. Imagine that, these guys elect the man who could wipe us out in an instant and they think we live on a planet entirely made up of Blockbuster Videos, Dunkin' Donuts and McDonald's. OK, maybe they're right – but they've never seen a medieval castle, a Roman ruin or wandered through the tangled streets of an ancient city. It's worrying.

By this time I was dying for a slash. I'd been bursting for around ten minutes but thought Tiffany too flighty a bird to wait for my return. But it was now either a visit to the bathroom or a warm dribble down my leg. I declared my intention.

'I'll be here,' she promised.

She wasn't. I rushed back to find her standing with two men. I sat back on my stool with an exaggerated flurry, although she gave no sign of returning.

Fuck it, I thought, I'm leaving.

'I'm off,' I said flatly as I marched over.

'Oh you're going,' she said, snapping out of her flirt. 'OK, let me give you my number.'

She fished round in her bag and handed me her business card.

'Make sure you call me,' she said as I left.

When a woman in a bar hands over a business card you have to wonder for the fate of romance. But it has its advantages. For a start, you know it's authentic. Any old number can be penned on a napkin. Second, it normally has an email address and you can get to work right away.

And Tiffany was a chatty emailer. She'd tell me about her lunch dates with Dawn, Suzanne, Dicky ''n' all' as if they were great chums of mine. I felt like emailing back saying, 'Tell Dicky he still owes me twenty dollars, the tight git,' just to see her reaction.

But I didn't. I kept it formal, with my few attempts at flirting falling a bit flat.

She was off to a concert on Saturday night with the Tiffany fan club, and I was welcome to come. I wasn't up for a massive night as Lauren and I were off to the Museum of Modern Art on Sunday, and I had high expectations of rapid sexual progress. And given that this was New York I had low expectations of a first-night shag with Tiffany.

But Tiffany was full of surprises. For a start, I arrived on Saturday night to find her looking amazing. She wore a bright-red miniskirt, black tights and knee-length laced-up boots. Her top was figure-hugging and her make-up was dark and heavy. She was dressed to kill – or possibly to walk the streets for money – and I was instantly aroused. It sure beat the Miss Jean Brodie style of first-date dressing.

And it turned out that this was a date. Although offered as a group activity, it quickly materialized that her friends were not invited and we weren't going to a concert. Instead she was keen to tour the dive bars in the East Village and Alphabet City, her old neighbourhood.

We trawled a few of these places, never lingering for more than a single drink and always getting involved with people, as if Tiffany was asserting her popularity. Tiffany seemed happy to chat about her old life in the East Village and steal glances in any mirror she could find. I was happy to tag along and listen, as well as steal glances down her ample cleavage.

At around 3 a.m., and with Tiffany somewhat unsteady on her heels, we ended up in a bar called 7b, on Avenue B and 7th Street. This place was famous for the transvestite scene in *Crocodile Dundee* and was packed with jovial, friendly people who all wanted to talk – or at least stand and stare at Tiffany's ample cleavage along with me. By now her eyes looked heavy and her lips especially pouty, having used her last bathroom trip to touch them up. So I started to gently stroke her long, straight, black hair. She closed her eyes and leaned into me like a cat receiving affection. Her head rested on my shoulder and she lifted her face towards mine.

'Go on, mate,' said Trevor. 'She's gagging for it.'

She took the kiss for a few seconds, moving her mouth with mine. Then her eyes opened and her mouth moved to a smile.

'Ummm,' she said. 'That was cheeky.'

Cheeky? She had practically thrown her mouth over mine. She was the cheeky one.

'You *are* forward,' she said.

This little vixen had an Orwellian sense of history, but I didn't mind. Being scolded for being forward beat kicking myself for being backward any day.

We went to one final bar, the Village Idiot at the bottom of Chelsea. It was a dump, although Tiffany loved it because it had a country-and-western flavour.

'Is this shagging music then?' I asked, determined to get back to the theme.

'No, shagging's much more fun,' she said. 'But I couldn't see any shagging music on the jukebox.'

'No Barry White, then?' I asked.

Again she sat on a barstool and again she didn't offer any money. We'd been in four cabs and bought six rounds of drinks but not once had Tiffany lifted a finger to pay. I was expected to shell out each time. In fact she said as much.

'I expect men to be gentlemen,' she told me. 'I expect men to pick me up, to open doors and to pay for dinner.'

It was her definition of dinner I was having trouble with.

Indeed, Tiffany seemed to think her only role in life was to have a dreamy look and offer her face up for the odd snog.

'I want to take things very slowly,' she said after planting another soppy kiss on my lips. But then she added, 'Why don't you come back to mine for a cuddle?'

209

Maybe this was Eddie Irvine's idea of slow, but it wasn't mine. And for New York it was warp factor five.

We caught a cab the short distance to her Chelsea studio and, after I'd paid the cabbie, we walked up.

'Elvis, Elvis. Hello baby,' she cried as she opened the door. A cat appeared and started purring. Tiffany picked it up.

'Say hi to Elvis,' she said, addressing me in the same childish voice as the cat.

Oh no, I was going to have to be nice to a cat – an allergy-ridden fleabag of a cat. And this cat wouldn't go away. It was as affection-seeking as its owner and demanded that any new visitor pay it full homage in the petting department.

For me, stroking a cat is like stroking a turd and not being able to wash my hands afterwards. I can feel the allergy shit on my skin, on my clothes, in the air. And I can feel it in my nostrils. Soon I'm sneezing, which means I bring my hand to my face. My neck reddens and I want to scratch my skin off. All in all, cats are not the perfect companions when a major seduction is on the cards.

Tiffany seemed unfazed by my problems and snogged me between sneezing fits. As we kissed she slid down the sofa until her left breast rubbed my right hand. After a final squirm my hand fully cupped it.

'Y'all such a naughty lil' boy,' she said. 'Y'all just keep pushin' your luck.'

I hadn't moved an inch.

I kissed her neck and ear and then moved down to kiss her shoulder. My hand moved up to her bra strap. I pulled it gently down her upper arm and her plump breast plopped out of both bra and lacy top.

'No, you mustn't,' she said urgently. She then pushed my head onto her nipple and started moaning loudly with pleasure. Her hand reached beneath my top and she pulled it over my head. I was now topless, although the movement shook up cat allergy shit and induced another sneezing fit. She ignored the sneezing and undid my trousers, rummaging around for Perky, although he was caught at an awkward angle and not easy to locate. Meanwhile I pulled down her top and began kissing both breasts in turn. I licked and bit her nipples and caressed her leg with my free hand, working my way up her boots, her tights and under her miniskirt.

This led to another, 'No, no, you mustn't,' and a second, successful, search for Perky.

Then she stopped, stood up and clinically undressed down to her knickers. This was major progress for a first date, although I felt a little disappointed. I'd been looking forward to undressing her myself and I was hoping to organize things so that the boots stayed on.

'Have you got a condom?' she asked, clearly wanting to get on with the job.

'I'm not sure I have,' I confessed, although I was really just trying to slow things down.

'Don't worry,' she said, and fetched one from a small box on the TV.

Tiffany moved to lie on the bed. Her whole body language now suggested speed, as if she was about to turn into a pumpkin and was determined to get a fuck in beforehand. In a clear 'let's get on with it' move, she lifted her backside off the bed and pulled down her knickers. Tiffany didn't look at me while she did this, as if she was undressing almost absentmindedly. 'I'm just removing my panties, tra-la-la. I'm assuming I'm on my own, tra-la-la.'

This gave me full access and a great view – I did like this American female habit of shaving pubic hair down to a small adolescent thatch. I placed my mouth on her fanny, kissing her lips as if it were a mouth. This intensified her moaning.

'WOAAHHH, WOAAHHH,' she cried, louder and louder as my tongue slid in and out of the opening.

Slowly I increased the pace, thrusting my face harder and harder against her pussy as she clung on to the back of my head and shouted, 'OH YESSS, OHHH YESSSS, OHH ROBERT, OHHH.'

She was so loud I assumed her neighbour sprang from his sofa and went to the list stuck on the fridge by a magnet.

'Hmmm, Robert,' he'd mutter looking down the list. 'Willy, Bill, Henry, Steve, Harry, Dicky, John. No, no Robert,' and off he'd go to fetch a pen.

She was soon pushing her fanny so hard into my face I could barely breathe, which encouraged the nose to twitch in preparation for another sneeze. I desperately resisted as Tiffany came to a crushing orgasm – the headboard banging the party wall in time to the music I could hear on the TV next door. By the end I was having to hold my nose to stop myself sneezing right in her and I was grateful her eyes were shut tight. If she'd opened them she might have thought I was complaining about the smell.

But Tiffany seemed oblivious to my problems. Straight after the orgasm she demanded I climb on. She pulled me level with her as I hastily put on the condom. She then thrust her fanny out and, uhhh, I was in.

And, like Krystal, Tiffany was no slow shagger. She wanted a hard fuck and she wanted to keep me well informed of my progress.

'Oh yeah, that feels so good,' she said. 'Mmmm, so good. Oh yeah, Robert, oh yeah. Don't stop. Oh yeah, fuck me good.'

I was tempted to ask her to shut up. It was difficult to concentrate through such a racket. Nonetheless I soon had a nice rhythm going and the headboard was again telling the neighbour that Robert was back on the job.

Then I felt something on my leg. It wasn't painful. It was more a weight, then another weight further up. The fucking cat was walking up the back of my leg. He was soon on my bum and up onto my back.

'Hello Elvis,' Tiffany cried as he came into view. 'Now you go and get down.'

We both laughed, although I secretly fantasized about setting the fucking thing alight.

'Snnnew,' I sneezed, trying not to get Tiffany full in the face. I moved my head aside and sneezed on her shoulder. 'Snnnew, snnnew.'

As I sneezed my body spasmed. This scared and destabilized Elvis, and I felt a series of sharp pains as the cat sought to improve its grip.

'Yeeow,' I cried.

'Elvis, stop that,' said Tiffany without conviction. 'Go on now you naughty thing. Shoo.'

It didn't get off. Instead he wandered down to my buttocks and started needling them as if getting ready to lie down.

'He's prodding my bum,' I said, nervous that the claws would return. Elvis then settled himself on my arse and started purring.

'Elvis,' Tiffany cried. 'Go away.'

Tiffany managed to move her leg so it was beside the cat and gave it a swift kick. To my relief he had no time to attempt to cling on and tumbled off, complaining.

With Elvis gone I returned to my rhythmic pumping.

'Now where were we?' I said, affecting a James Bond smoothness. And Tiffany was soon back to shouting at full volume.

'That Robert,' said the neighbour, shaking his head. 'A couple more minutes and he'll have beaten Willy.'

I did feel for the neighbours. It was around 5 a.m. and Tiffany was yelling the block down as she reached another climax.

And she was soon encouraging me to do the same.

'Come on Robert, yes, come in me, come on, come inside me.'

Now I may have been in two minds about the shouting, but this sort of order makes me instantly obey – with my usual single 'uhhh'.

Phil Parkes was the goalkeeper

It was 9 a.m. by the time I left Tiffany's. I staggered into a cab and was woken by the driver at 88th Street. My plan was to have a one-hour kip and a long bath before presenting myself at Lauren's at midday in time for our trip to MoMA. But it was 2 p.m. when I woke.

I felt so awful I had to take a cab the few blocks to her apartment near the Lincoln Center, and by the time I arrived I'd developed an acute stomach ache. This was an unusual hangover symptom for me – shrunken brain was my normal response. Perhaps it was the cat.

I ignored the 'All Visitors must be Announced' sign and walked straight to the elevator. The sign appears in every New York apartment block with a doorman and it bugs the hell out of me. It puts me in mind of grand balls and flunkies shouting, 'His Honour, The Esteemed Robert the Second' as I hautily stroll in and look for the Ferrero Rocher waiter. Not this time – I felt too shit to negotiate with a cheerful doorman.

Lauren answered the door warily. She wasn't expecting someone to turn up at her door and I assume she'd given up on this idiot long ago.

'Hiya,' I tried to be breezy. 'Sorry I'm late – I just overslept.'

She returned the jollity but I could tell she was pissed off.

We sat on the sofa and I tried to chat while Lauren regarded me with a detached coolness, her magnificent eyes revealing her suspicion. All the while I grappled with the stomach ache. It was a low dull pain that occasionally sent a sharp stab towards my heart. I winced with each turn.

'What's the matter?' she asked.

'Oh, nothing,' I said. 'Just . . . ohhh . . . a little hangover stomach ache.'

Lauren already had me down as an alcoholic. She'd seen me knocking back the vodka martinis the night we met as well as the beer and wine of our first date. Now she was seeing a pissed Brit on the downslope.

'Maybe it's your liver,' she said, mocking my discomfort. 'Perhaps you need a drink.'

I ignored the obvious sarcasm and instead took her literally.

'What've you got?'

She jumped to the fridge.

'Er, water, milk, orange juice, Coke.'

'Coke,' I said, aiming for a trusted hangover cure.

'Are you sure you're OK for MoMA?' she asked.

'I'll be fine,' I replied, putting on the full martyr. 'Just fine.'

We hit the street and I walked the ten or so blocks at a snail's pace, with Lauren's impatience eased by her increasingly cynical expressions of concern. My only response was to clutch my stomach and weakly return her smiles.

I was clearly in no state for a museum so Lauren suggested a coffee at Cafe Europa on Seventh and 57th. She bought a bagel and told me to eat it, although I thought I'd throw up any food. Nonetheless I picked at the bagel and immediately began to recover – especially after a noisy and prolonged dump in their restroom.

'Is that a load off your mind?' she said on my eventual

return. This woman had an English way with wit.

Finally, at around 4p.m., we made the museum.

We started on the floor that held the Impressionists and it became quickly apparent that Lauren knew very little about art. She asked me for my opinion on each painting and nodded in admiration at my replies. With no fear of contradiction I soon became carried away. I told her that Seurat blew paint through a straw, and Van Gogh used his fingers. I stated that Monet was an opium addict and hallucinated the clouds, and that Toulouse-Lautrec had an enormous willy – hence the tarts.

She wasn't sure how to respond to the last comment, although I noticed a single woman nearby shooting me a glance. In fact a lot of women in the gallery were on their own – many looking round as if interested in more than the paintings. Several held my look and one smiled at me. I became so fascinated I started dropping back from Lauren and tried to win smiles. It was certainly easier than in a bar.

The smiles and Lauren's admiration soon had me fully restored. And by the time we were herded out at 6p.m., I felt chipper. I suggested dinner and plumped for O'Neals' on 64th – just around the corner from her apartment.

Despite having a cool mini Statue of Liberty on the roof, it's a dull restaurant. It has a stuffy atmosphere that became positively asphyxiating after the arrival of two old women on the next table. One had a streaming cold and she continually sneezed into her napkin in a loud, exaggerated, New Yorky way. And because she didn't want to sneeze on her companion she turned her face towards us. And because she didn't want to snot up her napkin she only half brought it to her face. I could feel the sneeze hit me.

She spent the time between sneezes complaining to her mate. 'It's terrible, I tell you,' she'd moan, shaking her head. 'I've had it for six weeks – *six weeks*. And the fever – ayy yii yii. I tell you I almost died.'

'So what the fuck are you doing in a fucking restaurant sneezing all over my fucking pasta you stupid old bag?' I wanted to ask.

Of course what I really wanted to do was lean over and push her head in the soup. I'd grab her hair and ram her face into the bowl until the bubbles stopped.

'How's your cold now?' I'd say. 'Beats a Lemsip any day.'

Instead I watched my dinner turn to shit.

'I think the edge has gone from my appetite,' I said to Lauren, playing the unruffled Englishman that had her eyes smiling and her knickers wet.

I'd chosen O'Neals' because it was one block from Lauren's apartment – preventing an easy-to-leave cab ride.

'Never hand them an easy escape,' was Trevor's advice. 'They'll find one if they want.'

But Lauren was going to be no pushover. 'Here we are then,' she said by the entrance to her apartment block as if that meant goodbye. Strange, she'd been flirty all day – at least since I stopped clutching my stomach.

I was reluctant to give up so we chatted away while the busy street passed us by. After a while I grabbed her hand. Soon after that I took a bold step and moved in for a full kiss. She didn't object but, again, she wasn't exactly sucking my face off.

Eventually I just thought, 'Fuck this,' and asked, 'So are you going to invite me up?'

'Oh, you want to come up?' she said, as a question, not an invite.

'Yes of course,' I said, smiling sincerely.

'I see.' She was going to make me beg.

She really just wanted to give the impression of not being easy, but boy, was she making a meal of it.

'Yes, yes,' I felt like saying. 'You're not a slut. I get the picture. Now let's go up and fuck.'

'OK,' she said. 'But that doesn't mean anything, OK?'

What the fuck does that mean? It was like being lectured by an American mom.

'OK,' I said.

As expected, Lauren's apartment was very conservative – Christ, I was half expecting this woman to turn into Virginia Bottomley. I sat on the sofa with a Coca Cola (that was the best she could manage) and we listened to Bruce Springsteen (again, that was the best she could manage). Bruce was a local hero from her New Jersey hometown, which meant we had to endure his bland blue-collar 'life's a bitch' shite for half an hour. Eventually I could no longer stand it and rifled through her 1980s' collection for something more suitable. I put on Nat King Cole while Lauren turned down the lights.

After a while I started my usual trick of running my hand through her hair. I then moved in for a kiss. She sat and passively accepted all this. She accepted my tongue in her mouth, she accepted my hand massaging the back of her neck and she accepted me kissing her ear.

Ah ha – at that point her breathing began to increase and her hands started to rub up and down my chest.

I was wearing a loose sweater with nothing underneath so her hands were soon on my bare stomach and chest. I saw this as an excuse to do the same. I couldn't wait to reveal those breasts – they looked so firm and pointy.

But I didn't hurry. My hands swept over her bare back and down to her jean and knickerline, even clipping the edge of her panties with my fingers. One hand repeatedly moved over her bra strap.

She was sitting upright, facing me. I had one hand clasping the back of her head and massaging her scalp and the other now grabbing the bra strap's clutch and release mechanism. And with little resistance the bra straps parted and the cups fell loose at the front.

But it felt strange. The cups fell away almost too willingly, as if, as if . . . I moved my hands around the front – slyly, not hurriedly. I was right – it was a padded bra.

She wasn't entirely flat-chested. She had these little mounds with tiny pink nipples that I soon set about kissing hungrily. And Lauren pretended nothing had happened, and of course, nothing had – although I felt a little sorry for her.

I soon had her jeans off and was massaging the outside of her panties with Lauren lying back, eyes closed, lip bit and hand tightly clutching the back of my neck. Rather than pull off her knickers I tugged them gently aside by running my thumb underneath the hem. I run it up and down, each time moving closer to the line of moist flesh. I did it very slowly, trying to tease her.

'Wooaahh.'

With each stroke along her opening Lauren's ghost impression became louder. And once I slowly inserted my thumb inside her Lauren went wild. She thrashed her legs, dug her nails into my flesh and laughed like a hyena. And I mean like a hyena.

'HAHAHAHAHA,' she shouted.

'WHOOAHHAHAHAHAH,' now mixing the ghost and hyena impressions to great effect.

My God she was loud. What is it with American women? First Krystal, then Tiffany and now Lauren all shouting for America. But Lauren took the gold. The walls echoed to her moans. It wasn't late but I worried that the police would burst in yelling 'Freeze motherfucker or I'll waste ya.'

'WHOO, WHOO, WHOO HAHAHAHA HYAAA,' she finished off with an excellent police siren, moving exquisitely back to the hyena and the finale – an ironic karate chop. Bravo.

She quietened down but soon started to reach for my

219

buckle. And Lauren wasn't playing games when it came to undressing me. My trousers and boxers were round my ankles in no time and she immediately set about my todger. A man had obviously taught her the art of the hand-job and his instruction was bang on – fucking hard and fucking fast. I could have kissed him, although not while being wanked by his ex.

She grasped the stem as if her life depended on it. Blimey – I wasn't going to last long at this pace and pressure. I tried to remember the 1980 West Ham squad at Wembley, although I'm amazed I got beyond Phil Parkes. I tried to slow her down by kissing her neck and again playing with her vagina. She moved me away.

'I'm done,' she said.

'Fully cooked,' I quipped back.

'Actually a little raw,' she replied.

Then she did a delightful thing. She moved onto her knees in front of me. She removed my trousers and boxers, which had been sitting around my ankles, and she furiously wanked me off. I'm usually a bit of a silent fucker, rarely making a noise during sex bar the grunt at the end. But my God I moaned with pleasure as her hand coursed up and down my shaft.

To ease my excitement I grabbed her head tightly, clutching lumps of black hair and pressing my head to the top of hers. I could see down the curve of her slim back to the cheeks of her arse. It was a fine sight, but not as nice as the front view. She pumped my cock as if pushing air into a bicycle tyre. I could feel the sperm welling inside me, I could feel the tingle as it gathered at the base of my knob, deciding whether to go but needing that lift. I clenched her hair – fuck I was coming, I was going to . . . fuck. I sprayed spunk all over her small breasts and shoulders.

I looked into her eyes and smiled.

'Fucking hell, that was amazing,' I said.

She looked embarrassed. 'Have I still got any hair?' she asked.

'I'm sorry,' I said. 'I got carried away.'

'Don't be,' she said. 'It was exciting.'

Roarrrr.

FEBRUARY

New York, man, yeah, I can handle it

American weather is all or nothing. In fact, it's rarely nothing. New York has a sticky heat in the summer and is bitterly cold in the winter. In spring and autumn it rains a lot and it's bloody windy. And the rain. There's no pathetic spit'n'drizzle here. It just pisses down. One drop through the cool air and you know – give it ten minutes and the streets will look like Bangladesh in the monsoon.

So, of course, when the snow came, it came. I didn't hear any Americans saying, 'Oh look, it's trying to snow', oh no. Mr Snow sat down and had one great big massive dump of the stuff. New York became a candy-box scene overnight as the streets glinted white in the narrow sun. Snow heaped on parked cars and the fire hydrants wore white caps like a kitchen hand's hairnet. Any surface without a snowy crust looked incomplete.

New York looked beautiful, not least because the snow kept its colour. London's rare falls are rendered a grey mush within an hour. After a day it's no more than a filthy residue and within two days it's gone. In New York the snow lingered in great white piles until topped by a new load. And when it wasn't snowing the freezing temperatures turned the streets into ice sheets worthy of an Alaskan valley. Pedestrians gingerly picked their way along the sidewalks like unstable grannies. Unstable grannies stayed inside.

Ice is a key feature of the New York winter. Icicles drip from the overhanging traffic lights and form surreal cascades off the Central Park rocks. Everywhere is ice. Everywhere, that is, except the street corners. These became deep pools of black slush that make once familiar road junctions a leap into the unknown. How you wished you'd taken more notice of the depth of the kerb before the snow. Now your merest step may end in an ankle-deep plunge into icy slush, leaving you enduring the day with your trousers the shade of a student's wallpaper.

But the most annoying thing about the New York winter was how bloody cheerful it made the Americans. They loved it. It gave them a chance to wear silly woollen hats and stupid duck-hunting boots. It also gave them a chance to patronize foreigners struggling to cope with the freezing temperatures and death-inducing sidewalks.

'Oh, it's a mild one this year,' they'd say, with a nostalgic nod to notorious winters past, when men were men and people in Marks & Spencer's book of New York wore even sillier hats.

If the Americans enjoyed themselves, our gang of Brits all looked on death's door. Central Park late-summer tans disappeared as we became pale and drawn, like waxed corpses in a mausoleum. Nat had the appearance of a junkie. His eyes had black rings and he was constantly sniffing. He'd occasionally be found muttering, 'New York, man, yeah, I can handle it.'

Fiona developed bloodshot eyes and a red nose while I was permanently bunged up and carried the look of Bela Lugosi after a big night.

Still, I had an excuse. I lived in the only freezing apartment in New York. While most New Yorkers were complaining about their overheated homes, my place was like a windy underpass in Reykjavik. I'd lie in bed shivering, despite my thermal vest and John Wayne long johns. The only upside was the final completion of my terrace – just in time for a naked roll in the snow. But Serge had the engineering skills of a chimpanzee. He'd failed to include any drainage and the red-brick deck became a collection pad for rain and snow, even seeping through the taped-up French doors to flood the living room during a heavy storm or after a thaw.

And New York is freezing. Through January and February the NY1 TV station's little temperature gauge rarely climbed above thirty-two degrees Fahrenheit. Each morning I'd check it and each morning I'd groan. I'd then put on four layers of clothing, wrap my head in my West Ham hat and scarf and insist on cycling to 125th Street. Even with the layers, it was so cold my face felt like it was being attacked by a crazed acupuncturist. I'd force my way forward through squinting eyes and gritted teeth.

Cycling was a nightmare in the snow. The roads were like muddy farm tracks with two deep ruts for the car wheels. Occupying one of the ruts would result in hooting and abuse from the impatient New York traffic. But not occupying a rut was like cycling across a ploughed field.

I was determined not to be a fair-weather cyclist, although of course everyone in the office thought I was nuts and shouted jokey comments as I waddled by looking like the Michelin Man.

'Hey Ted, the iceman cometh,' one would shout to his mate, or 'Hey buddy, ya spotted a yetti on ya way in?'

I didn't mind. I saw myself following a long tradition of British pluck in the face of great odds and scoffing Yanks. Oh yes, I was Scott trudging south, Shackleton enduring the ice and Franklin pressing on though ravaged by a cruel wind.

When the winter did make cycling impossible I was forced to explore the city's public transport system. The System – by which most mean the Subway – attracts as much criticism as the London Underground, although there's no comparison. The Subway is better run and cheaper to ride. But, boy, is it ugly. The Subway is a series of brutal catacombs devoid of decoration. Iron girders are grateful for a layer of peeling paint, damp climbs every wall and water seeps onto the tracks. And at night there are no cute scurrying mice, oh no – just the odd rat looking well up for a ruck.

During the day, the gritty pace of the city is echoed beneath the streets. Subway trains clatter through the stations on the express line, adding to the rhythm of a busking bass guitar as it strums a line to anchor a sax. The husky tones of the sax echo round the stark platform while the commuters tap their feet. The local train slides in and the doors open, keeping time with the music. Even the announcer sounds like a rapper. 'Lex local, Lex local. Bronx bound, Bronx bound. 42nd Street next. 42nd Street next. Stand *cleeaarr*.'

Pssshhh, thump, clatter, clatter, rumble, rumble. And again the sax takes it away.

It's a shame the trains can't match the mood. Train interiors look like dole offices with hard, orange plastic seats bolted to a brown lino floor. They're stark and featureless with only the Spanish-language adverts for stimulation. You can't even stare at the map. It's positioned right behind someone's head so that a casual observer would assume you were checking the guy for lice rather than looking for your stop.

And when studying the map it's impossible not to conclude that the Subway's planners had a bit of a north-south fixation. Almost all lines start in the Bronx, head south under Manhattan's avenues and end up in Brooklyn – hence the platform signs at every Manhattan station entrance: 'Uptown and the Bronx' and 'Downtown and Brooklyn'. It makes the system look like spaghetti being scooped from a pan rather than the spider's web of the London Underground or the Paris Metro.

The east-west Manhattan traveller is reduced to the bus. New York's buses, like the Subway, have zero-comfort furniture and maximum standing space. But they're very nice to the elderly and disabled. They have a hydraulic platform for wheelchairs and the front of the bus can actually kneel to reduce the step up for the old bags. Yet my God, they're dull – single-decker white and blue affairs that blend in like wallpaper. No-one takes photos of New York's buses and there are no famous routes to make the eyes moist with nostalgia. Most simply nick the number of the road.

Instead people take photos of the yellow cabs. There must be a million of them infesting every street south of Harlem. Cabs monopolize whole traffic jams in New York and make Manhattan avenues look like streams from the neighbourhood's favourite fire hydrant – licences must be handed out like confetti at a wedding.

Not that I'm complaining. New York cabs may not be as clean as London cabs and they may be no more than a cramped back-seat bench with a great view of a perspex partition, but you can always get one, no matter what time of night. While London's black cabs abandon the streets after eleven – forcing people to use un-licensed cars often driven by illegal immigrants – every New York nightclub has a line of yellow cabs waiting out-side.

It's a comforting sight, although don't expect them to know the way – despite the city having the most obvious street plan on the planet. New York's clueless cabbies are no myth. I climbed into one cab at Grand Central and asked for Greenwich Village. After he took me to East Village I complained – only for him to drive on for a few blocks before accosting another cabbie and shouting, 'Glen-witch Willage?'

Not that New York cabbies give a shit. Most spend the whole journey on their mobiles and have no interest in transporting you efficiently from A to B. You have to tell them the address three times because they're not listening and they'll take you via the traffic black spots every time. For instance, it was quickly apparent that the best way from the Upper West Side, where I lived, to the Lower East, where I often hung out, was through the park and down Fifth. But these idiots would stay on Columbus, getting buggered as Broadway crossed by the Lincoln Center and getting buggered around 40th Street by the Lincoln Tunnel (that Abe sure does a lot of buggering).

Still, it would save me a tip.

Hung by the velvet rope

Contrary to popular belief, New York is not the nightlife capital of the world. Its nightclubs are eclipsed by London's to such an extent the top attraction for many clubs is a guest appearance from a British DJ. New York does lead, however, when it comes to the bars. Hip New Yorkers avoid nightclubs for the cool vibes of a bar and lounge. And with a 4a.m. close, many non-hip New Yorkers also prefer the bars – hence the city's obsession with the velvet rope.

New York invented the velvet rope, that intimidating barrier at a club's entrance that literally divides the 'in' crowd from the 'out'. And boy, does New York still hold the crown. If you don't fit the bill, forget it.

Luckily the accent helps – usually. The accent's a positive disadvantage if the guy deciding who's in or out is French, which was the case at Spy on Greene Street in SoHo. Spy is velvet-rope policy at its worst. I've never managed to successfully enter this bar, despite three attempts.

I tried turning up in the middle of the week with a mate.

'I em sorry,' says the Frog. 'We 'ave Stevie Wonder in 'ere tonight.'

So what? Am I going to nick his drink?

I tried turning up early with two women.

'I em sorry,' says the Frog. 'We are fool at the moment. I am only letting in my friends.'

His friends included a gang of tasty-looking women who didn't give him the slightest acknowledgement.

And I tried turning up late with a date.

'I em sorry,' says the Frog, 'but your girlfriend ees too ugly.'

Of course he didn't say that, but I no longer cared. I walked into the night shouting abuse and threatening to buy the place.

The whole enterprise seemed geared to proving me a loser. I wouldn't have minded but the French toerag was a spotty, ugly twat with a haircut out of *The Flowerpot Men*. He was hardly a good advert for the place – although now I knew why our forebears enjoyed giving that lot such regular beatings.

One possible entrée is to bribe the doorman with a twenty-dollar bill, but I've always balked at this practice. If I offered the Frog twenty bucks and he still wouldn't let me in I'd be in no doubt I was the uncoolest bastard to ever walk the streets of Manhattan. Better to leave some dignity in reserve.

Of course it's much harder for men than women. And it's especially hard for single men. On trying to gain entrance to Idlewild, a mock-up of an aeroplane on Houston Street (Idlewild was the original name for JFK

– yes the airport), the bouncer asked, 'Are you on your own?'

He said it harshly enough for me to detect this was a bad thing.

'I'm meeting some people inside,' I said.

'Are they women?'

'I hope so.'

He didn't laugh.

'Yes or no,' he said, adopting a manner that suggested he'd have found gainful employment in post-Depression Germany.

'Yes. Women,' I said, again suspecting this was what he wanted to hear.

'They'd better be,' he said. 'You've got fifteen minutes. Then I'm coming in to check you're talking to a woman.'

In fact it did me a huge favour. It was the best opening line I'd ever been handed.

The velvet rope is all part of New York's obsession with itself. The city's bars want to be hangouts for models and celebrities and would rather be empty than be a hangout for the masses. Of course, most would go out of business if they were strictly for the city's knobs, but impressions are everything.

But the whole celebrity thing doesn't say much for the intelligence of your average New Yorker bar punter. One chain of crappy bar-restaurants called Señor Swanky's states that it is a 'Celebrity Hangout' above the door. Who exactly? Stavros? I suspect they also claim their margaritas are world famous.

Once inside a cool bar it's often hard to see what the fuss is about. For instance this year's look appears to be 'Mode de la Building Site'. It's very odd, as if the owner ran out of money halfway through construction and decided to open anyway.

If wires dangle from exposed four-by-two ceiling joists, if half-plastered walls reveal brickwork in need of restoration, and if bare bulbs hang from RSJs, you're in a hot bar – or lost. To complete the image they should pour margaritas from cement mixers, dress their bar staff in oversized jeans to show off their arse cracks and ask them to greet each female customer with an ''ello darlin'', or the US equivalent.

Shit is certainly chic in New York. The coolest bars are in fucked-up areas covered in graffiti and litter. Dead bodies slump in doorways and the bars have the most basic decor, miserable staff and crappy toilets. All in all if the place looks like it should have been shut down years ago then you can guarantee you'll have trouble getting in.

And once you know what to look for, finding it can be a pain. For a start few have signs announcing that, indeed, this is the place you're looking for and welcome. Often the only giveaway is a hostile-looking bouncer and the velvet rope.

Such tactics are a deliberate ploy to avoid the dreaded B&Ts. The word on trendy hangouts is passed like encrypted information in wartime, and once discovered by the enemy the Manhattanites will flee to pastures new, where there'll be even more dead bodies propped in doorways and even less indication where the fucking bar is located.

But you don't have to descend into the twilight zone to be able to enjoy some of New York's best bars and lounges. The ones past their prime are more relaxed and you don't have to run such a humiliating gauntlet to get in.

One of my favourites is Pravda on Lafayette Street. Although in the poor-little-rich-kids part of town, Pravda is extravagantly wealthy inside. The bar's in a vault and is painted to look like the lair of revolutionaries. It has that studied, shambolic feel that Downtown bars pay a fortune to acquire. And the waitresses are all stunners.

They are tall, dark and slender with dynamic make-up and sharp hair. They wear black cocktail dresses and line up at the bar like the models in that Robert Palmer video.

Fez is also a good pose. While this year's decor of choice appears to be the fucked-up building site look, last year's was the Moroccan kasbah drug den, of which Fez is the best example. This was a real in-the-know place and it retains the feel despite its fading currency. You have to walk through Time Cafe on Lafayette Street to find it. A secret curtain opens and, with luck, you enter one of New York's most relaxing lounges.

Voyeurs of the New York scene should also try The Coffee Shop on Union Square. This place doesn't sound or look much, but it's developed a reputation as a hangout for classy chicks. One night Nat and I posed away to little effect when two leggy models came and stood by us. They were wearing nothing but lacy underwear. It was difficult not to ask.

'Oh, we're off to a party,' they said. 'He's a rock star – can't tell you his name.'

Sometimes I feel like the only person in New York not hanging out with celebs.

'It's great gear,' I said.

'D'you like it,' said one, giving me a strip-bar twirl to show her bum cheeks.

I couldn't think of anything witty to say so I simply smiled inanely. I was way out of my depth.

Watch your step

An early Friday night drink with the ex-pats. We were in a Nolita bar called Double Happiness, a basic basement in a rough area run by disinterested bar staff – you could

231

tell it was trendy. There was no sign – just a 'Watch Your Step' notice by a rusty staircase – rubbish piled up by the graffiti-ridden shutters above and the place had the look of a crypt. Oh yes, this was the height of cool.

But it was too early for the hipsters. This was the hour for the after-work crowd that shuffled up from the Financial District.

And as I waited an age to be served, my eyes cruised these knots of excited people. Naturally they rested on a gaggle of women sitting by the bar and drinking champagne. They had a collective sexuality that made the nose twitch and the senses rise.

My confidence had grown. Lauren, Tiffany, even Krystal in her way, had all convinced me that I was sex on legs. I had a cool stride and a confident smile. I had the walk of a man with an overused tool – the Bee Gees would have been proud.

The woman who grabbed my attention was small and dark, of course. She was furthest away, but our stares locked. Mississippi one, Mississippi two, Mississippi three, Mississippi four. Four seconds of eye contact. It was definitely the look – a sexual look. The one that says 'come and talk some shit.'

I rejoined Fiona's work gang. They'd grown in number and now included her boss from London, an event that was stressing Fiona. She'd been crying down the phone the night before because they were having trouble delivering some of their contracts – hence the arrival of the heavy hitter. Meanwhile, I'd yet to justify my presence in America, and it was fucking cold. It all combined to create an atmosphere of quick release. Life's a bitch, let's get pissed.

The girl with the four-Mississippi stare climbed out from her corner and we naturally fell into conversation. Fuck knows what it was about – I can't remember and it didn't matter. I'd learnt to relax with women. It was fine.

She fancied me or she wouldn't be standing here. Just don't be a jerk.

Although she was American, I can remember her telling me her name was Mary and that she was Scotch. I laughed and nearly asked if she was ten or twelve-year old, but then remembered not to be a jerk.

Instead I gave her my usual chat-up line.

'You're the best-looking woman in here,' I said, 'and I noticed you immediately.'

'Come here,' she said, grabbing my hand and walking me to two stools in a recess bar. We were a little way from the others, although still in full view.

'What'll you drink?' I asked.

'Cosmo,' she said.

The barman was right by us and by some miracle we were served immediately. In no time two silly Seventies Argos cocktail glasses appeared, brimming with a rust-red liquid.

'Here's looking at you, kid,' she said and we clinked glasses.

She knocked it back in one.

Now cosmopolitans are sickly sweet cocktails made of vodka, Cointreau, lime and cranberry and they have a powerful kick. This was some drinker, even for a Scotch.

'Drink up,' she said. 'Come on, it's my round.'

I winced as it rushed down my throat.

Her whole body language was so positive, so sexually geared towards me that I was quickly able to start running my hands through her hair. Her hand lightly clutched my thigh.

'Come here,' she said. 'You've got something by your eye.'

I shut my eyes and felt a light hand above my lid. Then I felt a lovely, soft kiss on my lips. Her hand rested on my cheek as she slowly rotated her mouth on mine.

It was beautiful. She wore a short black skirt and a

233

white exposed-shoulder top. And she'd just tricked me into a lovely snog within minutes of meeting me. My car advert fantasy had arrived.

'How shall we drink these?' she asked, picking up the Argos glass and composing herself for another downer.

'Slowly,' I said, keen to stop her rapid slide to oblivion.

'Spoilsport,' she said.

I took a mouthful of the cocktail and leaned forward to kiss her, allowing the liquid to pass from my mouth to hers. She drank in the cocktail, our tongues crushing together to absorb the alcohol. She was a lovely kisser: very gentle, very sensual. She broke, filled her mouth with cosmo and poured cocktail into my throat, the cold of the drink contrasting with the heat of Mary's tongue.

'You're lovely,' I said.

'Lovely,' she repeated with a tipsy giggle. 'So are you. I just can't stop kissing you. You're *sooo* kissable.'

She came at me again.

I had a storming hard-on by now. It was digging painfully into my trousers and creating a visible bulge.

We hardly spoke. Conversation seemed unimportant and, anyway, she really just wanted to carry on snogging.

Still, I made a few attempts.

'You have a lovely figure,' I said, using it as an excuse to put my hands on her waist.

'No, I'm fat,' she said. 'Feel.'

She grabbed my hand and led it to the side zip of her skirt. She then undid the zip and placed my hand on her bare flesh. Bloody hell, I was beating the car advert guy now. He only got a snog. I had my hand on her bare bum.

Blood coursed into my tool like steel rods being rammed into setting concrete. I stood up to overcome my discomfort. This allowed me to lean over Mary and give her a big face-sucking while my free hand cupped her head.

I felt her hand on my knob. Jesus Christ – the car

advert guy had been left for dead. This woman was playing with my knob in a crowded bar, and all within ten minutes of meeting me.

'Shall we go somewhere else?' I suggested, aware that we were in full view of the bar, including Fiona's gang. I could see Trevor's proud regard, his pupil turning in a sterling mid-term performance.

'You want to come back to mine?' she said.

I was thinking about a quieter bar or maybe a spot of dinner but she was suggesting we go back and shag. I was amazed. This just doesn't happen in New York – at least it didn't to me.

'Sure,' I said as coolly as I could manage, though it came out as a bit of a squeak.

We collected our coats and bags and I had a quick, rather difficult, slash. But when I returned she'd removed her coat and was standing with her friends.

'Ready?' I said, sensing something had changed.

'Yeah, yeah,' she said in a dismissive tone. 'Nice to meet you, give me your card, seeya soon.'

She was saying this as if quoting lines from the *Guide to being Fucking Rude to Men*. She was doing her utmost to dump me. I stood looking bewildered.

'I don't understand,' I said.

One of her friends stood beside her. She regarded me disdainfully.

'We thought *you* were leaving,' said the friend.

Indeed I looked like I was. I had my jacket on and Mary didn't. But what had it to do with her, anyway? Mary had wanted to leave, with me, and frigid bitch here could go jump in the Hudson.

I retreated to Fiona and Trevor.

'You look a bit stressed, mate,' said Trevor. 'Where's that bird you were virtually shagging a minute ago? That looked a banker.'

'I thought so too,' I said. 'I don't understand it.'

235

'I think her friends stopped her from leaving,' said Fiona. 'She's very pissed.'

'What's it got to do with them?' I said. 'She can look after herself. I was hardly going to rape her. It was more the other way round.'

'They were worried about her before,' said Fiona. 'They came and asked us about you.'

What? I couldn't believe it – puritan fucking America strikes again.

'I told them you were very trustworthy,' said Fiona. 'But when they looked round you had your hand in her skirt.'

It was all very embarrassing. Occasionally one of Fiona's gang walked by saying something like, 'Where's that girl you were snogging? Blimey, I thought you were going to have sex in front of us.'

The humiliation became too much and I made to leave. But Mary suddenly appeared next to me. She didn't say anything. She just stared, waiting for me to speak.

'I thought *we* were leaving,' I said. 'I was only suggesting dinner or a drink. You suggested your place.'

She didn't say a word. Instead she grabbed my now flaccid knob and reached up for another kiss.

'I'll get my coat,' she said.

This time I followed her, ignoring the evil stare from her mate. This time I wasn't letting her out of my sight. This time we made it to the street.

But Mary's erratic behaviour was getting out of hand. I tried to hail a cab but she walked beyond me and hailed her own. It screeched to a halt and she climbed in alone, although she clambered across to the far side and the door remained open. I hesitated for a second and then I walked over and got in.

'Tudor City,' she said to the driver, before turning to me. 'You're not coming in.'

Fine, fuck it. I wasn't arguing. I'd go with the flow.

She then held my hand and fell asleep as the cab cruised north. We rode the green wave of changing traffic lights and I rode my luck.

We arrived at Tudor City and she repeated, 'You're not coming in.'

'Wait for the firm no,' Trevor would say.

The trouble was I kept receiving the firm no – followed by a sharp retraction.

Mary was playing such an odd game I hadn't a clue about the rules. I stood on the street as she walked off without a word. I didn't run after her, I didn't even call. But she stopped and turned back.

'Come on,' she said, coming back and grabbing my hand.

She marched me into the Tudor City complex.

Despite its tiny size her apartment was a grand place, like an Elizabethan palace. She even had a four-poster bed, which I sat on while Mary went to the loo. When she returned she lay next to me and I moved to kiss her. She responded at first and I moved closer, kissing her neck and caressing her arms. But when I lifted my head to kiss her mouth she moved away. I moved with her and she turned her face the other way. I rolled on my back in surrender. As I did she got up and moved to the door. 'Thanks. Nice evening,' she said. 'Bye. Give me a call.'

I was furious. How dare she treat me like a potential rapist. I stormed out. Fuck her number – I wasn't into this shit.

Bob's Dodge

Despite the Hardon setback I was keen to carry on with what I now called my Energy Marketing Initiative. It was my best, well, only chance of survival in the States and taking it further involved getting in front of some energy marketers, most of whom are located in Houston, Texas.

I was up at four-thirty for a 6 a.m. flight. I persuaded myself this was fine. The first meeting wasn't until mid-morning and I'd already done the preparation. I'd pencilled in the three-hour flight as 'kip'.

But this didn't allow for the hyperactive kid behind me. For the whole journey I had to endure a one-boy riot while the rest of the aircraft snoozed. My back was constantly pummelled with rare quiet ten second breaks – when I hoped he'd fallen asleep or suffocated – shattered by a loud '*Krrrrpooowww*' as yet another jet fighter bought it.

With sleep impossible I watched the USA float by. The route to Houston from New York passes over a vast swathe of countryside: from Pennsylvania, through Virginia and Tennessee, and on to Texas via the Deep South of Alabama, Mississippi and Louisiana. And virtually the entire journey flies over a grid of perfect rectangular plots, each about a mile square, covering the whole landscape.

This grid is so emphatic it ignores any natural attempt to break it up. Rivers meander through a square without adjusting the lines in any way – the fences just sear through to the other bank as if they carry on underwater. Even mountain ranges prove little barrier. The grid lines charge up mountainsides without hesitation and tumble down steep inclines as if they didn't exist.

Land use changes abruptly at the fence and only at the fence, making the countryside look like a chessboard. One square may be deep pine forest with each surrounding square grazing meadowland or dusty crop fields. Some squares look abandoned or wild, as if they've never been claimed by the owner.

I could imagine the auction hammer banging down and the small man in spectacles shouting, 'Sold to the man with the scratchy beard and the dungarees – plot JJ147 Tennessee.' But old Scratchy Beard got drunk that night and drowned in a vat of moonshine.

This graph-paper landscape continues virtually all the way to Houston, although undetectable once on the ground and beyond the George Bush Intercontinental Airport.

Yep, that's right – the *George Bush* Intercontinental Airport. Amazing, isn't it? George Bush (senior) must have been the biggest nonentity to occupy the White House since Millard Fillmore (who? Exactly) and he now has a major international airport named after him. OK, Los Angeles has a local airport named after John Wayne but John Wayne was cool. He was a Hollywood cowboy with great underwear and who cares if he couldn't act. Naming an airport after a president whose most famous line was 'Read my lips, vote for Bill' or something, is like renaming Heathrow John Major International.

The unfeasibly wide highways which poured into Houston were full of vehicles of inexplicable origin – given that I'd just flown over a thousand miles of fuck-all. They were lined with vast car-sales plots and other messy out-of-town businesses, each boasting an enormous sign shouting for attention: 'Bob's Dodge', or 'Bradley's Tractors', or 'Jim's Jeep'. Profound stuff. They were simple whiteboard signs with plain lettering but they littered the view along the highway. Even smaller businesses felt the need to compete. 'EZPawn', 'Luby's Drive Thru', 'Vasectomy Reversals' – not drive thru I expect – and just about anything else imaginable – 'Fiesta', 'Carpet', 'Kettle', 'Wildfire', 'RV' – all with signs puncturing the sky. It looked like a Scrabble game for the gods.

Through this cluttered landscape the skyscrapers of

central Houston gradually emerge. The Downtown towers of provincial US cities just don't do it for me. Sure, many claim dubious height records. One of the towers is bound to be the tallest tower outside of New York and Chicago or the tallest single-use building but who gives a shit? You can't take on New York so why bother? It's like shouting, *'Coooeee*, over here. I'm important as well, you know.'

Indeed, New York creates an inferiority complex among other US cities, which adopt a variety of tactics to compete. First and foremost comes the nickname. Any US town with a nickname has really made it. Houston claims to be the fourth largest city in the US, recently overtaking Philadelphia, but Philadelphia has a nickname – 'Philly' – or even the 'City of Brotherly Love'. New York is the 'Big Apple' – although New Yorkers hate it – or 'Gotham', and Los Angeles 'LA' or the 'City of Angels'. Chicago is the 'Windy City' and Detroit 'Motor City'. San Francisco can manage 'Frisco' and New Orleans the 'Big Easy'. Even Boston has 'Beantown' but Houston, number four, so it claims, is, er, Houston – not 'Housty', nor the 'Big H', nor 'Oil Town'. Eventually the city fathers will spend millions on marketing consultants to find a nickname. They'll come up with something like the 'Big Slick' and Houston will know it's made it.

Provincial cities' second tactic is to build something big. But, again, there's no bridge, building or monument that shouts 'Houston'. San Francisco has the Golden Gate Bridge and LA the Hollywood sign, Washington the Capitol, Seattle the Space Needle and Chicago the Sears Tower. Even St Louis manages the Gateway Arch. Houston can't even manage an archetypal street scene such as the French Quarter balconies of New Orleans, the art deco fronts of Miami Beach or the cable car hills of San Francisco.

A third tactic is adopting a famous sports team. Dallas

has the Cowboys and Chicago the Bulls. But Houston's football team, the Oilers, buggered off to Nashville they were so bored. And Nashville can boast musical roots, as can Detroit, New Orleans, Memphis, Chicago and now Seattle. Houston's contribution to music can be summed up in one word: brief.

In short, Houston has an identity crisis. Even those cartoon maps of America tend to ignore it. They put a rodeo cowboy on this spot or maybe an oil well. They certainly don't put a crappy crop of skyscrapers.

When asked why they're proud of their city Houstonians point out that 'Houston' was the first word spoken anywhere other than planet Earth – by the Apollo 11 crew as they landed on the Moon. Funny, I always thought it was 'One'. Anyway, it's hardly a tangible symbol for a city – and difficult to prove. It could have been, 'Doobey, doobey Qwarkkizz splatzey, *whheee* [biggy biggy Martian, leapy, *whheee*].'

But Houston's biggest problem is that it's too darn hot. It's so hot, no-one walks anywhere, so the streets are deserted and there's no atmosphere. Indeed when people accuse Houston of being soulless they mean it literally. Everyone drives from their air-conditioned homes to their air-conditioned offices, having parked in an air-conditioned car park and walked through an air-conditioned walkway. Houstonians have become so conditioned to their air-conditioned world that it's almost impossible to walk outside. I learnt this on day two of my visit. Having stayed one night in a Downtown hotel I had to be at the company flat by eight-fifteen to meet a colleague called Mark. We were to drive on to a 9 a.m. meeting beyond the beltway.

Keen to get it right on my first full day I caught a cab from the hotel at seven-thirty. But those ten-lane highways were choked with traffic, as were the suburban boulevards. Every single Houstonian, it seemed, had got in his or her car and decided to sit in a traffic jam. There wasn't a bus in sight and almost all the cars had one lonely guy picking his nose or one lonely woman fixing her hair. The only vehicles with more than one occupant were the pick-up trucks ferrying gangs of Mexicans six abreast in the cab while a seventh guy sat in the back with the lawnmowers.

Eight-fifteen came and went and the taxi driver, a black African with a good knowledge of English football, started making noises about my bad planning. I should have allowed at least an hour for the three-mile trip, he said, not forty-five minutes. This was despite the fact we were driving away from Downtown. He said I should have known that it was going to be bad at this time in the morning and in his view Everton would be fine but Blackburn Rovers were in big trouble.

But I no longer cared. I was in as much shit as Brian Kidd. It was eight-thirty and Mark would be fuming. My mobile didn't work in Texas and the meeting was at least forty-five minutes beyond the apartment.

'How far are we from South Voss and Westheimer?' I asked.

'Two blocks,' he said. The traffic had moved no more than twenty yards in the last ten minutes.

'I'll walk,' I said.

'Walk?'

'Walk.'

'OK, if that's what you want,' he said, giving me a 'you're fucking mad' shake of the head.

And I soon worked out why. Blocks in Houston suburbs ain't like blocks in Manhattan. They're about a mile apart. It took me fifteen minutes to reach the end of block one as I trundled by DogMart and CatMart and Guinea Fucking PigMart.

And as I crossed the ten-lane boulevard I could see the waiting drivers' eyes following me across the road. I could also tell I was the subject of conversations in the rare car that had a passenger.

'Well would ya look at that,' I could see them saying. 'There's a guy in a suit walking. What in the name of God?'

They must have thought I'd broken down, or run out of gas, or been called on my way in and sacked – with an instruction to get out of the company car immediately. Maybe they were dreaming. Whatever – surely this guy wasn't just walking.

There was a sidewalk – at first. Broken and uneven, it was punctuated by abandoned street furniture and fallen DogMart signs. But block two didn't even bother with a sidewalk. Block two skirted a vast retail park'n'shop nightmare called EverypetunderthefuckingsunMart, or something. And they reasoned, not unreasonably, that no-one was going to use the sidewalk in a million years. So fuck it, they said, let's make it a grass bank. And I'll tell you what, let's keep the grass bank nice and green by watering it – constantly.

I squelched through the grass, my smart City brogues soon covered in mud. I did come across one other human being on the grass bank, a Mexican digging a hole for a new tree. He looked at me in amazement as I approached.

'Morning,' I said, trying to discourage the inevitable lecture.

'Shouldn't be walking here man,' he said.

'Evidently,' I replied, and stiffened my lower jaw.

Welcome to Wichita, it smells like shit

The Main Man missed my Houston meetings. He was an oilman and I wanted to talk to the power utilities. And

243

without the strength of his contacts, meetings were difficult to arrange and tough to conduct.

I'd gained my image of Texan businessmen by watching *Dallas*. Consequently I was looking forward to meeting giant guys wearing white suits and big Stetson hats.

'*Howdeedoodee*, Barb,' they'd say as they gave me a big slap on the back. 'Let's step into my *arfice* and have a *ceegharr*.'

But, of course, it wasn't like that. They were normal guys in normal suits. And normally they were rushed off their feet. Many would have back-to-back meetings and squeeze me in for twenty minutes. They'd spend the first half of my presentation thinking about the last meeting and the second half thinking about the next.

'So you see,' I'd say, 'we can take all your energy marketing Receivables, package them up and securitize them into the bond markets. I assume you'd be happy to remove those credit exposures to other traders and get cash upfront?'

Silence – and then eventually, 'Oh, I'm sorry. I was thinking about something else.'

They may as well have added, 'Something important.'

And that was my problem. These guys were traders, a breed not known for their patience. I was presenting what they saw as a fancy new concept that took months to implement while they were more concerned about the next trade, as well as getting this irrelevant Limey out of their office.

Even box-and-arrow diagrams failed to hold their attention for more than a minute. I handed out presentations full of them but they'd start leafing ahead. Then they'd slam the book shut and look at me expecting something more exciting. Meanwhile I'd just finished the 'we're such a great bank' intro.

One guy actually stopped me after less than a minute and said, 'No, not interested.'

He leaned forward.

'Now, have you thought about this?' and he started telling me his plan for using lots of my bank's money.

In fact it wasn't a bad idea. He was with a large trading company and expected commodity prices to rise, so he wanted to buy out the entire inventory of small commodity production companies so they couldn't sell elsewhere. He'd then hang on for the inevitable hike before selling the stuff on for a fat profit.

But he didn't want to take delivery of the whole lot in one go as that would create too big a dent on his balance sheet. So he wanted to set up a special company that took ownership of the commodities. Of course, the actual commodities went nowhere – they just sat in the producer's warehouse – but the producer didn't own the stuff anymore, although he'd be paid a small fee for shipping it to the trader, month by month.

And this is where my bank was to come in.

Our suggested role was to fund the special company that bought the producer's inventory. As the cash was passed to the commodity producer we'd be financing a cash-strapped small company and shift the payment risk onto the large trading guy, who'd pay us once the goods were delivered – thus paying back the loan. Sound familiar? It was Receivables finance, except it wasn't in a crap country. It was in the USA. We still had crap companies but he'd got round that by putting ownership of the commodities with a special company.

I was interested. In fact, given the way the other meetings were going, I was fucking interested. He told me to go to his company's other office in Wichita, Kansas – the next day. A flight was hastily arranged and I found myself on a small Learjet being buffeted by the wind as it headed north.

We landed at a cosy little airport in what felt like the middle of nowhere. Yet this place called itself Wichita

'Mid-Continent' Airport and a sign in the terminal declared, 'Welcome to Wichita, Aerospace Capital of the World.'

Away from the big cities, America loses all sense of worldliness. This allows hick towns in the back of beyond to develop a sense of purpose far removed from reality. Wichita can claim what it likes – no-one is taking any notice. 'Welcome to Wichita, Home of the World's Best-Looking Babes', or it could claim 'Welcome to Wichita, Official Center of the Universe', although judging by the lumpy women hanging around the airport the first claim would be more outrageous than the second.

I confess I had a secret ambition of mine fulfilled in Wichita 'Mid-Continent' Airport. I had my name announced over the tannoy. My name was echoing round the airport and I was to meet my man by a statue with some silly name – something like the 'Magic Flight' sculpture.

I made it to the small terminal lobby as the announcement was being repeated. I was standing by a small information booth in front of some strange little monument made up of bits of wings and things. And the repetition sounded a bit odd. I could hear it from the speakers and, yes, from this folksy little announcer standing in the booth right next to me. He was looking right at me as he spoke into the microphone. In fact the airport official, the man I had to meet and myself were the only people visible. As ambition fulfilments go it was a little disappointing.

Sorry Wichita but you really are Crapsville, USA. You certainly smelt like it. Once out of the terminal the whiff of cow dung hit me. That sharp shit'n'straw stench clung to my nostrils and had my companion apologizing, but like all Americans he was keen to talk up his town. And he told a good tale. Wichita's greatest claim to fame is as the birthplace of Pizza Hut. That's more like it, I thought: 'Welcome to Wichita, Birthplace of Pizza Hut'. This was no small claim and far more believable than some dubious nonsense about aerospace. But then he claimed that the aerospace boast wasn't so fanciful.

'You know that Learjet you came in on?' he said. 'Well, it was made right here in Wichita, Kansas, *yessireee*.'

His company, Uranus Industries, was housed in a rather smart blue-glass building on the edge of town – not that being on the edge of town should allow the mind to imagine a centre of town. The centre of Wichita looked like the edge of most towns. This felt like a blue-glass building had fallen out the sky and landed in the middle of the prairie.

But the atmosphere of the place was relaxed and friendly. Everyone smiled and said 'Hi' as you walked by – as if they either knew you or soon would. It oozed that family-raising atmosphere that America so craves. It was easy to imagine unambitious people saying, excuse me, bollocks to New York, I'm for a stress-free life out on the prairie and I'll get used to the smell of shit.

This was reinforced at lunch. After a meeting in the office – mostly spent receiving heartfelt thanks for making the trip to Wichita – I was taken to a local country club. I'd been looking forward to this. Since coming to the States I'd heard people talk of the country club 'set', and they sounded like nice places for grown-ups to hang out.

And the Beaver Creek Country Club was a nice place for grown-ups to hang out, *nodoubtaboutit*. It had the look of a Scottish hunting lodge: the sitting room was full of comfy chairs, the stone walls sported paintings of majestic stags wearing curious and surprised expressions while posing on craggy rocks, and the montage of Highland weaponry mounted over the fireplace looked capable of some serious arbitration in any clan dispute.

You couldn't help thinking the club had sent away to

247

the Scottish Hunting Lodge Kit Company, and ticked the XXL box for size. The fireplace was so vast US Steel could have knocked up some sheet metal in it. I suspect real Scottish hunting lodges are a little more compact, holding four nobs max while the beaters loiter outside.

And I doubt Scottish hunting lodges have fawning black servants in full waistcoat and bow tie. These guys dipped their heads when they brought a drink and had a 'yes massa' way about them. The club was trying to give the impression of a cotton plantation house – in the Cairngorms. Either that, or the Scottish Hunting Lodge Kit Company is also the Cotton Plantation Kit Company and the servant order got mixed up.

So what happens at a country club? Er, golf. That was the only discernible activity I could see other than pool in the – get this – Men's Bar. Indeed, my hosts told me many country clubs are men-only affairs and resist any PC legislation to allow women members. I find this strange. When I go out I at least want to look at women, even if I can't get one home, but these guys won't allow a female in the place, although I suspect this is a ruse to keep the wife away. There are probably plenty of women about – behind the bar or on a stage taking their kit off. Let's just hope it's not the women at the airport.

MARCH

How to marry a sex pest

Anyone on the New York dating scene quickly works out the routine. Man talks shit in a bar. Man gets number. Man makes call. Man pays for dinner. Man makes next fucking call. Man pays for next fucking dinner. Meanwhile, woman doesn't invite man home. Woman doesn't grab man's pouch. Woman doesn't even kiss man. Woman gives man kind look and says, 'Thank you and goodnight.'

In nine months there'd been exceptions, but this was the norm. And it was driving me up the wall.

Now maybe I'm an ugly bugger with no personality. Maybe. But this was happening to every single man I knew. Men in New York are destined to buy a lot of dinners and get in lots of masturbation. Certainly my credit card wasn't the only thing taking a pounding.

Janet was the latest beneficiary – of my credit card, that is.

Janet knew what she wanted. She was a fast-track go-getter: sharp, witty and ambitious. She was the cream of New York women and delightful company. Delightful, that is, until we started dating. She then stopped being a sharp, ambitious go-getter and became a fluffy passive girl's blouse.

249

She always waited for me to make the call. We'd have dinner at a restaurant *I* chose. She'd laugh at *my* jokes and pretend to be interested in *my* job. And then the cheque would arrive and she'd look down embarrassed, as *I* fumbled for my credit card.

Janet was the higher earner and was clearly better at her job. She spoke of directors' meetings and dinners with famous names. I tried to talk up the Forums and my dying umbrella plant but was no match, until the bill came. At that moment I became the boss and her success meant nothing.

After dinner we'd walk home and stop at the threshold to her apartment block. She'd then become coy, kiss my cheek and say goodnight and thank you. We were clearly attracted to each other and we were adult professionals living alone. But Janet was determined to deny her hormonal impulses. I could tell she wanted to invite me up but was fighting the urge – as if some behavioural standard was getting in the way.

I couldn't work it out and after a few dates I complained in frustration to a female colleague. She told me that Janet was following *The Rules*.

The Rules: Time-tested Secrets for Capturing the Heart of Mr Right is a little book by two frigid witches called Ellen Fakeorgasm and Sherrie Spinster, or something. And once I'd read them I just knew Janet had that bloody book at the bottom of her undies draw.

The Rules states that men know what they want and they love to chase. And for women to make themselves attractive they have to run away. When the man of your dreams approaches, it says, you must brush him off – persistently. Only then will he value you as a special person and come back for more. This draws him in and, like a Venus flytrap, the gates of marriage crash behind him.

Fine in theory, but a complete load of bollocks in practice.

Sure, men like to chase, but adherence to these rules doesn't make for a happy hunt with twists and turns and a shag at the end. It reveals misery and anguish for everybody concerned – especially the woman. And for New York women it's led to a demographic disaster worthy of a *National Geographic* special.

Some of these time-tested rules are worth closer scrutiny.

Don't stare at men

This isn't advice for the Subway. Women are not allowed to return a man's look anywhere: in a bar, at a party, at work. Women are to just smile at the room like a lunatic holding a fart.

Fucking great. The only 'time-tested' way of knowing if a man should approach a woman is banned. Men don't need long – maybe two seconds – but if a woman looks away or fails to make eye contact she may as well have 'FUCK OFF' written on her forehead.

At this rate the only men our girl is going to attract are redneck sex pests in from Wankov, Idaho. Any decent man would want at least some signal.

Don't call him and rarely return his calls

What? Is the follower of *The Rules* trying to marry a rapist? Not calling the man is just being passive, like a dainty Edwardian lady – so fitting for the rock-hard image of the modern New York female. But rarely return his calls? This is a stalker's charter. I have to chase a woman whose every action shouts 'hate'? If I kept pursuing someone who didn't return my calls I'd expect a court restraining order.

Of course, there's one advantage to the 'don't call him' rule. The man never has to finish with a woman. He just stops calling. It's great. I don't have to worry about composing Dear Jane emails, I can just forget her. Meanwhile she has to go through days of worrying about whether I'll call and weeks of her hopes slowly receding.

251

Shame – one call and she'd have been emotionally free to ignore other men in bars.

Don't accept a Saturday date after Wednesday

This one kills me. What if you met on Thursday? No date at the weekend will make things stale by the next meeting. You'll have forgotten her looks, why you made each other laugh, why you got on so well you ignored the fact she wouldn't look you in the fucking eye.

So not only is the woman supposed to be completely inactive, she can only accept your furious activity under the strictest circumstances. I have to have the planning skills of a bridge-builder to get a date at all.

Don't go Dutch on a date

Paying for dinner is supposed to be a sign that the man values the woman's company. Fine, but we don't mean one date here. My dining companion could retire on the dosh she's saved by the time *The Rules* suggests it's OK to even go halves.

What a load of shite. Most London women I know would view this as a patronizing insult.

'Don't try and own me, you creep,' they'd shout, and offer me a swift kick in the balls.

Yet in New York this is the one rule that is universally applied. In this city if a woman offers to pay half it probably means you've insulted her. In fact if she insists on paying half you may as well tell her to pay the lot, chuck the wine over her sexually neutral trousers and leg it. Either way you've had your last date with this chick.

Rule 15 (there are 35 in total): *Don't rush into sex*

Sex, *ha*. If India wants to solve its population problem they should publish the fucking thing over there. This book is the best contraceptive known to man. It convinces a woman she shouldn't invite her date up for at least three dates. And while they don't make statements about the best time to start shagging you can bet they're not saying 'Go on love, invite him round and fuck his brains out.'

Mr Happy here has to shell out for about a thousand meals and each time put up with a mere peck on the cheek before walking home to yet another expensive wank.

Of course *The Rules* are really telling women to use sex as a weapon. Yet all women know this – it's an instinct. It's how they use it that's the key. Women should try the following experiment in a bar. Take two men, ignore one and give the other a sneaky handjob under the table. See which one calls the next day.

But they won't. Women like Janet will doggedly stick to *The Rules* and blame past failures on not applying them diligently enough. And the older the woman, the more *The Rules* are supposed to apply. They must be even more determined to avoid eye contact and not return calls.

It's amazing. In the world's most innovative, brave, forward-thinking nation one stupid book has regressed women centuries (even the authors admit the 1950s). What they completely fail to realize is that the sexual revolution changed men as well as women. The feminists who did so much to create a balance within relationships should spit in disgust.

On our last date I told Janet about the English women I knew. I described how they were in charge of their own destinies. I spoke of them approaching the man of their choice, dragging him home for torrid sex and then discarding him as he pleads for more.

At the end of the meal she said, 'Robert, come back to mine.'

I turned her down and walked home for a very satisfying wank.

Hail to the handkerchief

So Bill Clinton masturbates. That's great. Why America finds this use of the Oval Office bathroom sink so embarrassing God only knows. I personally find this rather comforting. If Bill wants to slip off and have a quick one off the wrist then he gets my vote.

In fact I think wanking should be a presidential requirement, not some furtive peccadillo that's splashed across the tabloids. And during an international crisis it should be mandatory. In my short time in the US, Clinton has ordered bombings against four countries. And I just hope he had a wank before each decision. He should mull over Saddam's latest act of defiance in his bathroom while giving his todger a good seeing to.

'That bastard Hussain, defying the UN, I'm gonna bomb the crap outta him, I'm gonna . . . uhh . . . uhhhh . . . *ugghhh* . . . yanno who gives a fuck about Iraq anyway?'

Sexual frustration is a poor excuse for bombing a country.

And if he wants to find a comely intern to do the wanking for him, then that's also fine by me. Indeed, I would expect one of the more pleasurable early tasks of office to be checking out the White House babes to see who's up for the odd sly blow job. If that isn't the case then I certainly won't be running for president.

OK, I *can* see why Bill's behaviour has embarrassed the country. America needs to believe in its president because he is an icon – part of the glue that binds a fragile and diverse society – and the president is expected to treat the post with respect. And wanking into the Oval Office sink shows disregard for the job in the extreme, although I bet he wasn't the first. A portrait of this man is hung on the wall of every US government building in the world and if a pervy guy with a nice line in cigar tricks smiles back he's made a mockery of both the building and the office of the president.

But the US constitution is a funny thing. While the president is an icon, he's not the politician with the most influence over the life of the average US citizen. He's so constrained by the checks and balances on him that his only real area of freedom is in foreign policy. And if there's one thing that most Americans couldn't give a toss about, it's foreign policy. I'd like to think that as the US bombs each new dodgy republic the American people reach for their atlases to find out the location of their new enemy. But they don't. They reach for their remote controls and turn over to *Everybody Loves Raymond* or fish around for a basketball game.

The man with the most influence on the life of the average New Yorker is the mayor of New York. I like this. I know where the mayor lives and I can always go and knock on his door if he does something outrageous. Having said that, this particular mayor has done plenty of outrageous things – at least for such a liberal city as New York. Rudi Giuliani has reversed New York's slide into the moral mire. He's made New York a shiny, happy city full of law-abiding people. While much of this involves window-dressing laws such as closing porn shops and strip joints, he's also brought down crime levels to a thirty-year low.

His 'Zero Tolerance' policy has reduced New York from the murder capital of the world to around number fifty in the USA. This is a major achievement. New York was a forbidding place in the late eighties when I first visited. The whole city felt like a series of safe islands – such as Greenwich Village and Times Square – linked by yellow cabs to ferry you across the menacing void. Walk a few blocks in the wrong direction and your trousers quickly changed colour. Only madmen would ride the Subway, as they frequently did, and Central Park was a virtual no-go zone.

All that's changed. South of 96th Street there isn't a block that can't be walked safely at night and murders and rapes are big news. It feels like the safest major city I've ever lived in.

But Giuliani doesn't fool me. It's obvious that shutting porno stores and strip bars is a cheap and quick way to make an impact, as is forcing the police and courts to act like the Gestapo. Mending the roads and creating a decent education system takes time and is expensive. Why bother when the harassment of young ethnics is more popular and costs half the money?

Yet it almost backfired on him with the shooting of Guinean immigrant Amadou Diallo. A squad of plain-clothed cops mistook the slight, unarmed figure of this street peddler for a brutal rapist and shot him nineteen times. Rudi then made a major political mistake. At first he stood by his officers – alienating the black com-munity. Then, as the pressure mounted, he dropped the cops – alienating the middle classes that accept the odd dead immigrant as the price for a safer New York.

Rudi's image as Gotham's saviour took a battering in those weeks. City Hall was besieged by protesters and Rudi himself looked a lonely figure. In fact he looked des-perately in need of a comely intern to wank him off. And the more I watched him struggle with the media the more his face seemed to say, 'not getting it'. It may explain why he shut down all the strip joints – he was just too tempted.

Away from shooting immigrants, Giuliani's gesture politics invades my life to a degree impossible in Britain. The city is awash with rules. Every Wednesday I have to sort my trash into three piles: one for plastics and glass, one for card and paper and one for all the other shite. Actually I do nothing of the sort. It all goes in one black bin liner and bugger recycling. But my violations resulted in a fine for the building. So now I walk my bag next door and they get fined for my violations.

Another law makes me declare that I don't live with any children under ten, and if I did I wouldn't throw them out the window (I may have misread that one).

Meanwhile, restaurants are forced to display three signs: the number of people safely allowed to enter, that employees must wash their hands after having a slash, and a demonstration of the Heimlich manoeuvre to be applied to anyone choking to death on a fishbone.

He's even made a cab ride a nightmare. Every New York cab has to play an inane message telling me to belt up. This law really bugs me. I can ignore the recycling and step over anyone choking to death but I have to wait for Adam West or Dan Ingram or some other nobody to cheerfully order me about before I can get in a row about the route with a cabbie.

'Remember, life isn't a movie – so belt up for safety.'

I wish they'd belt up for my sanity.

WIMMINN

The beat pounded my brain. Thump, thump, thump. It was a deep house beat that urged the body to respond – to nod the head, shake the shoulders, tap the feet. Thump, thump, thump-thump-thump. It was New York lounge music – chilled. It was less techno than British house. You didn't have to thrash about like a skinhead in the away end. This was voyeur's music, more relaxed and made for scanning a posey bar.

And I scanned – despite my deranged focus. I'd be

257

unsteady on my feet by now and my voice would be slurred, although there was no obvious manifestation of it to me. I felt fine, pumping even. But it was 2 a.m. and I was pissed.

I'd stuck to beer until midnight in an effort to postpone the inevitable. Yet enough vodka now coursed through my veins to fuel a space launch, and any hope of pulling a woman had evaporated in an alcoholic fog.

Alcohol rendered my ability to attract women diametrically opposed to my desire. I felt as horny as a charging rhino. I would have shagged a moose. And I mean a moose: antlers, big fat nose, dopey look, the lot. Yet I was so pissed I doubt a moose would have shagged me. As for New York lounge women – they weren't even going to talk to me. I needed to head for the dive bars of Amsterdam Avenue where the moose roam free.

I knocked back my seabreeze and staggered into the street, and was immediately stopped by a guy pondering whether to enter. 'What's it like in there?' he asked.

'Sokay,' I slurred. 'No wimmin lo.'

What I meant was, there were no women prepared to talk to a pissed English fuckwit like me. But it was enough to convince him not to enter. He walked alongside me.

I think my plan was to head for Moonlighting because I started walking 'up' Columbus when the majority of Amsterdam bars were 'down'. I expect my reasoning, such as it was, focussed on the fact that Moonlighting was a dark, noisy, tacky disco that would mask my inebriation and solitude.

But now I had a pulling partner. I was no longer a sad, pissed loner. So I suggested we stop at Merchants NY, a posh bar with a reputation for high-quality women.

His name was Brett and he was a good-looking lad. He had black, spiky, gelled hair, like someone out of those Eighties *stu-stu-studio* hair-moose ads. He said he came

258

from California, which explained the look. New York men are either grungy types or slicked-down Wall Streeters. They're not salon-selective beauty boys like this guy.

We chatted for a bit, although I wasn't paying much attention. I was too pissed and too busy looking round for women to try and converse with my new pulling mate, although the bar was virtually empty.

'Werzal la boody wimmin?' I cried. 'Gaww issa bad nigh. Lere musbe norny birds conven, conven, convenssion goin on summair. Crisi'd luv to no ware latson.'

He nodded and laughed, although I think he hadn't picked up a word. 'We shoo goata Moonlightin,' I said.

'Where's it at?' he asked.

'Eighty-fiff and Amstam,' I replied.

'Is it good?'

'Nois shit,' I said. 'But la wimmin are dirt.'

'Tell me,' he said. 'Do you ever go the other way?'

'Oshore,' I said. 'I go loverway all time.'

I gestured south, towards Downtown. 'Issgreat.'

He looked at me uncertainly. He left it for a minute and then said, 'Do you like guys?'

'Oshore I lie guys,' I said. And I did. I'm a friendly chap. I'll talk to anyone.

'My bes friendsa men,' I said. 'Well, menan Veeowner.'

'I mean bisexual,' he said. 'Are you a bisexual?'

This one floored me. It seemed a strange question to come out of the blue. Here we were, two men desperate for a shag and he wonders whether I'm bisexual?

'I dunno,' I said.

And I didn't. It was 2.30 a.m. and I had the blood-alcohol level of a doodlebug. I didn't know very much at all. I couldn't recite my times tables or spell any difficult words. All I knew was that I was prepared to fuck a moose at that point, although I was presuming it would be a female moose.

There was a bit of a pause, and I realized that Merchants NY was virtually dead.

'Cumon Brett,' I said. 'Les go find sum wimmin.'

'I know a place Downtown,' he said, and finished his drink. 'I'm parked outside.'

This surprised me. I'd assumed Brett was also pissed. He certainly had an excited look about him. But I was happy to climb in the Cherokee Jeep and motor off Downtown. What did I care? I was off my face.

In fact I was so off my face I was losing any tangible grip on reality. The warmth and comfort of the car made me sleepy and I couldn't focus on the line of lights in front of me as we rode the green wave down Columbus.

To wake myself up I opened the window and cold air startled my face into life. Brett placed his hand on my thigh and talked excitedly about where we were going.

'Man, yeah, chicks. We're gonna hit a bar I know where the action's hot man. I mean *hot*.'

'WIMMINN,' I shouted out the open window. 'I want WIMMMINNN.'

Brett looked at me a little nervously and squeezed my thigh a little harder. I finally noticed.

It was cool, I thought. This guy's from California. Californian buddies spend all day squeezing each other's inner thighs, don't they? Brett and I were great Californian buddies together, weren't we? Still, I readjusted my seating position and he found reason to move his hand to the automatic gear stick.

We were now by the Lincoln Center and the green wave stopped. We were caught by a red that wouldn't change as we hit it.

Brett's hand returned. But this time it was rubbing the bulge in my trousers. It wasn't an aggressive rub. It was more an exploratory, check-it-out-for-size rub. I sat staring out of the window while a pissed idiot inside my brain stumbled to his feet. He lurched towards my consciousness, waving unsteadily at my crotch.

'Lurk, lurk,' he slurred. 'Eeess wubbing, esss wubbing yo clock.'

I couldn't understand.

'Esss wubbing your clock,' he kept saying.

It sounded important so I screwed up my brain in concentration. He took a deep breath, mustered all his available co-ordination and shouted, 'Ees rubbing ya cock.'

It came through. Fucking hell, this bloke had his hand on my knob. I moved it away. Brett looked a little uncomfortable and adopted a fixed smile.

'I want wimmin, mate,' I said. 'WIMMINN.'

I didn't say it aggressively. I just reminded him, although Brett's earlier question was now sinking in.

'I'm heading for women, man,' he said. 'I'm heading for women.'

'Lats alwite len,' I said.

'Look man,' said Brett, 'you're fucking horny, right?'

'Orny as an orny fing mate,' I said.

'You wanna fuck, right?'

'Fuck I wanna fuck,' I said.

'Well you're gonna get a fuck, man,' he said, his smile relaxing.

'Gweat,' I said and continued to shout, 'WIMMINN,' out of the window.

His hand returned. It was now aggressively rubbing my knob. This wasn't a check-it-out rub. This was a prelude to a handjob. Oh, fuck. What was I going to do?

The pissed idiot in my brain didn't have to go through the whole pantomime this time. He just shouted, 'Lurk, es doin it agen.'

Brett wasn't a bad guy. I liked him. But he wasn't going to get his chops around my knob, oh no. And it was obvious that his promise of women wasn't going to materialize.

By now we were around the Port Authority bus terminal on 42nd Street. We were in the heart of Hell's Kitchen and it was gone 3 a.m. At the next red light I mumbled something like 'Goin lurk wimmin' and climbed out of the car. I staggered to the east side of the street with a vague idea this would lead me to the bright lights of Times Square. I started walking up the incline. I was still incredibly pissed, but with a resolve that drove me forward.

What the fuck? I was lying on the floor. My hands stung from the fall and I had difficulty getting up. That was odd, I thought. That was fucking odd. It felt like I'd been pushed. I sensed someone behind me. No hesitation now. I was on my feet in an instant and turned round to see Brett. His face was flushed and his eyes ablaze. He was also holding something in his hand.

'You fuckin' cockteaser,' he said.

Adrenalin pulsated through my body, pushing aside the alcohol. It felt like a police raid at a party. Well-'ard uniformed giants steamed through the happy knots of pissed-up ravers, instantly changing the temperament. I was in sharp focus.

He plunged forward and a glint or flash appeared by my stomach. I felt something. He retreated and stood there. He stood there for no more than a split second. In that time I looked down to see he was holding a blade – it looked like a Stanley knife. He was holding it at the end so that only the inch-long steel blade was visible. He looked ready to use it again. He had no time. My fist cracked into his jaw with a mighty force. It didn't feel like me. It felt like someone else's fist. It felt like the adrenalin police had taken over and I was just obeying orders.

His head swung back violently and he started to fall. It was one hell of a crack. My hand reacted. It didn't feel like someone else's fist anymore. It felt like my knuckles had imploded.

I didn't see him hit the ground. By the end of the split second I was running up 42nd Street towards the junction with Eighth Avenue.

I finally stopped running at around 46th Street. I didn't feel too bad – exuberant, in fact. My heart pounded and the sweat trickled inside my shirt.

By 48th Street I became worried I'd been stabbed. I inspected my clothes. Nothing. No sign of any penetration. He was obviously an amateur at using that blade, thank God.

Next, I worried about Brett. Going by the way my hand felt, it must have hurt. I imagined him lying in a pool of blood on 42nd Street. Maybe the police were drawing a white line round him and Kojak was on his way. I hailed a cab to get me home, asking him to drop me a few blocks short of my street – just in case.

Picking their bogey

He first appeared at the internal Forum. I was presenting the Uranus Industries transaction and there he was, sitting in our conference room wearing a couldn't-give-a-shit expression. The transportation guys were up first. They were being roasted by Braveheart's London pack and I hastily reread my notes in a desperate search for missed angles.

They called him High Pockets because he had no hips and his trousers rode high up his torso to compensate. Like a lot of Americans it didn't occur to him to wear a belt.

I'd met him before. He'd been part of my early tour of the boutique. I remember he liked the Receivables structures but thought the deals themselves dogs. He gave me about five minutes, spending four of them telling me that he'd signed over one hundred and fifty deals, many of which had the flavour I was showing him. The inference was that he could do my shit with his eyes shut. Except he wouldn't – because it was shit. The deals were too small and in lunatic countries. Now piss off I'm busy.

I didn't expect the Uranus Industries deal to interest him either. Again, this was small change – no more than $50 million – and it involved dodgy companies. Sure, the double-A-plus-rated Uranus was our payment risk, but the commodities still sat at the little guy's warehouse and could disappear at the first whiff of bankruptcy. I'd been talking into the speakerphone for about a minute before he interrupted.

'Oh, this stuff's easy,' he said. 'You just strip out the yield on the hedge and create some paper. Let the producer retain the risk on the underlying. That way he'll be obliged to perform in order to win the full PV.'

The speakerphone emitted an expectant silence and everyone in the room looked at me, waiting for an answer. But I didn't have one. To me it sounded like High Pockets was going to impress some fool called Peevee by doing a strip under a hedge.

Eventually someone in London said, 'But the producer has to surrender ownership without receiving full payment.'

'Yes,' I said hesitantly. 'Ownership moves to a special company.'

I hoped it was relevant.

Without missing a beat, he said, 'Then the SPE issues a note obligating payment of the full PV at delivery. I mean you weren't planning to realize full value of the inventory back to the producer upfront were you?'

'I er, yes, er,' I stumbled.

'Well you'd be left with the full price volatility. I mean there is a hedge on this stuff, right?'

'Well, Uranus—'

'Uranus will blow it up your ass if the price moves against them.'

High Pockets looked at me with a goofy smile. It was a smile that said, 'I'm fucking clever,' but it was still a goofy smile – like a dumb cartoon character about to step off a cliff.

'Now we could look at hedging it ourselves,' he said, 'but it'd be expensive . . .'

And on it went until I was thoroughly flummoxed. At the end Braveheart said something like, 'You two sit down together and then come back.' I could hear sniggering coming from the phone.

Why High Pockets was in our Forum was a mystery – as was the fact that a vacant office had been stacked with full-looking cardboard boxes.

I knew High Pockets' area of expertise was pretty much where I wanted to take the Receivables product so the prospect of him joining the team should have delighted me. And if Flatcap had pulled me into a room and said, 'Son, meet High Pockets – he's going to get you your first pair of red suspenders,' I'd have said, 'That's great, I'll chuck these Hush Puppies away then, shall I?'

But instead I had to endure two grown adults pretending they'd formed a club without me and I wasn't to know that the first gang meeting was behind the bike sheds at break.

Eventually I'd had enough and marched into Flatcap's office for an explanation.

'So, er, what will High Pockets be doing?' I asked Flatcap.

'Son, we're very lucky to have him,' was all he'd tell me.

In the end High Pockets told us himself. 'There's to be no more commercial bank thinking round here,' he said. 'I'm here to turn you guys into investment bankers.' Strange – my business card already had the words 'investment banker' printed on it.

But I liked this a lot – I just wished his employment hadn't been treated like a covert CIA special op. I liked it so much I allowed High Pockets to patronize me every time we spoke, although it felt like I was being debriefed after a defection. 'Forget your Old Bank past,' I was told. 'From now on you must think only New Bank.'

This was a mantra that brooked no dispute. The minute the Old Bank tag was applied I had to retreat. The office should have painted 'New Bank good – Old Bank bad' on the side of the building.

But New Bank thinking had some curious quirks. For a start it involved a strange vocabulary. High Pockets thought my deals looked 'ugly' because their rating would be 'underwater'. But he thought they might be attractive to 'yield hounds'. These hounds would require us to 'noodle' the numbers and possibly 'juice it up' to get an improved rating. Then we could 'bar bell' or 'turbo' the payment-stream to reflect the investor's wishes. Only then would we 'hit their bogey'. But first I'd have to 'chop off my finger' and even 'lift my skirt'. At that point we'd see if it 'sucked'.

New Bank thinking also involved having a ridiculously messy office. High Pockets never managed to unpack and the boxes remained stacked against the glass partition as if fortifying himself against all the Old Bank thinkers outside. The office itself looked like he'd bundled a mass of paper and thrown it to the ceiling. His desk, walls and computer quickly became dotted with tiny Post-it notes – as if the computer had cut itself shaving and little yellow stickers now mopped up the blood. He also had around a thousand foolscap notepads half-used and a million biros, again all thrown about as if a child had just had a tantrum.

Of course, the scene was to give the impression of a maelstrom of activity. Here lies the Centre of the Universe, it was saying, and at its helm – the Master.

New Bank thinking also involved lots of conspiracy. I doubt the plot to kill Kennedy involved this much secrecy. It was certainly beyond me. Phone calls and meetings would take place within a Masonic pact and emails would be circulated to certain individuals and not others, even those clearly involved.

Of course dimwit here wasn't in on the plan, so like an idiot I'd forward the emails to the forgotten party, assuming High Pockets didn't know Ginger was on the team and that he'd benefit from the knowledge. This would have me summoned as if hauled in front of the escape committee of a POW camp.

'We deliberately avoided giving Ginger the information, you idiot,' I'd be told.

'But I thought Ginger was on the team?' I'd say.

'That's Old Bank thinking,' I'd discover. 'And I'm not sure Ginger's fully onside re the tunnel op. He's too friendly with the commandant.'

But despite High Pockets' peculiarities, I soon learnt to trust his navigation of possible deals. He was right about Uranus and he liked nothing more than being rude about my Energy Marketing ideas. With his help they soon started to acquire a New Bank veneer.

'You've got a business here,' he said, almost surprised. 'We can noodle the numbers until we find their bogey. Then we'll chop off their finger and suck it.'

At least I think that's what he said.

Ralph and Calvin have a laugh

American men dress like shit. And I don't mean the grungy wannabe tramps of the Lower East Side. They're trying to dress like shit, and doing a sterling job. I mean middle-class, professional American men. I mean the men that don't think they're dressing like shit. I mean men that are, in fact, trying quite hard not to dress like shit.

Their favourite shit is Polo Ralph Lauren. That silly little man on horse splodge is sewn on just about every shirt and sweater in middle-class male America. They even have it on their socks. It amazes me. I can't believe that such a crap-looking logo has become so dominant. Every time I see it I think the guy's dribbled pasta sauce on his shirt or his pen's leaked. I don't think he's bought the height in male fashion.

But US men love it. They love Ralph because it allows them to have a frontal lobotomy in the style department. They don't have to think. If it has the sauce splodge, it must be good. Other than Ralph the only shirt a casually dressed American office worker will consider has his company's crest. What? Let's not even get into that one. In the UK he'd have been debagged on the spot and thrown off the roof as a brown-noser.

Anyway, I'm convinced old Ralph's having a laugh at the expense of the American male. Why else would so many American men wear disgusting stripy polo shirts? These aren't cool stripes, oh no. They're shit stripes – poorly grouped bands of clashing colours and varying widths. And why else would he encourage fat middle-aged men to wear tight polo shirts to reveal every roll of their gut?

In fact, American clothes designers seem to have collectively decided that ageing men should flaunt every crap bit of their body. While the standard trousers for our middle-American man are the frontal-lobotomy chinos, more and more are sporting jeans by Ralph, Calvin and a few other jokers. And these jeans like nothing more than to show off a sagging male arse to full effect.

But it isn't just saggy arses that are revealed by this. The only jeans cut to reduce even the most ample backside are Levi's, yet Levi's are condemned as gay on this side of the Atlantic. Yep, my favourite 501s are for homosexuals, which may explain some of the problems I've been having. And it turns out your average American rejects as gay virtually every make of American clothes I've ever admired. Gap: gay. Banana Republic: bandits. J Crew: queer. Abercrombie & Fitch: fags.

The US makes some of the best clothes in the world. But not for Mr America, oh no. He'd rather wear shit. At least it's straight shit.

This definition of straight and gay clothing can be perverse. For instance, poncey slip-on shoes that reveal, wait for it, white socks, are very common amongst family-loving suburban men. Yet macho Caterpillar-style walking boots are avoided as, yep, gay.

Such clothes are condemned as they have style and style is for faggots. We're now at the epicentre of the American male psyche. This is one mother of a heterosexual society and gays are condemned to ghettos such as San Francisco and Manhattan. Homosexual acts are illegal in nineteen of the fifty States (carrying a life sentence in Idaho) and it took a State Supreme Court decision to overturn anti-gay legislation in a further six (including New York).

Any manifestation of faggoty behaviour is a definite no-no for Mr Middle America. This includes creativity, style and, most definitely, any show of emotion or contrition. Only gays cry. Only faggots compromise.

Surprised? So was I. My TV image of the American man was someone who'd have no trouble showing his emotions. I thought they went round hugging each other and getting all quivery-lipped on a mate's night out. But American TV is lying.

Real American men are taught to keep quiet and 'kick ass'. They're taught to be Masters of the Universe: autonomous, controlled, unemotional. The model American male is a number-crunching non-thinker wearing Ralph Lauren. He reserves any emotion for the Giants or the Yankees or the golf course. Sure he shouts when he hits a par three, but is he the slush bucket of the Gillette adverts? Is he fuck.

So are the Brits so great? Of course not – we invented the stiff upper lip. But there's been a seismic shift in British male behaviour in the last ten years. The post-Ecstasy generation of British men have learnt to enjoy cooking, dancing and cunnilingus. They've realized why the Italians are so reluctant to go to war – if food and sex are this good, why bother? They even cry at the odd movie and do the occasional spot of washing-up (steady on). Sure they still like footy and beer and big tits, but they've broadened their interests. And I haven't spotted the same progress here, even in New York.

My guess is it all comes down to history. This is a tough country created by rock-hard pioneers. They had to rear cattle and raise a family, all the while keeping one eye out for Big Horn and his braves. America wasn't created by men going misty-eyed at *You've Got Mail* and offering to do the hoovering.

Such attitudes don't augur well for women. In many ways American women are a product of American men. If they're prudish and conservative it's because American men demand it. American women are less liberated as a result. I wasn't expecting this, especially in New York. I was expecting the world's most independent females. What I found were women terrified of being labelled a slut.

At home the word slut is falling out of use because it's no longer relevant. She's a slut, you say? Oh, right – you mean she's in charge of her own body and enjoys sex. Not so in the States. Once placed in the slut bin, a woman stands no chance of meeting a decent man and making a nice middle-class suburban life for herself. No husband for you, oh no – just the odd passing trucker inviting his mates to a gang bang on the pool table.

This influences women's behaviour far more than they think. Not only does it make it tough for a randy bugger like me to get a shag but, even when I do, the anti-slut propaganda kicks in again. I'm convinced it's why so many American women are so passive in bed. Any hint of a bit of carnal knowledge and, yep, it's truckers and pool tables for you.

But I actually like American men. They've got one great big redeeming feature (at least in New York). Unlike your average British male, they have no problem keeping their aggression under control.

I saw a classic example of this after the Lewis-Holyfield fight at Madison Square Garden. Around five thousand Brits made the journey to cheer on the West Ham boy. I came across three of them in a bar on Amsterdam after the fight. You couldn't miss them. They were chanting 'Looisss, Looisss,' at the top of their obviously English voices.

I was curious to know the result. 'Fucking travesty, mate,' shouted one in a raucous cockney accent. 'Cunts.'

He aimed the last outburst at the room as if the bar was somehow responsible for a dodgy bit of maths by one of the judges.

'It's kickin' off in Midtown,' said another. 'And the filth are soft. They don't know what's 'it 'em.'

'Yeah,' shouted the third. 'And we want a fucking ruck now.'

He looked truculently round the bar, hoping to catch an American eye to kick in.

'I wouldn't bother,' I said. 'Americans aren't up for aggro. It's not in their nature.'

'I don't care,' he said. 'It's in mine and I'm up for it.'

He staggered about bumping into American men who'd then say, 'Hey I'm sorry, excuse me,' as if it was their fault. At one point he placed his neat vodka on the side of the pool table only to be handed it back by a player.

'Sorry, friend,' the player said, 'but I'm gonna knock this over.'

The Brit became bristly and tried to square up to the American, who gave him a curious look. Then the Yank leant down to line up his shot, not understanding what the Brit was trying to do.

New York men may be badly dressed emotional retards, but at least they're not thugs.

APRIL

You look like porno star

	Rating	Considerations
Krystal	AAA	Stole my heart but I was a tart
Lauren	A	A US Virginia Bottomley – no chance
Tiffany	AA-	Too high maintenance to endure Elvis
Mary	A	Scotched by her puritan friends
Janet	BBB+	Ruled herself out of contention.

Finding the right woman in New York was proving difficult. American women meet their husbands at high school or college or grad school or work. They don't meet them in singles bars on the Upper West Side. This left me trying to bluff my way into a US high school or finding a woman at work, neither of which filled me with great anticipation. My office was for thirty-something suburbanites. The only single women seemed distinctly provincial in mind and body and I knew I'd soon die of frustration. And anyway, they weren't exactly throwing themselves at me.

So what was I to do? I could trawl the second division options, of which New York had plenty. Starbucks was supposed to be a great place to meet single people, but it looked like a great place to meet fucked-up crazies to me. Then there were the coffee shops at Barnes & Noble bookstores. But, again, the crazies seem to have bagged all the best seats and the rest were nicked by students trying to avoid buying textbooks.

Next, I'd heard of singles supermarkets. Fairway on Broadway was perhaps the most famous. But I couldn't work it out. Sure, there were plenty of fit, single-looking women crashing trolleys round the aisles, yet they looked a bit busy buying groceries. What was I supposed to do? Go up and tell them they were the best-looking woman in the place?

I did try Fairway a few times, but on one occasion I met my landlady. We had a bitter exchange. She complained I'd yet to buy a rug for the apartment (to comply with yet another New York law) and I countered that I'd buy a fucking rug just as soon as she'd sorted the fucking plumbing. And she could reach for her own fucking pickles. Fairway lost its appeal after that.

The final option was the gym. This is a New York fave. I'm told just about every unattached female hangs out in the numerous New York Sports Clubs. They work out in full make-up, waiting for Mr Right to bump into them by the water-cooler. But my office had a gym in the basement and the lure of the free facilities was too great. My workout partners, therefore, were the thirty-something men listening to Bruce Springsteen and wearing frontal lobotomy Polo Sport. Anyone appearing in full make-up was asking for trouble.

So what was I left with? Art galleries? Evening classes? Approaching women in Central Park? It all seemed like losers' territory to me. Besides, I've always hated those men I see approaching women out of the blue. Singles bars are one thing, but hitting on a female leaning over the melons at Fairway must be fucking annoying for the woman. I needed a method where there was at least some certainty they wanted to be approached.

I'd been reading *Time Out New York* since my arrival, mostly for the nightclub and restaurant reviews. But I'd quickly tire of these and search the mag for other amusements. I was soon at the back, with the personals ads.

Unlike Drip, where everyone answered the same questions, each *Time Out* advertiser had around thirty words to encapsulate themselves and their desires. Words were carefully crafted to extract the maximum impact. The key appeared to be the headline. While many said 'Handsome, Sane, Professional', or something else expressing 'Cherokee Jeep owner, frontal-lobotomy suburban life ahead', others wanted to project their urbane sophistication. 'Thrift Stores and Dive Bars', stated one – implying 'artist' but really saying 'skint'. 'Sugar Daddy in search of Diva', said another. This was a blatant appeal to be financially abused by a gold-digging bimbo – a sure sign he was hideously ugly.

I noticed *Time Out* had a web site, so spent a spare lunchtime trawling through more of these adverts. I was being drawn in. I could tell I was going to succumb. I needed a headline. A key word was English, and another, romantic. Both pressed the right buttons in the American female psyche. But I sounded a bit soppy. I also needed something that said entertaining, that said I was a laugh to hang out with. 'Witty English Romantic'. I had my headline.

The text was less important and I paid scant attention to the final element, a recorded message to greet any enquirers. I thought I'd repeat my body text but the recorded advice stated I should expand upon the advert. Before I knew it the dalek was commanding 'Record after the tone – beep' and I was on air.

Fuck. 'Ohh, er, ah, hello, er this is Robert. I've er, not, er, prepared anything for this, er, obviously. I'm English, yes, as you can probably tell. Er, I live in New York, yes. Obviously. Er, and I'd like to meet a woman. Er, also obviously. Yep, yep. So, er, if you'd like to meet me then leave a message. Obviously.'

I slammed the phone down. I'd completely fucked that little exercise, obviously, and I assumed any listeners would write me off as a liar. 'Hey, if that guy's witty then call me Beatrix.'

It was a fortnight before I had the courage to check my voicemail box for messages. I keyed in my code and waited an agonizing ten seconds before receiving the judgement of the single female population of New York.

'You have . . . four replies.'

Fucking hell. I grabbed a pen and paper.

'Hey Robert this is Amy.' She had a doirty Noo Yoirk brogue. 'I jus' love your *akkscent*. Ya sound so cute, yuk, yuk.'

She didn't. I pressed to move on.

'Hiiii, this is Belinda.'

She sounded nice – a standard college-educated American woman.

'Your message made me laugh. I too haven't prepared anything. Just to say that I'm a single woman in New York. I work in the fashion industry and I'd love to meet. Give me a call.'

I scribbled the number – very possible.

'Hi Robert, I'm Caroline.'

She sounded very businesslike.

'We should see if we can schedule some time. My diary's hell for the next fortnight but there's a window on Friday when I'm out with some friends. If I call you from my cellphone and tell you the bar, you can drop by and we'll chat.'

276

What? She should have added 'and don't forget your résumé.'

No thanks. I pressed to move on.

'Rawbert, dis is Eva.'

Blimey – she sounded like a Russian shot-putter or someone out of *The Munsters*. It was scary.

'I am Hungarian. You have handsome voice. Are you handsome man? Email me.'

Of the four, Belinda sounded the most promising. I called and we chewed the fat for a while, mainly about different New York neighbourhoods. I told her I lived on the Upper West.

'Oh, exposed brick walls and a house plant?' she said.

I was impressed. It was Daryl Hannah's line from *Wall Street*. Belinda was definitely worth a date.

We met in a restaurant on Columbus called The Avenue. I wasn't disappointed – she had short black hair and a toned figure. And she was confidently dressed, with figure-hugging trousers and a leather jacket. She was also attractive.

Over dinner, we discussed the pitfalls of personal-ad dating. She stated that most of the men were ugly losers with no social skills and she clearly felt such an exercise was beneath her. I assumed I was being told this as a co-conspirator. What I think she meant was, 'We're too good for this, aren't we?'

She said she was 33 and wanted to start a family. This seemed to be a bold cards-on-table move to despatch the time-wasters. It was certainly efficient. This time-waster couldn't pay the bill fast enough.

This left me with Eva the Hungarian. I emailed her and she immediately responded, again asking if I was 'hand-some man'.

She also attached some photographs of herself. I'd expected a battleaxe to match her voice, but I found *Superwoman*, literally. In one shot she was at a

277

fancy-dress party in said super-heroine garb, another had her swigging straight from a champagne bottle and in a third she was draped over some furtive Latin lover type. He looked pretty chuffed and you couldn't blame him. She had long blond hair, a cheeky look and a stunning figure. In fact, she looked just like Sharon Stone. I asked for a date.

But it all seemed logistically difficult. She'd said she was a journalist, but this turned out to be a voluntary spare-time job. She was really a housekeeper for a swanky Park Avenue Jewish couple. And this couple were so loaded they were nervous of the servants organizing a heist of the silverware, which meant that Eva couldn't use the phone. Eventually she rang from a call box. 'Meet me at Starbucks on 87th Street and Lex,' she demanded. 'In twenty minutes.'

She had a voice it was wise to obey.

I sat in Starbucks trying to look cool. I crossed my legs, but dismissed it as effeminate. I sat upright with my legs open, but it looked too uptight. So I leant back with right ankle resting on left knee, but it looked too cocky and I nearly tipped the chair over.

I tried reading my trusted *Economist*. I tried staring out of the window at the busy Upper East Side scene. I tried counting the holes in the honeycomb ceiling tiles. Nothing could hold my attention. I was just too nervous. The thought of meeting a beautiful woman had done it again. I was going to fuck it up, I could tell.

I was contemplating running away when she walked in and lined up at the counter. And as she browsed Starbucks, I realized my advantage – she didn't know who I was. I could have been the fat guy eating with his mouth open in the corner. I could have been the dorky nerd with the laptop and Walkman. Or I could have been the sensible-looking guy with the Ralph Lauren shirt and side parting.

'Are you Rawbert?' she said, taking me by surprise.

'Er yes, how did you—'

'Oh, thank God,' she said in that shot-putter voice. 'I thought you one of others. I was about to walk out.'

What a lovely comment. I leant back with my right ankle resting on my left knee.

'Why you advertise in stupid magazine?' she said. She certainly knew how to say the right things.

And there was no caution. She knew I'd find her attractive and she immediately felt able to flirt.

'You like me, no?' She said, at one point, with a coy 'Will there be anything else sir?' French maid look, 'You handsome man, very handsome.'

She spoke of her many suitors: her wedged-up, married employer; the editor of the Hungarian-language rag; the owner of the Hungarian restaurant on First Avenue. All had sworn undying love and untold riches. But all possessed some fatal flaw that kept her on the circuit.

At each pause she'd return to her favourite theme – the fact that she found me attractive. My self-esteem was going through the roof, although I found the comment 'You look like porno star' rather difficult to interpret.

I suggested a drink, by which I meant a proper drink in a proper bar, rather than the sterile pretension of McCoffee's. We went to The Gaf on 85th Street, a lively Irish pub which Eva claimed had the best jukebox in New York. Her tastes were spot on. The bar resonated to The Verve, Oasis, New Order, and the Stone Roses. It was like a Mancunian's night out as we sat on high stools and drank Tanqueray and tonics.

She didn't understand much of what I said. And she'd aggressively ask, 'Wat?' after my every utterance. But she was pleasant company nonetheless, mainly because she was such a babe and clearly attracted to me. After a while it seemed natural that my foot rested on the rung of her stool. It even seemed natural that her hand began

279

to rub my calf. She winked at me and said, 'Nice legs.'

It had been a while since I'd met a woman so sexually confident. I needed to respond in kind. I rested one hand on her leg and began to lightly play with her hair with the other. As my brushing became firmer she closed her eyes and leant in with her mouth open. It was a lovely kiss. Her mouth felt so young, her lips so alive. Her face fell into mine like it was a moment she'd anticipated all her life. It was electric. I held her head and kissed her cheek. She whispered in my ear, 'You want to sleep with me, no?'

'I want to sleep with you, yes,' I said.

'Not yet,' she said. 'At weekend.'

She said I could call the Park Avenue palace, but only at certain times. She fished in her bag for pen and paper and pulled out the sales label for a bra. She wrote her number on it and handed it to me.

'36C,' I said, reading the label.

'You'll see,' she said.

The weekend started in forty-five and a half hours.

Where the heat is on

Mandy had stored my fidelity in a special folder. While I tried to shag my way round New York, she sat in London pining for her faithful man. It wasn't a good situation.

I didn't feel like a two-timing bastard. I thought I was operating within an unstated mandate. And it was Easter before her expectations of total fidelity began to dawn on me. In fact she said, 'If you're unfaithful to me, you're history' – a fairly stark indication that the sun was up and the coffee was on.

I opened my mouth to protest but then closed it. Instead I nodded and tried to hold her searching gaze.

Images of Eva, Krystal, Tiffany and Lauren floated through my mind. And it wasn't just their faces. My brain became an orgy of orgasmic expressions and wanton genitalia. I changed the subject as soon as I could.

But it played on my conscience. I knew I had to clear things up and I nervously broached the subject once safely back to a telephone relationship.

'I'm just saying that if a beautiful woman jumps on me in a nightclub, it's going to be hard to resist,' I pleaded.

Some chance in this city.

'But you promised fidelity,' she said.

'No I didn't,' I said. 'I gave four definitions of fidelity and I couldn't abide by definition number three – faithfulness to one's spouse or lover – remember?'

I was wary. Her voice seemed strident.

'Yes you could,' she said, and within a minute I was reading the specially preserved chain of emails that ended with me, indeed, stating my lack of problem with definition number three.

'It was . . .' I stopped.

What could I say – it was a typo? It was the charter under which she'd been living, for Chrissake.

I realized her trips over had not been the frivolous no-questions-asked sessions I'd assumed. Seen from her side they were the very moments our lives were complete. I was going to have to sort it. And it was going to have to be in Miami, the site of our next frivolous, no-questions-asked session.

Miami has a reputation in the UK as a destination for Dave Dagenham and family, but in fact they tend to head for Orlando and the Mickey Mouse resorts further north. Miami Beach is the sophisticated end of Florida and an architectural gem. The smooth lines and pastel shades of the art deco buildings aren't just on the seafront. They cover several square miles and make the town look like a giant box of marshmallows.

Miami Beach is a battle between the smart art deco chic of monied America, and the brassy energy of the Hispanics. Latin America begins at Miami and every dusty street and clapped-out car resonates to the pulse of salsa music. And while Ocean Drive has mainstream American bars aplenty, Miami's most happening nightlife is in the Latin dance bars such as Mangos.

Mangos was my kind of place. The waitresses wore skin-tight leopardskin suits and took it in turns to jump on the bar and shake their bodies to the music. They'd become so carried away with their dances they'd end up leaning against the wall and pumping their arses as if being rogered from behind. Such pumping was the signal for a beefy bouncer to climb on the bar and complete the picture by, yes, rogering her from behind. It was enough to make you wish you were Cuban. Even the tamer stuff in front of the band seemed little more than mock sex acts involving grinding torsos and groping hands.

I couldn't help thinking that such dancing must be responsible for Latin America's population problem – bugger the Pope and contraception. A couple of sessions on the dance floor and you'd be so fired-up you'd skip the foreplay.

But evenings watching couples showing off their sexual technique and days spent hanging out on the beach weren't going to solve my relationship issues with Mandy. And after a few days she'd finally had enough of this idiot's inability to bring up the subject.

'Am I just wasting my time here?' she asked over dinner.

'What, in Miami?' I said. 'We're on holiday, you're supposed—'

'Nooo,' she said. 'You know what I mean. Us. Is this relationship going to go anywhere?'

Oh Christ. This was a step on from promising fidelity.

'You mean, can I commit?'

'Ah,' she growled in frustration. 'That word.'

'That's what you want to know, isn't it? Does this end in marriage?'

'Not necessarily,' she said, looking down and toying with her pasta.

'I can't tell you,' I said. 'How can I know that? Mandy, we'd been seeing each other a week before I was sent to America.'

'Two months actually,' she corrected. 'And it's been over a year now.'

'Has it? When was the—'

'Oh forget it,' she said. 'I knew you wouldn't remember so I didn't bother reminding you.'

Mandy fell silent for moment.

'Look,' she said eventually. 'If I am wasting my time you will tell me, won't you?'

'Yeah . . .' I stopped in mid flow.

I wanted to be honest with her – I really did. But I couldn't. Every time I looked into those eyes I saw the pain it would cause her. This was the man she was waiting for and he was overseas – trying to get laid.

But she seemed happy now. She attacked her pasta with gusto and thought about what to wear on the beach the next day. She had the answer she wanted – I'd tell her if she was wasting her time. My silence was saved in a special folder.

After dinner we wandered over to the beach. The palm trees swayed above and the waves crashed in the dark, subduing the noise of the neon-fronted bars on Ocean Drive. Couples strolled arm in arm on the walkway as roller-bladers and joggers dodged passed.

On the beach a gang of Chinese kids had built an enormous sandcastle. It was a fantastic citadel of crenellated towers, belfries and chambers, many containing small candles that glowed in the evening air. There was a bucket for money and a sign leant against a ghetto blaster saying, 'Here since 6 a.m'.

I gave them a dollar – oh how they thanked me.

'You should listen to this song,' said Mandy, at the ghetto blaster's melancholic broadcast. 'It's weird – it really speaks to me. Listen to the words.'

It was 'Ocean Drive', by the Lighthouse Family – a song of hope for a broken heart. Of a bruised soul abandoned by an arrogant lover. Never mind, it said, one day you'll be strong and realize he was no loss.

Emotion overwhelmed me. I screwed my face but it was too late – tears poured from my eyes. The Chinese kids stopped pretending to put the finishing touches to their castle and stared. Mandy noticed my hand tighten on hers. I turned away and stormed off. Shit. I didn't want her to see me crying. I knew how she'd react.

'I'm sorry,' she said when she caught up. 'I didn't mean to upset you. I don't mean it really. I love you.'

But I wasn't crying at the words. I was crying because I felt such a git. I felt guilty and I felt sorry for myself.

'I'm no good,' I said, sobbing. 'I let everybody down in the end. I do.'

I mumbled the words onto her shoulder as she held me. Roller-bladers and joggers were now slowing down like rubberneckers at an accident. I was beginning to feel a bit self-conscious.

'No you don't,' she said. 'You haven't let me down. Come on, let's go back to the hotel.'

She seemed content on the walk back, rather than the more thoughtful woman of the last few days. She'd got what she came for – that special folder was filling up.

Choppers on the roof

Braveheart was in town. You could tell Braveheart was in town because all the senior vice-presidents were in work by eight, hadn't left by six and wore a shirt and tie. And they smiled a lot. We were a busy, happy office, oh yes. We weren't a back-stabbing bunch of whingers, oh no. Flatcap put on especially fatherly airs, the moaning hierarchical senior vice-president treated the assistant vice-presidents like human beings, and even High Pockets came out of his office occasionally.

Braveheart spent a lot of time in High Pockets' office. While not a word could be heard, the body language was giving clear signals. Braveheart leant back in his visitor's chair and put his feet on High Pockets' desk.

'I'm delighted you've joined the department,' he appeared to be saying. 'And, as you can see, I'm the fucking boss around here, so you'd better toe the line.'

High Pockets divided his time between Braveheart and the Bloomberg screen.

'I'm delighted to be here,' he appeared to be replying. 'And as you can see, I don't give a fuck whether you're the boss or not.'

But Braveheart wasn't here to play power games. He'd finally had enough of the Greenwich office. We'd spent too much time complaining and not enough time producing cash. In fact we hadn't produced any cash since my Brazilian soya beans deal, and that just sat on the balance sheet like a fat sow after a good lunch. Heads were rolling – again.

'I could close you down,' Braveheart said at the supposed-to-be-jolly drinks session. 'You're just not coming good.'

His prophecy was quickly fulfilled. The next day all the

AVPs were out. The only exception was Barry, the laid-back Aussie. He was being transferred to London. Two American AVPs were being laid off and the rest sent back to the commercial bank. Of the deal teams, only the transportation guys remained intact. They were working with High Pockets on a potential bond deal that ticked all the right boxes.

But they were the only survivors. The energy team was being disbanded in Greenwich, giving the Main Man in Houston complete control this side of the pond.

'Awesome,' he'd have said. 'Fucking awesome.'

Then came the big news. Flatcap was going back to London. He told me this himself, adding, 'I think you should also consider a move back.'

I pondered this statement for a day – it made it sound like I had a choice. I was here because I was told to be here, and I'd be there the minute I was told to be there. Resigning was the only alternative.

Of course he was just softening me up for the inevitable. He took me to lunch. Well, when I say he took me to lunch he bought me a sandwich in the cafeteria – he was from Yorkshire, after all. We sat by the window just out of range of the laughing American workers in their stripy shirts. They all looked very happy, as they should. No-one was about to tell them they were on their way back to cold, miserable London. Flatcap wouldn't look at me. His eyes rested on a boat in the harbour. I knew what was coming.

'Son, you're going back.'

'When?'

'In the next few weeks. Just get the odds and sods sorted here first.'

Fuck it. I didn't say anything for a while. I munched on my sandwich and stared at the boats. They looked lovely in the spring sunshine. Greenwich was such a nice place to work.

'It's good news,' he said. 'Charlie Bristols, the new director, is creating a team and he wants you in it. He specifically asked.'

'But I don't even know him.'

'He saw you at the Offsite in November,' said Flatcap. 'He liked you.'

'What? I was shit at the Offsite. I spent one day being abused by Braveheart and the next with the mother of all hangovers.'

'Well he liked your ability to absorb both abuse and alcohol,' said Flatcap.

He laughed because he'd made a joke. But it was a hollow laugh and he laughed alone.

It was such bollocks. Bristols had been told to take me by Energizer Bunny and Braveheart – I just knew it. He was on the Wide Boys team at the Offsite, like me, and he'd been thoroughly unimpressed with my contribution – especially the ten-point deduction.

'What about the Energy Marketing Initiative?' I asked. 'It's just starting to come together.'

'Son,' he said, looking at the boat. 'I just don't see it. Hardon came to nothing. Uranus came to nothing. Where's the juice?'

This was obviously Flatcap's attempt to try and learn New Bank parlance, but I understood. He thought the initiative was shite.

'But High Pockets says—'

'Son,' now Flatcap was being firm, 'count yourself lucky. A lot of people are losing their jobs here. You're safe.'

'I'll take the gamble,' I said. 'Give me until the end of the year and sack me if it doesn't work.'

He dismissed the challenge with a chuckle.

'I know son,' he said, looking intently at a particularly nice boat. 'It's a pain to move here, but once here it's hard to leave.'

But it pained us both to be going. I'd learnt to love America. I thought it the goofiest country on Earth, but one with such a remarkable array of redeeming features it was impossible to come away feeling negative. I loved the generosity of the people, the way dishes come with free extras like soup and salad, and coffee that's topped up with pleasure. I loved the fact that purchases come with hidden discounts, not hidden add-ons, that barmen give away free drinks, that people want to be your friend, that someone will say 'bless you' when you sneeze in public and stand by ready to perform the Heimlich manoeuvre if you're coughing. I loved all that. It shows such an acute sense of humanity. In Britain we only know how to rip each other off and to put each other down.

'No-one ever took it seriously did they?' I said to Flatcap. 'They all thought the Energy Marketing Initiative a load of bollocks, didn't they?'

Flatcap really couldn't be bothered. This was a week when he was sacking half the remaining department, when he was being sent back after little more than a year, and when he was having to face being condemned as Old Bank. He was in no mood to argue with the one guy he thought had done all right out of the mess. They knew they'd sent me to a tough office and I was being helicoptered out.

'Son,' he said with finality. 'Just count yourself lucky.'

What he meant was, 'Nice try son, now shut up and get in the chopper.'

'So give me two months,' I said. 'Two months, then I'll go back to London. If I go now I've failed.'

'Son, you've not failed—'

'If you make me stop now of course it's a failure. I was sent here to originate Receivables deals in Latin America and to get us in with the boys upstairs. I was stopped from doing both. I've reinvented myself. OK, it's taken some time, but I've done it. I've created a whole new

288

business here and by June we'll have the juice.'

I was virtually on my feet. I'd put on my most dramatic voice, the music should have pitched up in the background, the stripy shirts should have stopped laughing and turned to listen, Flatcap should have stopped munching his way through his sandwich.

I had a mission.

'Give me until June,' I said.

'Oh what the fuck,' said Flatcap. 'Energizer Bunny's head of Energy. He can fucking deal with it.'

He went off to prepare for a sacking.

I didn't hesitate. I needed all the support I could get. I rang the Main Man.

'Hey Big Boy,' he said over his speakerphone. 'How's Mandy?'

'Fuck Mandy,' I said.

He picked up the receiver.

'Look, do you see a business for what I've been doing with the energy companies?'

'Mate, I don't,' he said. 'I've looked at it and I just don't. Hardon fucked up. Uranus fucked up. I mean, where's the juice?'

Oh right.

'What if I could show you I had a business?'

'But how, Big Boy?'

'By getting us a deal by June,' I said. 'You know it takes time to build something. I feel I've only just started.'

He was quiet for a moment.

'I know what you're saying,' he said. 'You want me to put a word in with Energizer Bunny so you can stay until June.'

'Bang on,' I said.

'Let me think about it,' he said. 'I'll call you back.'

He put the phone down without saying goodbye – at least the Main Man knew how to ham up a good drama.

He also knew how to be a sly bugger. He'd been

worried about one of his clients for a while. They were triple-B minus and were on negative watch by the rating agency. This meant a downgrade was likely and they'd fall though the investment-grade barrier. They were heading for the junkyard unless something could be done.

The Main Man came back to me in less than an hour.

'Hey Big Boy, do you owe me big time or what?'

I could hear him clapping and getting excited.

'I've just spoken to Energizer Bunny,' he said, 'and persuaded him to let you stay until June.'

'Well I never,' I said. 'I . . . I . . . thanks.'

'But Energizer Bunny says you better get a deal done – right, Big Boy?'

'Right,' I said.

'Oh, one other thing, Big Boy,' he said. 'Could you take a look at Dickhams, down in Tulsa.'

I agreed. What else could I do – go home?

Might as well face it

Sex with Eva was astonishing. 'That was astonishing,' I said.

'It was nothing,' she said, in her dark liqueur accent, as if to say 'you wait'.

I imagined weekends spent in dungeons, punctuated by the occasional whipping from a rubbered-up Eva. I wasn't sure I could handle it. I was being driven nuts as it was.

I'd bought her dinner in Delphini, a romantic eatery close enough to my apartment to avoid a cab home. Not that I needed to play tricks. She behaved as if being bought dinner was the most romantic gesture of her life, second only to the gift I'd given her earlier. Mandy had turned up in Miami with the new Armani cologne called ' . . . he/él/etc', having bought herself the ' . . . elle/she/etc', version. It was a nice gift but an awkward aftershave to sit in my bathroom in New York. It said girl-friend with ' . . . elle/she/etc' version lurking. So after parting with Mandy at Miami airport I bought a spare ' . . . she/elle/etc' and presented it to Eva.

'Oh, it is fantastic,' she said. 'Rawbert, you so kind. You such handsome man.'

'And look,' I said. 'I bought the men's version for myself. They connect, see.'

I demonstrated how the bottles fitted into each other in a mock shag, just as Mandy had shown me. Eva took the two bottles, held them in the shag position and pressed the ' . . . he/él/etc' so that it sprayed into the ' . . . she/elle/etc'.

'Later,' she announced.

I couldn't wait.

This was going to be one dinner bill worth paying. Eva had even arrived at my apartment with a large weekend bag.

'What shall I wear?' she said and proceeded to get changed in front of me. 'You like dress, no?'

She held up a dress.

'You like bra, no?'

She showed me a bra.

'I change bra. Don't look.'

I turned away.

'Why you not look?' she said angrily.

After dinner it seemed strange inviting her back. She'd arrived with half her possessions, for chrissake – of course she was coming back. And the fact she'd spent half the dinner saying 'you handsome man' and running her foot up my calf suggested major sexual progress was on the cards.

Her skin was amazing. It was like running my hand

along powered silk. She sat on the couch, waiting to be kissed. Her black dress hung loosely from her shoulder, waiting to be removed. And her sleek back held a tempting bra-catch, waiting to be released.

I didn't kiss her breasts immediately. I kissed her arms, her shoulders, her neck. But her breasts pointed at me, the nipples like sharp berries begging to be picked, pleading to be eaten.

'You take off your pants,' she demanded.

Although she'd clearly learnt her English here, her voice retained a Transylvanian menace. It said, obey. It said, 'I whip, you scream.' And it said colossal erection swinging from stomach. She took me in hand and moved her head down my torso muttering 'handsome man'.

I'd never had a blow job like it. I thought blow jobs were blow jobs but . . . blimey. She held it very tightly at the stem and pulled back the skin to the edge of pain. Then she moved up and down like a cylinder head on a piston. She sucked hard.

'Wooahhh, wooahhh,' I cried.

I just couldn't control myself. I was screaming the place down. It was as if every nerve ending in my body was focused on my swollen helmet, which was doing a good impression of an over-ripe beetroot. It didn't feel like I was about to come. It felt more like I was going to faint.

'You take me from behind,' she demanded, turning round and offering me a view you'd pay extra for in a hotel. 'I want you inside, now.'

I'd barely recovered from the blow job but knelt behind her – in no mood to disobey. She felt back and guided me in.

'Ohhh.'

Now it was her turn to cry.

'You handsome man, ohhh.'

She felt fantastic. It was a different dimension. Her

taut cheeks slapped against my stomach. Her back arched away to rise for her slender shoulders. Her long blonde hair cascaded around her neck. It looked incredible. I was fucking this stunningly beautiful woman from behind. Hollywood couldn't invent a better scene.

'Ohhhh, Rawbert,' she cried. 'I orgasm for you, ohh-hhh.'

I was determined not to come too quickly. But the view, her moaning, her grasp – it was just too much. I pulled out.

'Why you stop? I want you fuck me,' she said.

'I would've come,' I said.

She turned to me.

'I want you come in my mouth,' she said.

She went back to the blow job. I could see her lips clutch the shaft, her hand tightly holding its base.

'Jesus woaaah,' I said. 'Jesus woaaah.'

I couldn't stop, 'Ohh Jesus.'

She didn't change pace, she didn't retreat – her eyes just searched mine for a reaction as I erupted in her mouth.

'That was astonishing,' I said.

Eva was the cocaine of sex. You had to have it and when you couldn't have it you thought about it constantly. Every date was a prelude to the next fix. And between dates you'd relive the memory and mess up the sheets.

Eva saw things differently.

'We have gone too fast,' she said after our first session. 'You will not like me now.'

'No, no,' I said, still trying to recover and in no state for a major reassurance session. God knows why she needed it. An angel on my arm and a tigress in bed – what man wasn't going to beg for more?

But that was the key to Eva. Somewhere in there lay a deeply unconfident woman. To say her behaviour was ambivalent was an understatement. She may have sounded like Dracula's mistress but she behaved like Jekyll and Hyde.

If I didn't call for one day I'd have a furious Eva shouting, 'Why you not call?'

Yet if I called she'd bark, 'Not now,' and put the phone down.

The minute I said I had trouble making a date she'd bring up some man that was desperate to marry her and had been begging for a chance. And, of course, my rival suitors were all millionaires – even the Hungarian journalist. What I should have said was, 'Fine, enjoy yourself', but I couldn't. I was too addicted.

I was also captivated by her beauty. Actually that isn't strictly true. I was more captivated by my friends' captivation of her beauty.

'Bob, she's lovely,' said Fiona as Eva wandered off to the restrooms. 'And she's so into you. It's amazing.'

'Fucking nice arse, Bob,' said Trevor as his eyes followed Eva's wiggle.

It was only after such statements that I'd look at her and think, 'Yeah, fucking hell, she's gorgeous.'

Eva was tall and blonde with sculptured looks, whereas I tended to like sultry, small, dark women. And I'd never really fancied Sharon Stone. Sure, she's not ugly, but she's not triple-A – at least not in my book.

And Eva's ability to be 'so into' me had a capricious edge. After a few Tanqueray and tonics, another side of Eva would emerge. This was a side that not only flirted like mad when she met Nat but also arranged a date with him at the Guggenheim.

'I don't want man that just want sex,' she declared loudly in the bar. 'I'm intelligent woman. I want man with culture.'

Nat sat slightly back from her. He caught my eye, nodded towards Eva, opened his eyes wide and shook his head.

'Mad as a fucking hatter,' he was saying.

Great – I'd introduced Sharon Stone to my mates and she'd turned into Vlad the Impaler.

For whom the bell tolls

'Good news,' said Mandy during one of our testy daily calls. 'I'm coming to work in New York for a month.'

'Great,' I said.

Even though we were on the phone I adopted a fixed smile.

'Well don't sound overwhelmed, will you?'

'No, no, I can't wait,' I said. 'When?'

'Friday.'

It was Wednesday.

'Blimey, I mean great, great. Where are you staying?'

'With you,' she said.

'What?'

'Don't worry, it's only for the weekend. Then I'm in the SoHo Grand.'

'Great, great,' I said.

Fuck. Eva was due on Friday night. She'd turn up with her stuffed weekend bag as usual. Constellations were about to collide.

'Eva, how's things?'

'Why you call? I tell you before—'

'Look I'm going away. I won't be here at the weekend, sorry.'

'Where you go?'

'Houston, something's come up.'

'At weekend?' she sounded disbelieving.

'It's urgent, sorry.'

'Are you dating other woman?'

Blimey, just come out with it, why don't you?

295

'I wish,' I said.

'You *wish*?'

'No, no,' I said hastily. 'It's an English expression—'

'You wish you dating other woman?'

Now she really was angry.

'Nooo,' I said patiently. 'I meant I wish it was pleasure, not work. I'll call you when I get back.'

Mandy arrived at JFK around six. The earliest I was going to be in town was seven. I told her to go to the 86th Street Starbucks and wait. I'd cycle straight down from 125th.

New York for a month – what a pain. I was due home in June and had determined to enjoy my remaining freedom. Bugger finding the wife, I'd earmarked the final two months as 'shagfest'.

And New York appeared to be dripping with sexual tension. Spring was here and the women were back in full bloom. Every turn brought angular, bare shoulders, smooth legs and magnetizing g-strings visible through sheer skirts.

My sap was rising. I could sense a good-looking woman and my eyes would automatically rise to check her out. The scanner was permanently on. I could be dozing on the train and it would wake me up for a babe. I could be avoiding death-by-bus on 125th Street when the radar would decide the woman on the sidewalk was worth a look. And I could be about to meet my girlfriend in Starbucks when my peripheral vision would clock a tasty female waiting in line. Except this tasty female was Mandy. My automatic scanner had picked my woman – what a doll. I couldn't wait to get her home.

But this was a weekend for getting out of the apartment. It wasn't Eva's call I feared. She'd been sorted. It was other women, usually ringing late at night (an American habit). Melanie from Miami was wont to call me after one of her drunken nights out, as was Betty.

Betty was a silly woman I'd met in Jake's Dilemma on the night of the Lewis-Holyfield fight. She'd tried her best to be sophisticated, able to deal with a guy talking shit and a romp in the sack. But it was beyond her. She turned soppy the next day and rang me every time she went out in Manhattan with her chums. The fact she was married didn't help. He was some inattentive couch potato in Queens and I feared a baseball-bat beating from his mates. She wasn't worth the risk.

The Empire State, Ellis Island, Statue of Liberty, galleries, museums, the lot. I'd made it to Sunday night without mishap and that was my only concern. She'd be in the SoHo Grand tomorrow and I could relax, so I thought. But Monday was a Bank Holiday in the UK and Mandy's colleagues weren't due in New York until Tuesday. She was staying an extra night – fuck.

'Well, why don't you go to the hotel early?' I said, rather clumsily. I was desperate to get her out of harm's way.

'What?' Her eyes filled with tears.

I felt like a wife-beater.

'You knew it was a bank holiday at home. You knew I was staying until Tuesday. I can't believe you're such a pig. Why do you want me to go?'

'I don't, I'm sorry, I just didn't realize,' I stammered. 'It's the idea of having to go to work with you in my bed.'

Oh gawd, it cost me $150 to get out of that slip.

Mandy spent Monday pottering around the Upper West Side while I spent the day having little panic attacks at work. Would she find the condoms? Would she find my stash of women's phone numbers? And what about the Kiehl's massage oil? I expected to arrive home with a collection of offending articles on the coffee table next to my ripped suits.

Instead I arrived home to find the apartment clean, the bed made for the first time ever, flowers in a vase, my antique clock wound and ticking and dinner on the table. The place didn't know what had hit it.

But it wasn't all domestic bliss.

'Betty rang,' she said, searching my face for signs of discomfort.

'Oh right,' I said, trying to sound nonchalant. 'What did she want?'

'She just told me to say she rang.'

Silly fucking bitch. She knew I lived alone. Why didn't she put the phone down when a woman answered? But Mandy seemed pretty cool about it and I thought I'd successfully managed to change the subject.

No such luck.

'So', said Mandy during a pause at dinner, 'who's Betty then?'

'Who?'

'Betty.'

'Oh, Betty,' I said, desperately buying myself some time. 'She's part of a gang I met. She occasionally asks me out when their gang is out around here. I don't know why *she* calls. I get on better with the guys.'

'She probably fancies you,' said Mandy.

'Yeah, well,' I said. 'Who can blame her?'

Mandy bought the story.

'Brrrrr.'

The phone broadcast its manly single tone into the room. I stared at it as if it had never made such a noise before.

'Phone's ringing,' said Mandy.

Yes, yes, I knew the fucking phone was ringing. I just didn't want to answer it.

'Aren't you going to answer it?' she asked.

'Er, yeah,' I said reluctantly. 'I'm just worried it may be someone from work.'

'So what?' she said. 'What are they going to do, drag you back to Greenwich?'

'I just don't want to speak to them,' I said, resolved to let it ring until the Bell Atlantic message minder took over.

'Don't be silly,' she said. 'And it may be for me. I gave them this number.'

She picked up the phone.

'Hello,' she said.

Her faced creased.

'Sure, who is it?'

She handed me the phone.

'It's someone called Eva,' she said. 'For you.'

Fuck, fuck, fuck.

'Hi,' I said.

'Who's that woman in your apartment?' said Eva.

She sounded very angry.

'Pardon,' I said.

Fuck, fuck, fuck.

I stood up and walked around the room with the phone under my chin. I went to do some washing up. It had been done. I looked to bag the rubbish. It had been done. I started to clear food packets from the worktop.

'Who's that woman?' she was now shouting.

'Oh, a friend,' I said.

I tried to say it quietly so Mandy wouldn't hear.

Mandy sat eating her dinner, her ears flapping like an elephant's.

I had to find a bin bag under the sink. I bent my head into the cupboard and mumbled into the phone.

'She's just staying here for tonight.'

'Wat,' Eva barked. 'Speak loud. And stop doing things while I talk to you.'

I laughed.

'Yes, ha, ha, ha.'

'Wat? Are you drunken?'

'No, ha, ha, ha.'

'Are you dating woman?'

'No, she's . . . Look, I'll call you tomorrow.'

'Tell me, you dating woman?'

'Sorry, can't hear,' I said. 'I'll call you tomorrow. Bye.'

As I put the phone down I could hear Eva shouting abuse.

There was silence for a while.

'So I'm just a friend?' said Mandy.

Oh shit, this was going to be expensive.

The next day I received an email.

'Robert,

You lie me. You dating bitch woman. Fuck off pig. You ugly man. I fuck Nat. I marry millionaire. Have shit life, Eva.'

A response seemed inappropriate.

MAY

Lie, you bastard

The SoHo Grand is one of New York's trendiest hotels. The doormen look like secret-service agents and the decor has an industrial feel: functional straight lines, stainless steel and frosted glass. The rooms are the height of cool. They have CD players, mock NHS bathrooms and black and white post-war New York street life photographs. The whole place just says 'now' – or at least 'now and, er, the 1950s'.

At the weekends I virtually moved in. It was great to sit and order room service, to watch a movie, to crack into the minibar and to occasionally give Mandy a good seeing to – all courtesy of the company. And when we did venture out we were in SoHo, New York's coolest district.

Mandy and I were getting on fine. We always did when we were together. She was easy company and by far the sanest woman I'd met in the last year or so. She even rationalized my behaviour in New York.

'I don't really want to know what you get up to here,' she said at one point, 'but I like to see your reaction when I ask. Your eyes panic.'

Oh fuck. I could never be a poker player.

And Mandy was starting to deal me some tricky hands. I felt like a murderer with the proverbial net closing in,

301

whilst Mandy acted more and more like Columbo. Her latest venue for a session of 'just one more thing' was Balthazar on Spring Street, one of SoHo's liveliest restaurants.

'So you never did explain who Eva was,' she said.

'Oh I met her in Starbucks,' I said. 'She wanted to get into banking so we got along. She's a bit of a pain, always asking for favours.'

'She's got a funny accent,' she said.

'She's Hungarian,' I said.

'Oh well,' said Mandy, trying to bury the ghost. 'As long as nothing happened.'

'No, no,' I said.

This menu was awfully complicated. I had to concentrate very hard.

'Hiya, howya doin'?' said the waitress who'd come over to make sure we were paying attention to the menus and not just chatting.

New York waitresses are a special breed. It's not that they come with attitude. That's true of all New Yorkers. But most waitresses are in New York trying to break into TV or fashion or world domination and use waitressing to pay the bills.

It's all so breezy, breezy. She wants to chat and make jokes and you'd better laugh. She reels off the ubiquitous specials as if delivering Hamlet's soliloquy and she ain't the slightest bit interested in whether you're in the middle of saying something when she's about to offer you dessert. Oh no, she just butts right in. A guy could be on one knee with a ring box open and she wouldn't give a fig.

'Dorothy I've been wanting to ask you for a while, will you mar—'

'How you guys doin' for drinks – more wine?'

But my relationship with Mandy was heading in the opposite direction.

302

'You would tell me if you were unfaithful, wouldn't you?' she asked.

'I thought you said you didn't want to know, that you . . .'

I stopped when I saw the trap. It was too late.

'I never said that,' she snapped. 'That means you *have* been unfaithful, haven't you?'

'Er, I . . . er.' Nothing came. It would have been such an obvious lie after the last statement.

Why was I such a dimwit? The clever answer was, 'Of course I'd tell you. You know I can't lie to you.'

Now I was fucked.

'You have, haven't you, you have? I don't believe it, you have.'

Her face filled with pain.

It was too late to deny it.

'Just once,' I said. 'It meant nothing. I hated it.'

Again, what a dimwit.

'It's never too late to lie,' Trevor would say. 'If you're found with your head in a woman's crotch, say you were sucking out a bee sting. Get caught shagging her from behind, say you were demonstrating the Heimlich manoeuvre. In the nude. Never, never, never just hand out the info over dinner.'

'Why did you tell me?' she said.

'What do you mean?' I said. 'You asked.'

'Why didn't you lie?' she said. 'I didn't mean you should tell me.'

I really was lost. A minute ago she denied she didn't want to know. Hell will freeze over before I understand the female mind.

'I want to go,' she said, standing up and rushing to the door.

'Mandy, wait,' I called. But it was too late.

The couple on the next table looked at me as if to say 'Why didn't you lie, you knucklehead?'

As the waitress came over to deliver the specials speech and crack a few jokes, Mandy was already in the street and in a cab. Fuck it.

At that moment I realized I loved her. Here I was looking for a soulmate in New York when she was in London all the time. And I was about to lose her. I grabbed the cab behind and followed.

She let me in her hotel room, although she'd clearly been crying.

'You can't stay,' she said. She was calm but firm. 'I need to be alone.'

'Don't pack me in,' I pleaded.

'Huhh . . .' she went to speak but stopped.

Her eyes filled up as she stared out the window at a crop of New York water towers.

'Just go.'

'Look, things are changing for me,' I said. 'I thought I was here for good but I'm coming home now. You're my woman. I see you as a life partner.'

'Oh that's the carrot, is it?' she said.

'I love you Mandy and I'm sorry.' I turned and left. And I *was* sorry. I didn't want to lose her.

Over the next few days I became the model boyfriend and slowly won her back. Soon my infidelity was forgotten, but it was clear – there was to be no more nonsense.

After a fortnight, Mandy's deal collapsed and she went back to London. And New York seemed empty without her.

Bernie the bolt

With Mandy back in Britain my sexual needs didn't simmer down. In fact they boiled away like quick-cook spaghetti with the pan lid on. I felt ready to explode. I'd wake up in the morning with a painful erection, wanton thoughts followed me through the day and sleep was impossible before Perky had been thoroughly exhausted through exercise.

The trouble with this particular form of exercise is the need for visual stimulation. Every man who admits to masturbating will tell his girlfriend that he wanks over a mental image of her. It's a nice lie, but he's normally wanking over the visual image of pictures in a magazine. Men just aren't mentally ambidextrous enough to wank and conjure images, especially of girlfriends. Help is required.

The key to a good wank mag is fantasy. When locked in the loo or bedroom with a mag I'm not masturbating, oh no. I'm actually with Staci or Candi or the Reader's Wife of the Month. And it's important to get this fantasy as close to reality as possible. So while full sex with this woman is rejected as unrealistic, the illusion is that it's her performing the service and not me. I'm on that beach or by that pool and it's her hand round my boner.

Staci's pose and position in the fantasy is all important. For instance, while she wanks me off, she must look into my eyes. After all, if Staci was really wanking me off I would expect her to look into my eyes. And this is where the fantasy takes over. Staci looks into my eyes and makes encouraging noises. I concentrate hard on her face, aware of the body below but too polite to fully stare. Her face sneers (next page) as if to say 'Come on Robert, come on me.'

She's now on her knees with her mouth slightly open. I've wet my hand and concentrate my strokes at the tip. Her breasts fall from her chest and swing to the rhythm. She's good and ready. She wants me to come on her tits. She offers them to me (next page). She cups them and thrusts the nipples forward. Oh, Staci, oh *wowwww*.

I was in a great country for wanking. The porn's superb. Like the food, there's more of it and it's better quality. This encourages better service, but it also encourages addiction. Within a few randy days of purchasing a magazine it's redundant. The models are rejected for having the wrong pose, or having the right pose but with the wrong look, or having the right pose and look but having their arms up so they couldn't realistically be wanking you off, or having the right pose, look and arm placement but being located on a page you can no longer open.

And like all addictions it's progressive. It's easy to move up the scale towards ever-greater obscenity. *Playboy* is dismissed early on but soon the naked women and all-girl romps of *High Society* aren't enough. Then you need the mock sex acts of *Hustler*. The guys have lumbering hard-ons that Staci grasps tightly and pretends to suck. But it ultimately goes nowhere. There's no climax. Then you discover *Cheri*. This is a magazine that seems to recognize the progressive nature of porn addiction and tries to push the boundaries for you. Mock sex acts result in the man coming on the woman. And before you know it the couples are at it on the page in front of you. Of course, these sex acts require a twist in the fantasy. Either King Dong's in the sesh with you and Stace, or you're him.

Whichever, it's a small step from stills of copulating couples to videos. And it would be much easier to resist this step if they didn't sell the videos alongside the mags in the newsagents. There seem to be no restrictions on their sale, even with Giuliani's frustration-induced tightening.

Once on the videos, the slippery slope beckons. Eventually you watch them so often you start noticing some of their quirks. For instance, it's nearly always the same guy. After watching a couple of these videos I'd say

306

I knew this guy's willy better than my own. I'd certainly seen it from more angles.

And old Leather Dick has a strange way with women. For a start he keeps slapping them on the bum like he's geeing-up a horse.

'Ya, gal, ya, ya.'

You expect John Wayne to appear and warn him about the cattle rustlers.

He also has a habit of moving from whatever sexual position he's in to deliver his climax right in her face. And rather than complain about this, as I'm pretty sure any of my girlfriends would, the women seem to encourage it.

He also has no trouble involving passing neighbours and friends who don't seem in the least bit shocked that Leather Dick is shafting some strange woman kneeling on a sun lounger. He occasionally shakes a newcomer's hand without even breaking rhythm. And, yes, the newcomer's soon getting stuck right in there as well.

It really does warp your sense of reality. You need to have made sure you're fully back to Earth before nipping down the deli for a bagel. Indeed, watching any normal TV afterwards requires some adjustment. Even watching *Friends* becomes a little strange. You expect Chandler to fuck Monica on the couch while greeting Ross – without breaking rhythm, of course.

At this point it's best to arrange to meet people and go out. I arranged to meet Nat and his new girlfriend Sal. Unlike Nat's previous dates she refused to take any shit about his ex, Jill, and had a witty, aggressive manner that I'd missed in women. Although American, she'd spent enough time in London to like British men and to have had that apple-pie crap beaten out of her. She was a confident woman and had with her a confident friend – Rose, who was in from Long Island for the night. The three of them sat in a divey Lower East Side bar called Max Fish,

307

with me completing the foursome.

Rose was glad of my arrival. Nat and Sal were content to swap banter and have play fights on their own, and Rose needed someone to pay her some attention. And she was a good talker.

Rose had that all-American look of long, blond hair, wide eyes and healthy skin. American females just ooze good breeding. But Rose also had a disconcerting masculinity about her. She had a large jaw and mouth and a strong build. She was the sort of girl who was good at athletics at school and you'd avoid in kiss chase for fear of getting your head kicked in.

I didn't really fancy her. Not that it mattered – my pulling days in New York were over.

Max Fish became crowded around 1 a.m. and we had to scrunch up on the bench seat. Soon the seat was so packed I had to dangle my arm behind me to avoid putting it around Rose. But this position encouraged me to face her, even though we were sitting bang next to each other. And while talking my right hand was free to emphasize my speech. Or I could place it on my leg when listening. Or I could tap her leg lightly when she was close to finishing a point I wanted to argue with.

And she then did the same. It felt fun, so we got into a mock row in order to carry on tapping each other's leg. Then the leg tapping became so frequent it seemed pointless retreating. Soon the stomach began to tighten, the adrenalin began to surge, the hairs on the arm picked up and Mandy seemed an awful long way away.

It was easy now. I'd graduated. I knew what to do. Touch arm, touch hair, touch cheek. Look at eyes, look at mouth, back to eyes. Pause. Move in for kiss. I didn't need green lights. I could go on amber – she'd flash the red if she wanted to.

'That's my boy,' said Trevor. 'You don't need me now. You're a master.'

And Rose was no passive New York kisser. My God no. Her tongue was down my throat like a Jack Russell terrier. I almost gagged. It was as if an iguana was having a fit in there.

We left Nat and Sal throwing pepperoni at each other in Ray's Pizza and caught a cab north. As we rode the green wave, I didn't think of Mandy. She was safely stored in a separate room of my brain. She was hidden from the sight of me snogging Rose, although this tongue felt capable of crashing through the wall and chasing Mandy off the sofa. My only worry was whether the tube of hand cream and the loo roll were still by the TV.

Rose was incredibly responsive. We spent most of the taxi ride snogging and we were undressing the minute the apartment door was closed. Before I knew it we were in the bedroom and she was giving me an aggressive blow job.

'Your cock tastes good,' she said. I'd heard exactly that line delivered to Leather Dick earlier. He'd responded with something equally blatant but I didn't reply – I really didn't want to tell her I was going to fuck her up the ass and come in her face.

But Rose's reproduction of the fantasy was proving problematic. She was now giving me a rough handjob. She was kneading poor Perky as if making bread and he protested loudly. I had to move her off.

By now we were on the bed and I suggested she undress and lean back, although every move was accompanied by an annoying commentary.

'Oh yeah, take off my panties? Oh yeah, lick my pussy? Oh great. Oh Robert, oh. That's good.'

But this wasn't like Tiffany. She wasn't getting carried away and saying things through pleasure. She was giving instructions. And she was just warming up.

'Higher, higher. Up a bit, up a bit,' she shouted as she became more excited while I performed cunnilingus.

I felt like Bernie the Bolt.

'Left a bit, right a bit, down a bit. That's it, keep it there. Keep it there. Yes, yes.'

This went on for an age. Once my tongue found the spot (look it wasn't obvious, OK) I tried desperately to maintain its position as she slowly climbed the ladder. But one slip and she was back at the bottom and barking at me to push her up.

At one point she even said 'It doesn't normally take this long.'

Not a comment calculated to inflate my ego.

But each climb got her further up. Eventually – and we are talking at least half an hour – she grabbed my head and forced it against her opening.

'Just there, just there,' she shouted.

There was no need to give orders as I had little choice but to obey. My face stung, my tongue ached, my leg had gone to sleep – it was agony.

'Yes, yes, yes,' she panted, using my head as a virtual dildo and ramming it hard against her vagina. 'Yesssss, ohhhh, yeessssss.'

She finally relaxed.

'Well done,' she said after a pause and in a 'there's a good boy' tone. I thought she was going to throw me a choccy drop.

Twenty-four hours in Tulsa

'This is crap,' said High Pockets. 'You're showing me an Old Bank deal. You're just not hitting their bogey.'

'So how do we hit their bogey?' I asked, somewhat exasperated.

'We offer them a swaption.'

Oh gawd, here we go.

'What's a swaption?' I asked.

'It's a swap on an option,' said High Pockets in a tone that suggested 'come on, get with the programme. Sharpen up, willya.'

'And, sorry, how does this hit their bogey?'

Within a minute of walking into High Pockets' office I was lost. It was like having a conversation with one of the Clangers – it all sounded familiar but it made no sense at all. You prayed for the Soup Dragon to pop up and say something intelligible.

On this occasion High Pockets was destroying my plans to help Dickhams maintain its credit rating. They had a ton of energy marketing contracts with all sorts of weird and wonderful names and I wanted to bundle them up in a securitizable package and give the asset-backed guys upstairs something to sell. Dickhams could then use the cash to pay back some debt and please the raters. And High Pockets had agreed to help as long as he was allowed to accuse me of being Old Bank at least twice in every conversation.

He wasn't such a bad guy. He loved the fact he could confuse me in an instant but then he'd put on his goofy, cartoon-dumbo face and explain it in very simple language.

Eventually I'd say, 'Oh I get it, hey, that's quite easy really.'

He'd nod at the magnificence of his power of explanation.

'When you strip away the jargon,' I'd say cheerfully, 'we're just plumbers – putting this bit of pipe to that stop and that bit of pipe in this tank.'

He gave me a look as if to say, 'Never tell that to the client.'

And with a High Pockets' approved presentation in my pocket I was bound for Tulsa.

These out-of-the-way American cities are very strange.

311

For a start you never quite get to the centre. I walked the entire length of Tulsa's Downtown area expecting every corner to reveal a big shopping mall or a square full of bars and restaurants. But I never found it. I'd walk one street that reminded me of the service area behind Sainsbury's in Chelmsford. It was full of skips and loading bays and other unappealing shit. This would cause me to walk hurriedly to the next block, assuming that I was behind something exciting. But all I'd find would be another line of skips and a few more loading bays.

And there was no-one about. On the whole of my Tulsa walk I came across one other pedestrian, and he was a tramp lying asleep on a bench in an otherwise deserted street. The city appeared to have paved this street solely for this guy's benefit. On hearing my footsteps he woke and beckoned me to join him, assuming that another pedestrian must be a fellow bum. I declined.

Towns like this really depress me. No amount of money could make me live in one. They are nothing but urban breaks in the prairie. I'm sure Tulsans will be horrified at my ignorance of the fantastic shopping and entertainment on offer in the city, but it will be in some out-of-town mall with a vast car park. Imagine visiting a British town and being told you'd yet to see the place because you missed the Supacentre out on the ring road. You'd be on the next bus out.

It was a pity Tulsa was so dead, because I had a night to kill. I was hoping to complete the Dickhams visit in a day, but a strange thing had happened in the meeting. I first presented my proposed structure to a trader. He looked at it between taking calls, talking to colleagues and negotiating with his secretary about some sporting event he was due to attend. But after about fifteen minutes he began to focus on it properly.

He said, 'Y'all jus' hang on a second there boy', and

made a call. 'Chip, y'all should git yersel down here and have yersel a lil look at this.'

Chip turned out to be from the treasury department. He looked long and hard at the box-and-arrow chart in the presentation. I was waiting for one of them to say, 'This diagram don't make no sense, boy. Where's the goddam bogey on the swaption?'

But they didn't. Instead they asked a couple of questions and nodded.

'I think Hank ought to take a lil look at this,' said Chip.

After a while about five people had been called and they all stared hard at the diagram. By now I'd run out of copies so I'd drawn it on the whiteboard. They kept asking questions they'd already asked, as if they were just confirming it to themselves.

'So y'all take the contracts and put them in this here special company?'

'Yes,' I said, fighting a desire to say 'yessirree'.

'So y'all monetize the total value of these contracts through a loan to the special company and they pass the money on as a prepayment for the contracts. So it's not debt for us?'

'No,' I said.

'So we can use that cash to repay debt?'

'Yes,' I said.

'Well Chip, y'all be happy with that.'

'Yessirree,' said Chip. 'Those rating agencies are bustin' my ass about our level of debt.'

'And this special company now has all the risk of our customers not paying, so we can release all those credit reserves we have against those names. Well Hank, y'all be happy with that.'

'Yessirree,' said Hank. 'I need to do more business with those darn traders, and the credit boys upstairs keep on stoppin' me.'

'And this here swaption thing – what in God's name does that do?'

Oh fuck – here we go.

'All the swap does is turn the risk on these contracts from something you don't like into something you do,' I said. 'You hate the credit risk on these buyers, right?'

'Right,' said one.

'But you don't mind the fact you carry price risk on the commodity you're selling, right?'

'Right,' said another. 'It's our business to run the price risk on commodities – we're traders.'

'So the swap turns the fixed price of the contract into the floating price of the market. You now have a price risk, rather than the current credit risk, because if the buyer collapsed you'd just sell the gas or power in the open market and give the proceeds to the special company. The option bit is that you can choose when to use the swap.'

'You know,' said Hank. 'I'm an engineer by training and that's the first time I've understood what an investment banker's been darn well telling me. Either I'm gettin' smarter boy, or y'all good at your job.'

'He ain't gettin' no smarter,' said Chip.

'Well,' I said, getting a bit cocky, 'if you strip away the jargon we're just plumbers really – putting this bit of pipe to that stop and that bit of pipe in this tank.'

They had a bit of a conflab in the corridor and then came back.

'Boy, y'all jus' got yersel a deal.'

I was amazed.

The only problem was I had to hang around for a day while their lawyers organized a letter of engagement. I didn't mind. I was going to hit the town and get pissed.

I was staying in a Downtown hotel, hence my walking tour in search of stimulation. Finally I found Orpha's

314

Bar, a real dive with a tatty pool table and twangy music coming from a knackered jukebox.

The only spare stool was next to three Native Americans, all of whom were asleep. I pitched up and waited for the street-hardened, ageing blonde bombshell to serve me.

'What beer have you got?' I asked, thinking I'd see what the local micro-brewery offering was like.

'Bud,' she said.

She noticed the snoozing Indians and slapped her hand hard on the bar.

'Hey will you guys wake up,' she shouted. 'You know you're not allowed to sleep in the bar.'

They stirred. She turned back to me.

'So wat'll it be, honey?'

As the choice seemed to consist of 'yes' or 'no' – or possibly honey – I said, 'yes'.

'Harrummphh ha,' said the Indian guy next to me, wiping the sleep from his glazed eyes. He was talking to me so I shook my shoulders in a mock laugh. This encouraged him.

'Hey, harrummmpphh rougharough?'

It was a question but I hadn't a clue what he'd said. It didn't matter; he nodded off again.

The barmaid came back and slapped the beer so force-fully in front of me that the top half-inch spilled onto the bar.

'Hey,' she shouted, hitting my neighbour. 'Wake up John, or yer out. Get me?'

'Hattumpph hahumph,' protested John.

I'd never met a real live Red Indian before so I was a bit disappointed he was so pissed. I was also a bit disap-pointed his name was John. I was hoping for a Little Foot or Big Willy or that old Two Dogs Fucking joke.

His head moved backwards and forwards in an effort to get me in focus – his eyes obviously no longer capable of adjusting for distance on their own – and he kept talking and gesticulating. He was also getting a bit emotional.

'Rumpfa sergeant,' he said, proudly pointing at his upper arm. 'Rumppfha humph Vietnam.'

He poked his chest. 'Humpha humph purple heart.'

He laughed, so I joined him. His face dropped in anger and he hit me on the arm, not hard. But he was trying to get his point across and I should take it seriously, whatever it might be.

'Hummphha dumpfha machine gun: ahh, ahh, ahh, ahh,' he mimicked a machine gun. 'Hullupahu all dead.'

It didn't sound like a very pleasant story although I wished I could have followed it because I was interested. Never mind, he was impressed that I'd made the effort so he harumphed incoherently to the barmaid, who lined up four shot glasses with some liquid in them.

'What is it?' I asked John.

'Harrumpha mash,' he said.

'Mash?'

'Mash,' he confirmed, and knocked his back in one, as did the others.

But this wasn't the mash that came with sausages and beans back in Essex, oh no. And now the three Indians looked at me expectantly. Oh fuck. I took a sniff. It smelt like it would fizz the paint off a battleship. I took a sip, blimey.

'Na, na,' said John, taking the glass off me. 'Notlilat. Lilis.'

He knocked it back, slamming the empty glass on the table. I wasn't too upset to lose my gift.

I decided to leave but had no clue where to go. I asked the barmaid.

'Well,' she paused, and thought hard.

It was as if I'd asked her to name the state capital of Delaware, although I'd simply enquired about food. Where to get something to eat in Tulsa? Hmmm, tricky.

'Well howdya like *barrr-beee-que*?' she said, perking up.

'Love it,' I said.

'Well there's Billy Ray's on the Bollox County Road to the south-west.'

This lifted my spirits. Billy Ray's *barrr-beee-que* – it sounded mighty fine.

And I wasn't disappointed. It was a scruffy, wooden shed on the edge of some crappy industrial estate. It had those crazy angled tin smokestacks coming out of the roof and a line of old pick-up trucks by the front door.

Inside I was confronted with a scene from Planet Fat. Every customer looked like they'd been rolled to their seats. There was a group of men, a family, two young lads and two middle-aged women – all as fat as a house. I'd found the world epicentre of obesity. My waitress was comparatively attractive because she only had three chins and her arse was only of magnificent proportions compared to the preposterous scale of her colleagues. She obviously saw herself as the local beauty as she was very flirty, flashing her eyes at me and leaning over to explain the menu.

Not that the menu needed much explaining. It had catfish or ribs with all the 'fixin'. But she wanted to explain it anyway to allow me a view of the yawning cliffs of flesh that formed her cleavage.

I ordered the ribs.

'An what y'all be drinkin', darlin?'

'What beer do you have?'

'Bud.'

The ribs came on a tray – literally. No plate was offered and no knives and forks. I had to ask for eating irons, which caused a ripple of curiosity throughout the restaurant. After a faff they arrived and I tucked in, leaving shallow cut lines on the plastic tray.

The restaurant lost its relaxed atmosphere. Small

children stared hard and the adults had hushed conversations while shooting me the odd glance. I loved it, and held the knife and fork in a deliberately poncey way in order to increase their excitement.

But things soon settled down and the ripple of curiosity dissipated. They'd checked outside for my spaceship and, having satisfied themselves I'd come in peace, ignored me. In fact, I felt quietly accepted. I ordered a second Bud and sat there basking in the cosy ambience of the restaurant.

Goofy men in baseball caps had raucous laughing chats and the plump women in catalogue shorts occasionally gave one of them a jokey slap for a comment. The twangy tunes of 'WLIZee All Country Radio' wafted around the warmth and the odd knackered truck pulled up outside, causing everyone to stop and check out the new arrival.

I was happy. I'd come to the middle of nowhere to prove I could walk around Wall Street in red suspenders but I'd done it. I was New Bank. I was chicken.

It felt great – I wouldn't go home a failure.

Christmas-crackered

'Maybe I shouldn't have come back tonight,' said Rose.
  'Huh,' I said.
  'At least not with a guy who has to get up at seven.'
  'Right,' I said.
  She was clearly trying to get a reaction.
  'I mean, don't you care?' she said, moving up a gear.
  'Care about what?'
  'About me. About whether I get what I want from this.'
  'Did you want to come back to mine?' I asked.

'Yes.'

'Did you want to make love to me?'

'Yes.'

'Then you got what you wanted.'

As I recall, she'd manipulated it. She'd telephoned offering the tickets. She'd persuaded me to come even though it was a weeknight, and she'd made noises angling for an invitation back to mine.

Not that I was complaining. She'd bought two tickets for a ballet performance of *Romeo & Juliet* at the Lincoln Center and wanted me as her escort. Although Rose was supposed to have been no more than a one-night diversion off the straight and narrow, this offer pressed all my buttons.

I'd wanted to see a ballet because I'd never seen one. I wanted to go to the Lincoln Center because I'd never been. And having seen *Shakespeare in Love,* I wanted to see *Romeo & Juliet.*

And once sat in the red, Christmas-cracker box magnificence of the Lincoln Center, and once Rose had put her arm through mine during the performance, it seemed appropriate to invite her back. She didn't seem to have an alternative plan. She wasn't going to make it back to Long Island and Sal didn't even know she was in town.

What was I to do? I intended being faithful to Mandy, I really did. But Rose didn't really count. I'd already blown it in that respect. I couldn't be unfaithful with any *other* new women.

But I was already beginning to repent.

'I wanted an orgasm,' said Rose, like a child demanding candy.

I was slightly taken aback by her frankness, although I really just wanted to go to sleep. I wasn't ready for a major debate on how different genders are emotionally influenced by the expectation and reality of sex –

especially on a Tuesday night with work in the morning.

'I'm sorry I didn't manage it,' I said.

'That's not what I'm saying,' she said. 'Oh why are you reacting like this?'

'Like what?'

'Like you don't care.'

'Rose I do care. But I need to go to sleep.'

'It's just that you made such a fuss in Max Fish about being an unselfish lover.'

I knew that line was going to come back and haunt me. It had been a throwaway comment. I'd been talking shit in a bar. So what?

'And now you want me to just suck your dick and then roll off and go to sleep.'

I didn't answer. I hoped the silence would be enough for her to drop it. Sure, I'd been a bit selfish, but I wasn't ready for a thirty-minute square-bashing session at the entrance to Dante's Inferno. I'd had a bad day at work and I didn't need someone shouting 'Higher, lower, left a bit, fire,' just before bedtime.

But Rose wasn't ready to stop.

'Did you say you were jealous of that guy in London because you wanted to fuck me?'

'No.'

Oh gawd, this was getting out of hand. Again I'd been talking shit. I'd said any bollocks to get what I'd wanted. I was being a bloke. Didn't she get it?

'How would declaring my jealousy make you fuck me?' I asked.

'Of course it would,' she said. 'It's obvious.'

Playing the ignorant guy didn't work anymore. The genie was out the bottle. She'd been on a trip to London and shagged a guy in Hammersmith. I knew that declaring my jealousy would make her go all gooey and make her want to shag me. It was an unspoken game and the rules didn't bear scrutiny. I resented the exposure.

'I feel so used,' she said. 'You got me back here to suck your dick and fuck you because you were jealous and now you won't give me an orgasm.'

Oh Christ. I'd had enough. I was going on the offensive.

'Look,' I said. 'Maybe we're just not sexually compatible.'

And I meant it. Rose was hard work. If some rent-a-dick in London managed to bring her off then good luck to him. Given how long it took me last time – as well as the schoolma'm lecturing I had to endure – I'd like to buy him a pint. We could swap stories of Rose's muff.

But Rose wasn't happy to hear about our incompatibility. This seemed to turn the argument in an unwelcome direction – *my* selfishness was now *our* incompatibility.

'You think we're incompatible?' she said in an incredulous tone.

Oh no, I could tell an hour-long bout of soul-searching lay ahead. A bout that would, no doubt, have to end with another sesh at the coalface just to prove me wrong – and give her an orgasm.

I was keen to avoid the scenario opening up in front of me. I sat up and put the light on. I could see Rose's underwear strewn on the floor in not-so-fascinating little bundles. She had those apple-catcher panties favoured by American college girls and her underwired bra looked capable of stopping an avalanche. And I wished she'd put them on and fuck off. If I'd blown it, fine. I was a dick. Now get dressed and sling your hook.

'You think we're incompatible?' she repeated.

'Well clearly I can't turn you on,' I said, 'and that's an issue for you.'

'I didn't say you couldn't turn me on,' she said. 'You can when you don't want me to just suck your dick so you can roll over and go to sleep.'

321

Why did she keep using that expression? It really grated.

Rose had now metamorphosed into a hideous monster. I had the 'Thing from the Deep' lying in my bed and I wanted her out. I sat with my back to her while I tried to find the right words.

'Look I really don't feel I can face some big row at this hour,' I said. 'Perhaps you should go.'

A bit blunt, but I said I'd try to find the right words. I didn't say anything about finding them.

Rose glared at me. I guess she may have been nervous of being thrown onto the streets of New York at two in the morning. Those crime-free streets may look a little different in the middle of the night, especially to a young, white, middle-class girl from Long Island. So when she adopted her best sergeant major manner and insisted on staying, I detected enough fear for the non-bastard side of me to relent. But she could bloody well move over and keep still.

In her own way, Rose encapsulated my frustration with American women. There really was no sense of mutuality. Rose's confidence manifested itself by demanding I perform. This was no different to the passive American women I'd come across – sometimes literally. They were equally dependent on the male performance. It's either lie back and take it or lie back and demand it. Where's the climb on and give it?

I'd had enough. Part of me was mentally clearing the decks for a return home, but a larger part of me had lost all respect. If I'd told a British woman I was jealous of her shagging another bloke she'd have told me to grow up. Here my envy was seen as chivalrous – a fight over the keys to the chastity belt.

And once sussed, it's difficult not to hold American women in contempt. Everything about them looks compliant. That hair. I once thought it showed an ability to

322

prosper while remaining feminine. Now I see it as a desperate attempt to look like Barbie in order to please Ken. That svelte figure – Barbie again. Ken likes 'em skinny. And those nails – has Ken told you about his handjob fantasy?

I guess I needed to go home. I needed women who could strike me down with a devastating comment, who could chew me up and spit me out. I didn't need women who just swallowed what I gave them and complained when I didn't return the compliment.

JUNE (ish)

It's sport Jim, but not as we know it

At last, the Knicks lost the playoffs and New York could get back to normal. The city's basketball team had consumed the interest of New Yorkers for weeks. Normally chatty bars and restaurants whooped and cheered every Knicks point. Even aloof establishments succumbed to the fever and installed a TV for the team's run to the finals. Less aloof establishments completely lost control and erected giant screens. New York loved it. I hated it.

Don't get me wrong, it's great to see a city get behind its team, especially as the Knicks were the underdogs. But it didn't fit New York's don't-give-a-shit image to become so carried away. Isn't this America's cynical city? Isn't it a bit provincial to root with such abandon – especially for guys squeaking round a sports hall in long vests? And doesn't this sense of unity make New York look, well, small? Shouldn't the city have a dozen basketball teams – so while one district goes wild, eleven close the curtains?

The trouble was I'd brought too much sporting baggage from home.

As the unfortunately named Knicks went down to the even more unfortunately named Spurs (of San Antonio), I couldn't help noticing that every game in the series

324

ended something like 98-96. Such a score delights the Americans. It means they can whoop and cheer for the whole game. It means they can watch the entire spectacle in the hope and expectation of victory. And it means a nail-biting finish.

But Brits find such a score nonsense. It tells them the only significant event occurs in the last ten seconds and they needn't watch the rest. What's the point of cheering a basket in the first quarter if the opposition immediately squeaks off and equalizes?

Such scores explain the problem Americans have with soccer (sorry, it's what they call it). It's not that they haven't the patience to wait for the goals – although they haven't – it's that they can't see the significance of them when they arrive.

Proof came during the European Cup final in May. I persuaded a Greenwich bar to show the tie (between Manchester United and Bayern Munich) and a few American colleagues joined me out of curiosity and for an afternoon off. But after ten minutes someone said, 'Hey Bob, nothing's happening. I'm bored.'

They quickly gave up and muttered about the basketball repeats on the other channel. And when United scored twice in injury time they couldn't understand my excitement. You could hear them dismissing it, 'Phoof, just two points. This Limey should follow the Knicks. He'd get to jump up and down a hundred times and it'll still be decided in the dying seconds.'

And while not all US sports are as high-scoring as basketball, they all feed a public with the attention span of an energy trader. TV is to blame, of course.

Action, ad, action, ad – that's the mantra. Steady development of fascinating contest, ad, further development with a half-chance on goal, ad – that's a disaster. The worry is not losing the viewers during the ads but during the sport. Couch-potato thrills come cheap on US

TV and sport needs to keep the buzz to maintain the viewing figures.

The Brits think differently. Any sport that sits well with TV scheduling we dismiss as illegitimate. After all, we're weaned on the Beeb, the natural home of sport, and the BBC happily fucks up its programming for extra time or a follow-on. Also it carries no advertising and positively delights in dreamy ponderous sports that fill up the entire day, or week.

Americans don't know what they're missing. Sure, they have the Golf Channel, but the constant ad breaks rob the viewer of the essence of the event. If you miss Mike Atherton adjusting his box between overs or Colin Montgomerie's caddie wiping down his wedge, you're losing the very elements that make it worth watching. That caddie was annoyed he didn't use the nine iron, and Atherton's ballsache is wrecking his innings. But you wouldn't know – although Ford's new four-wheel drive comes with nought per cent finance.

The nub is that Brits have trouble seeing US sport as sport at all. And this touches our very notion of America as a legitimate nation. The fact that the US has sports played nowhere else reduces its status. Superpowers are super because they're better. They don't run off and invent their own games. So you're number one, you say? Oh yeah, even Iran beat you in the World Cup, and where's the cricket team?

The extent of this isolation is only apparent to non-Americans who live here. Only then is every read of a newspaper or flick through the TV channels an adventure into an unknown world. Seriously famous people have well-known pasts that I hadn't a clue about until I lived here. It's like landing on another planet to find the Martians excited by strange groups exerting themselves in collective formations. 'It's sport, Jim, but not as we know it.'

My ignorance was revealed when I shared a flight with Ernie Banks (his name was on his cap). Every other bugger on the plane adopted the smiley cheerfulness of people near a celebrity. Yet I was at a loss. My neighbour filled me in. Mr Banks played shortstop, or something, for the Chicago Cubs in the 1970s. He was one of their 'all-star' players and spent the following two decades wearing a baseball cap with his name on it and making everybody grin on aeroplanes. But I bet he doesn't go abroad much.

Americans are so esoteric about their sport that, like isolated Midwestern towns, they can make spurious claims without fear of contradiction. Several Americans told me that Michael Jordan is the most famous sportsman in history (sorry, Pele). Many New Yorkers claim that Madison Square Garden is the world's most famous sporting arena (sorry, Wembley) and that the Yankees are the world's best-supported team (sorry, United – though not that sorry).

But no Brit will admit any of this. To us, the Americans break the cardinal rules of sport. For a start there's no grit. The arenas are too comfortable – no concrete terraces and cups of Bovril. And they have poncey names – imagine Burnley playing at the Rose Bowl. The pitch is too clean – no muddy field or snowy pitch – and the players too protected – no cauliflower ears or twisted noses.

But that's just the trimmings. The sacrament of sport is the loyalty. And where's the fucking loyalty? This isn't just a fan thing. The relationship between a team and its city is tenuous. Clubs tend to move about, not only between suburbs but from one end of the country to the other. The most famous such move was the Brooklyn Dodgers' flight to Los Angeles in the 1950s, but that was just the beginning. Wholesale team movement is now a regular feature of US sport.

Creating fan loyalty in such a situation is impossible. Take the case of the Cleveland Browns football team. Cleveland was rather proud of its team until it buggered off to Baltimore and became the Ravens. But this was only fair on Baltimore as their team, the Colts, had buggered off to Indianapolis. Cleveland then got a new team, called the Browns. Meanwhile the Oakland Raiders had just moved to Los Angeles, decided the city was nuts and moved back to Oakland. This was a pity for LA as their other team, the Rams, had buggered off to St Louis. But St Louis was delighted because its own team, the Cardinals, had buggered off to Phoenix.

Given such whims, you can't blame the fans for avoiding the tribal, and therefore emotional, loyalties we Brits attach to teams. For instance, the people of Houston shrugged off the loss of the Oilers to Nashville and began following their old rivals the Dallas Cowboys. It's as if Newcastle United left for Dublin and the Toon Army said, 'Oh well, Sunderland for us next season.' The Toon Army would rather burn in hell – although they'd lynch the Newcastle board first.

Talk of the Oilers and Cowboys brings me to the names. I love 'em. It's such a great idea to have names that reflect the locality (unless you're from Nashville). There are historic names, the 49ers and the Patriots, industrial names, the Steelers and the Packers, and geographic names, the Heat and the Seahawks.

Britain has tried to rebrand some lesser sports by adopting American naming techniques but so far we've got it badly wrong. Each time we fall into the trap of alliteration – the Bradford Bulls, the Wigan Warriors – something US teams tend to avoid.

My home county of Essex is a bad offender. I don't care about imported American sports teams, such as the Chelmsford Cherokees (American football) and the Chelmsford Chieftains (ice hockey), although it's been a while since Red Indians roamed the plains of mid-Essex. But the Essex Eagles for the cricket was a complete cop out. Oh yes, how I remember those eagles perched on top of the runner-bean poles.

In true American fashion there's a sport tailored to every type of individual. If you're tall and black, you play basketball. If you're old and unfit, you play baseball. If you're a huge lump of lard, you play American football. And if you're dangerously violent and Canadian you play ice hockey. But this doesn't leave much room for new sports such as soccer. So soccer has taken off in a big way amongst women. Every Sunday half the public parks are given over to small girls playing matches in vaguely familiar strips. Of course, they have all the right gear: the latest in net technology, corner flags, Fifa balls and even podgy refs with official purple tops.

Women's soccer has become so popular that the US-hosted Women's World Cup has been playing to capacity crowds in stadiums like Soldier Field and the Rose Bowl (both bigger than Wembley). Not that it stops a British lad from scoffing.

'D'you think she'll pull her shirt over her head if she scores?' said one as we watched in a bar.

'Imagine those thighs wrapped around your neck,' said another.

'I hear those Swedes are a tasty side?' said a third. 'Shit at football though.'

And then we became serious and said it wasn't natural. Birds kickin' balls indeed – trust the Yanks. But trust the Brazilians, Germans, Italians, Swedes, Norwegians, Dutch and Russians as well. They were all in the tournament. In fact the only major absentee was England, the country that invented the game – not that we cared or anything.

Of course, the biggest problem with American sports is that they're boring. I thought cricket was dull until I

329

saw a baseball game at the Yankee Stadium. The action takes place in a fraction of the field and there are no thrills such as the bowler's run-up or the bowled-over stumps. Yep, baseball makes even cricket seem exciting. The highlight was the ground staff's YMCA routine at half time.

And the crowd made it no better. I was in the bleachers – the Kop or Shed end of the stadium. These guys were tough but their singing was pathetic.

'Boston sucks, Boston sucks,' was the most sophisticated chant they could muster, despite a fierce rivalry between the teams. They needed some English hooligans to teach them the art of chanting.

We could start with the mild 'You're not singing anymore', move on to the threatening 'You're going home in a London Ambulance', and finish with the flagrantly offensive 'Who's that lying on the runway?'

'Let's go Yankees' was a bit tame in comparison.

'Let's go home,' I said to Nat.

Yo bro

A strange thing happens to New York on summer weekends. It empties. Obviously we're not talking pre-disaster evacuations here. Not everyone leaves. The old Chinese woman in my launderette still asks me if I 'lie starch'. The middle-aged Greek in my diner still tells me the football news from England. And the young Puerto Rican in the deli still serves me while talking on the phone or shouting at his assistant. But anyone who is anyone is not in New York past 6 p.m. on a Friday. They're in the Hamptons, a group of posh annex towns on Long Island.

To be left in New York come Saturday is to be a nobody. The nightclubs are strictly B&T and the Broadway shows are for tourists. New Yorkers are not shopping in Barney's or dining at Le Cirque. New York (or more accurately, Manhattan) has moved a hundred miles east and is having a pool party or a beach barbecue.

Not that you can blame them. The city heat is just too much. Walking with anything more than a soporific slouch is impossible. Even a trip to the deli is an effort and results in another soaked shirt. And forget eating alfresco. Sidewalk restaurant tables sit idle as brunchers and diners flee into the air-conditioned interiors.

Such heat makes life unbearable without air conditioning. And, of course, my millionaire's slop house didn't have any – unless you count two clanking ceiling fans only good for hot air circulation. I lay with a damp towel over my face for two sleepless nights before I surrendered and shelled out three hundred dollars to a dodgy AC salesman with a new van.

Air conditioners are heavy squat lumps that sit jammed in an open window. This prevents the window from being closed and locked but makes your apartment no less secure. Anyone climbing up and opening the window from the outside will be found dead on your return. I realized this while trying to install the bugger.

The box carried simple instructions that a child could have mastered – as long as he was an Olympic weightlifter who'd brought his mates. It stated that installation required two people, which was one more than I possessed.

Person A (me) pulls up the window and holds it open.

Person B (also me) places the plastic unit holders on the sills.

Persons A (me) and B (me again) lugs the bastard machine into position.

Person B's free hand holds the plastic unit holders in place while Person A's free hand gently drops the window onto the unit.

Person A was the back of my neck until I risked being strangled between machine and window. At that point Person A (my neck) had to swap with Person B (my hands) and Person B's former role was fulfilled by my knees. However, my knees weren't up to the job and would have prematurely tested the built-in security mechanism had not Person B been quickly redeployed. This left neither Person A nor Person B holding the window and it slammed down to scatter the plastic unit holders and dent the machine.

It was worth the agony, and the impression of trying to sleep in Concorde's hangar. My bedroom felt like a September morning in Cumbria. To walk into the living room in the middle of the night was like entering an oven. It would have been impossible to sleep in such heat.

But thousands were forced to try, thanks to the power company. ConEdison plunged a large part of Harlem into a sweaty blackout (the TV called it a brown-out) as it lost the struggle to meet electricity demand – probably due to a power marketer demanding $7,000 a megawatt.

The community leaders accused the company of racism, although commercialism was a more likely cause.

'Shit man, we're outta power,' said the panicky controller at ConEd. 'Somewhere's gotta go. Downtown's gonna sue, Midtown's gonna sue, Uptown ain't gonna sue – sorry, Harlem.'

Yet this time Harlem may sue. Their response came from lawyers and politicians rather than rioters and looters. Most people coped by organizing street barbecues and by rallying round for ice.

Harlem looked at its most scenic in the heat. Carefree gangs loitered on the stoops shouting 'Yo bro' at passersby. Old men sat in shady chairs playing dominoes and chess. And the kids turned on the fire hydrants, allowing clear water to cascade into the gutters as if from mountain streams. The older kids used tin cans to direct the water skyward and created great fountains for the smaller kids to play in. They screamed with delight as showers sparkled in the summer sun and splashed onto the sidewalk. It was one of the most New York scenes you could ever hope to see – even if the occasional hydrant king directed the jet my way as I cycled by.

But summertime made all of New York's streets rampant with activity. Little businesses that had disappeared for the winter suddenly returned. Hot dog stalls, fake gear pedlars, coffee stands, newspaper sellers all came back with the warm weather. I'd forgotten how vibrant New York sidewalks can be – especially when all the movie-makers were about.

Summer prompts a crazy amount of TV and movie filming on the streets of New York. And my street seemed to be Media Central. Although lined by two ordinary rows of brownstones, every week saw roadside parking banned to accommodate convoys of trucks and caravans emblazoned with statements like 'On Location', or 'Movies on the Move', or 'Is this Fucking Cool or What?'

One week the entire street was blocked off and guys with big cigars sat in directors chairs right in the road. Thick cables and perplexing light stacks were cast around the street, making bike navigation a nightmare. Far too much equipment was operated by hordes of people all pretending to be in charge. Some rushed about with clipboards and walkie-talkies. Others shouted orders that were ignored.

Everyone looked important – except me and the neighbours. We just gawped in wonder. But we were kept informed by a notice taped to our front door which stated that they were filming something called *A Travesty* and instructed us to act normally, keep our windows shut during the rain scene and not complain when they filmed late at night. In fact they were going to completely fuck up our lives for a few days but so what – would we rather they'd chosen 89th Street?

New Yorkers are supposed to respond with a cynical irritation at such intrusions. Not me. I thought it was great. For a start they made the street look lovely. They removed all the rubbish, which was starting to smell in the heat, and brought in lots of small conifers, large potted plants and wrought-iron benches.

And I just couldn't help looking out for someone famous. Most of the neighbours also found excuses to linger, rather than do their usual plunge into anonymity. Some went the whole hog and set up deckchairs and picnic tables. Even the street grouch – a role I'm hoping to fulfil myself one day – got in on the act. He tutted, shook his head and said, 'Aye-yi-yi, they've taken over the whole street, aye-yi-yi.'

Oddly, the grouch spent the entire week outside his building – perhaps to make sure they returned the rubbish once done.

When not watching movie-makers I was using my terrace. I moved the landlady's nasty garden furniture outside and resolved to eat dinner each night while overlooking the backyard greenery to the gentle whirr of the air-conditioning units. Too bad I came home one night to find a statement from City Hall taped to the door.

'ILLEGAL CONSTRUCTION NOTICE
Terrace at the rear of the building, adjoining apartment
    four.
Construction undertaken without proper authority.
Notice of due demolition – by Order.'

Fucking great. The old witch had achieved her final coup.

'It's not your concern,' she told me when I called.

'What do you mean it's not my concern?' I said. 'I took this apartment on the promise of an outside terrace. It took six months to complete and now has to be demolished. And you tell me it's not my concern.'

'It took one month to complete and you still have a terrace,' she said.

I couldn't argue without risking a cardiac arrest (mine, that is: I'd have argued like hell if it had encouraged her to drop dead).

'Anyway,' I said, 'I'm giving you notice I'm leaving. You've had your last rent from me. I'm going back to England – where landlords are accountable for their actions.'

'Oh you're leaving, are you.' Her voice sounded almost joyful. I hadn't heard this tone since her flirt on my first viewing.

She couldn't wait to get me out, although I knew it wasn't personal. New York rent rises are restricted for sitting tenants. This encourages landlords to make tenants' lives a misery so they'll leave after the one-year lease is up. They can then whack up the rent above the City's statutory limits.

New York landlords – doncha just love em?

Get lost, you tosser

'We're going to have a little chat later,' said Mandy as she joined me in the early evening sunshine outside the Hamilton Hall pub.

It was Friday, and the happy gangs were getting ready for a night out by knocking back vodka and Red Bull on the terrace outside Liverpool Street station. I'd been in London a week, although wasn't yet a Londoner. Charlie Bristols had got me over for his own mini Offsite, but I'd

335

spent most of the time finalizing preparations for being repatriated. Everything was planned. I'd be home by the beginning of July. The timing annoyed me. I'd arrived just after 4 July 1998 and I'd leave just before 4 July 1999. Having spent a year in New York I'd miss the most important day in the American calendar. It made the year feel incomplete, which was fitting.

Mandy was the compensation. Oh how she couldn't wait for me to come back. Her life would fall into place with me home. I just knew she'd been pausing at estate agents' windows. I could tell she gazed at the wedding photos in the local rag. And I was certain she was regarding her local churches from a different perspective.

But Energizer Bunny had pulled me into a meeting room on that Friday morning.

'Mate,' he started. 'We're fucking happy with the way things are going now. Charlie's team is going great guns. Your energy marketing shit is working out. And you even seem to have cheered up a bit. Do you want to stay in the States?'

'Love to,' I said.

There wasn't a flicker of hesitation. I wasn't expecting to react so emphatically. It was a pain in the arse to stay. Everything was arranged for me to come back in a few weeks. But fuck I wanted to stay. I was delighted. I loved America. I loved New York. I'd been hiding my feelings to make coming home easier.

Mandy went ballistic.

'How long for?' she shouted.

'At least to the end of the year – maybe longer.'

'Well there's no need to sound so pleased,' she said, and slammed the phone down.

But she'd recovered her composure by the time we met outside Hamilton Hall. She was even sweet and loving as we cruised across London on the Central Line, having given up hope of ever finding a cab.

We went for a drink in a pub called the Lemon Tree at the back of the Coliseum. It used to be one of my favourites because it had a cosy atmosphere and was frequented by opera singers who'd mince in after a performance and bitch about the orchestra, but it had suffered a restoration and was now a soulless drinking den. The opera divas had gone, to be replaced by the usual West End mix of office workers, thugs and tarts.

'So it's the end of the year at the earliest?' said Mandy, toying with a glass of wine.

'Sounds like it,' I said. 'But you know our place. It changes its mind all the time. I could be back in London next month.'

'I doubt it.' She paused, took a sip of her wine and steeled herself. 'Rob.' She'd taken to calling me Rob because no-one else did. She owned Rob. 'I can't wait any longer,' she said.

'Oh dear.' That was all I could say.

I wasn't sure what she meant. At first I thought she was complaining that we'd yet to eat and I'd suggested a drink as an alternative. Women can be incredibly impatient when it comes to food.

But then she added, 'I can't wait for you to come back.'

'It's only until the end of the year,' I said.

'You've just said the company keeps changing its mind,' she said. 'I bet they keep you there longer.'

There was more. She was trying to keep the chat on track despite the fact I wasn't really paying attention.

'I can't promise to be faithful,' she said.

'Oh dear,' I said again, as if she'd told me they'd run out of nuts.

I remained calm. She might get off with some bloke, but I could live with that – in some ways it would make me feel better. After Rose I felt I'd let Mandy down and

337

she needed an equalizer. She loved me and that was all that mattered.

'Well I'd rather not know,' I said.

And I suppose I didn't really believe her. Women are genetically monogamous, aren't they? Fucking everything in sight is a male instinct, isn't it? Women spurn quantity for quality, don't they?

The subject was closed. Let's enjoy the evening. I took a big slug of my pint and looked around at the bar.

'It's such a shame what's happened to this place,' I said. 'It was a real find in the old days. Oh well, that's progress.'

I looked back to find Mandy crying. It wasn't a lament for the ruined pub.

'Mandy, don't worry,' I said in a panic. 'Look, everything will be fine. You'll see. Time will fly by. And I bet you won't be unfaithful, I bet you can't. You love me too much and, anyway, I'm not going to be unfaithful to you. I love you.'

This really opened the floodgates. It was becoming embarrassing. People were turning round with that look – the one that says women think you're a bastard and men wonder whether they can kick your head in and shag your grateful date.

'It's too late,' she sobbed.

'What?'

'I've already been unfaithful,' she blurted.

Now obviously I was shocked by this, and jealous and hurt and all that shit. But I prepared to rationalize it.

1) I'd lived in New York while she lived in London,

2) I'd been trying to shag anything that moved,

3) occasionally I'd succeeded,

4) and like an idiot I'd confessed.

The jury wasn't going to take long deciding I had it coming.

'Take it like a man,' they'd say.

And I did. I'd live. It almost felt like a release.

'Oh Mandy,' I said. 'You didn't need to tell me. But you have and that's OK. Obviously I'm hurt but I'm in no position to argue. I'll get over it. You know – it may be a blessing. We can look each other in the eye now.'

That was it as far as the floodgates were concerned. They were overwhelmed. Mandy let loose with wails of noisy sobbing. The Thames Barrier was going to have to be alerted if this carried on. By now the men in the pub were getting restless. I mean, a weeping bird on their manor just wasn't on. This geezer was cruising, he really was.

'Oh, you don't understand,' she said, trying to hold back the tears long enough to get the words out. Then she dived into another sob session and couldn't speak at all.

I didn't understand what? I didn't understand that she'd been unfaithful? I didn't understand that someone as loyal as Mandy had shagged another guy? I didn't understand that for her to do that was a major step? That she wouldn't jump into bed with just any bloke while seeing me. That this man had obviously worked his way into her affections. That they meant a lot to each other. That my staying in the US had made up her mind for her. That she wouldn't want to be unfaithful to him – by carrying on with me.

I understood.

'I'm being chucked,' I said. 'This is the end, isn't it?'

Now we were in trouble. Forget the Thames Barrier, it just wasn't going to hold it. Tears poured from her eyes in great torrents of water. The table was wet with drips, her eyes were red and her tissue sodden.

339

'I'm sorry,' she said. 'I'm really sorry.'

I leant back and put my hands to my face. I kept repeating, 'I've been fucking chucked. I don't believe it.'

'Are you all right, love,' said one of the Neanderthals, finally unable to contain his desire to exploit the opportunity. He scowled at me.

'Oh get lost, you tosser,' said Mandy. 'Can't you see this is private.'

I shrugged at him as if to say, 'women, what can you do?'

He slunk back to his laughing mates with a greatly reduced penis.

What a great girl. And to think I'd fucked it.

Where do all the ducks go?

I sat in the Greenwich boardroom, amazed. On a vast screen a white van cruised past a skip. Next to the skip a group of office workers emerged from a pub and walked towards us. And in the foreground a man pushed an empty market-stall cart into an unseen lock-up. I was watching the East End of London – as it happened.

I guessed it was Wentworth Street, one of my favourites as an angst-ridden adolescent. It was perfect for walking along with collar up and hands in pockets with its closed down markets and decrepit old tramps. It was so full of the miserable atmosphere of that part of London it could have been the backdrop to a Ralph McTell video.

The reason I sat in Connecticut and watched my youth walk by was because of something I'd said to Braveheart. I'd told him I objected to the Forums. I said they might seem like a jolly pisstake when you're sitting in London,

340

but they felt like trial by humiliation in Greenwich – you couldn't see expressions and could hear coughing, shuffling and the odd incoherent comment from the back.

'Leave it with me,' he said.

And here I was, waiting for the first video conference Forum to begin. It meant a move to the boardrooms in London and Greenwich, but that was fine, almost an incentive. It also meant we could direct a camera three and a half thousand miles away while waiting for Braveheart and his entourage to sweep in.

And I wanted to check the view. It was the view I'd shown the Receivables team on a chilly spring morning last year. It was the beginning of my journey and I felt I was about to present something of a conclusion.

I was presenting the Dickhams deal to the Forum. After Braveheart and his entourage swept in I made it brief and snappy and was soon rounding up, saying, 'We'll make one million dollars from this in the first year and it doesn't involve lending a cent of our own money.'

I could see them all smiling back at me; Energizer Bunny, Charlie Bristols, Rip Van Winkle – even the newly repatriated Flatcap.

'This is exactly the sort of business we need to be doing,' said Braveheart. 'Well done.'

'Nice one, son,' said Flatcap.

'Isn't it the good case that Receivables deal in the States we have,' said Rip Van Winkle.

'This definitely hits their bogey,' said High Pockets, beside me.

'Awesome, fucking awesome,' said the Main Man, unfortunately still condemned to the speakerphone because of a lack of video link to Houston.

And all those half-heard comments from previous Forums? They turned out to be the balance-sheet geek mumbling 'This will take us to our optimum book position before quarter-end – there's one hundred and seven available against the forecast', or something equally banal. It wasn't some clever dick saying 'what a load of bollocks' after all. Oh how I enjoyed that Forum.

But I didn't enjoy being back in New York. I'd flown home on the previous Saturday with an enormous sense of emptiness. It wasn't just that I hadn't eaten all day after spending the night on a mate's floor. It was because I'd sat in Business Class surrounded by men staring at their laptops.

As soon as we were airborne they'd started updating their spreadsheets or knocking out memos. They were so absorbed they didn't notice the late sun pour through the windows in broad shafts. The cabin looked like a medieval cathedral and the crew translucent angels. But only I noticed. The others just shut the blinds to avoid the glare on their screens.

It summed up the city I was heading back to. New York had lost its soul. It was no longer an urban hell and an artistic paradise. It was no longer somewhere you could make your fortune, get laid, take copious amounts of drugs, fuck your brain, lose your fortune, shoot your new girlfriend and get taken out by the Mob – all in the space of a Virgin Supasaver weekend.

New York was now about having two jobs so you could afford the rent. It was about cagey dating where a good CV was more important than any spark of passion. And it was about staying clear-headed for that 7 a.m. conference call and the Sunday morning half-marathon.

While London was throwing off its inhibitions New York had become a prude. It had taken a long, hard look at the mirror and resolved to join the gym.

Even the crime had given up. In my entire time in New York I hadn't seen a single cop car rush to an incident. All the whoo-whoo sirens were ambulances carting grannies about or fire trucks with posing hunks leaning out the window.

The police just lumbered around being given coffee and donuts. Kojak had been laid off years ago. Stavros now had his own coffee stand. Cagney and Lacey were soccer moms out on Long Island. And New York was no longer the setting for nightmare street movies. It was the setting for romantic comedies like *You've Got Mail* where the biggest crime is the opening of a bookstore on the Upper West Side.

But at least I had my friends in New York – or so I thought. I arrived back to find Fiona and Trevor keen to tell me their news.

'We're going to San Francisco,' said Fiona. 'The office in New York is ticking along and we're off to start up in California.'

'Great,' I said.

'Nat and Ricky are coming with us.'

'Great,' I said.

'Still, you've made lots of friends so you'll be fine. You've got all your women to keep you company.'

Oh yeah, all my women. My apartment just wasn't large enough to deal with them. I had so many women I stopped in a bar on the way home rather than face the consequences of my popularity.

It was the grottiest bar on 72nd Street and it was empty apart from the bartender and me. She was watching the Women's World Cup but was happy to be disturbed.

'Where is everyone?' I asked.

'Oh they're all in the Hamptons I guess,' she said.

She was small and dark. She had an attractive but intelligent face and an appealing smile. Physically she was just my type, but for fuck's sake – I was just so tired of all that shit.

'You don't seem so happy,' she said. 'New York not treating you right?'

'Oh it's the heat.'

'It looks deeper than that,' she said. 'Come on, unload. It's just you and me in this place so you may as well.'

'OK,' I said with resolve. 'How do I meet a woman like you?'

She rolled her eyes, thinking I'd just wrecked her friendliness with a come-on.

'No,' I said. 'It's not a line. I'm not trying to chat you up. I can't seem to meet the right women in New York and I want some advice. Honest.'

She relaxed a little. 'Where d'you meet these women?'

'Singles bars, mostly.'

'Well you won't meet someone like me in a singles bar,' she said firmly. 'You'll meet shallow women who have no thoughts of their own. And they're usually looking for shallow men.'

'Well where do women like you hang out?'

'Me. I'm always in here,' she said. 'I own this place – for my sins.'

'And what attracts you in a man?' I asked.

'My boyfriend,' she said.

I wasn't unhappy with the comment. Sure she was cute but I really wanted the advice. Now I knew it would be genuine.

'Well what attracted you to your boyfriend?'

'He didn't talk shit,' she said. 'Men think women want to hear shit and they complain when they end up with an airhead, or a woman who hangs on their every word, or just a money-grabbing bitch. Women like me judge men on whether they can hold a conversation.'

She was getting into her theme now. She leaned towards me on the bar counter.

'And just because we're talking, it doesn't mean I want to date you. And don't just try and have sex with me. Sex isn't a relationship – it's sex.'

I vigorously shook my head. I won't, I won't.

'Women love sex but they can get casual sex anywhere,' she said. Her tone changed and she sneered,
'Hey, d'you wanna fuck me? Of course you do.'

My heart shot to my mouth but I quickly realized she
was talking rhetorically. None the less my vigorous shake
became a cautious nod.

'That's not what I want,' she said.

I went back to a slow shake. I was terrified of making
a false head movement.

'If I just fuck you it's not special [shake]. It's special if
it's with someone you respect [nod] and I won't respect
you [shake] if you expect me to go to bed with you within
minutes of us meeting [nod].'

Then she stopped. Not because I'd nodded when I
think I should have shaken, but because the women had
just scored (a goal). We watched the replay and started
having a general chat about the state of football in the
US. To be honest I was rather relieved to change the subject.

She played soccer and so did her sisters. Her brothers
thought it a boring girl's game and weren't interested.
She watched the 'EPL' as the English league is known
here, and we had a chat about Manchester United.

'Are they your team?' she asked.

'No,' I said. 'They're the team for people who don't
know who else to support.'

'Oh yeah, the Dallas Cowboys used to be that here.
Who are your guys?'

'Oh, you'll have never heard of them – West Ham?'

'Yes I have,' she said. 'Harry Redknapp and Frank
Lampard.'

'Blimey,' I said.

'And you had that Israeli guy who was kicked in the
head by that fat Welsh striker.'

'Blimey. That's amazing.'

345

'Not all American women are bimbos you know,' she said.

'Will you marry me?' I said.

She laughed.

'Too late,' she said. 'My boyfriend's already asked and I said yes. But I'll keep you in mind.'

'Congratulations,' I said.

It had a hollow ring – it felt way too late.

I decided to walk the long way home, although the summer air now carried a chilly tinge. I felt inadequately dressed in the breeze and I walked up Central Park West with my hands in my pocket.

I passed the Dakota Building – the famous site of John Lennon's assassination. Not that you'd know. There's no plaque or memorial. It was ripe for some comedian to draw a chalk body outline on the street, complete with round spectacles. But New Yorkers wouldn't do such a thing – too much respect.

The tramps were bedding down for the night on the benches and shook cups as I passed. I gave one some change.

'Thank you sir, God bless you sir,' he said, almost bowing.

On the next bench a tramp had a radio playing. The music had a stirring emotional feel and an announcer was speaking in a proud voice.

'We hold these truths to be self-evident,' he was saying. 'All men are created equal, that they are endowed by their creator with certain inalienable rights, that among these are life, liberty, and the pursuit of happiness. That to secure these rights, governments are . . .'

It trailed off as I crossed 77th Street. I'd stopped listening anyway. What a load of bollocks – while that statement was being penned the US had an eighth of its population in slavery.

Such thoughts made me realize I was in one hell of a

346

weird mood. So weird that I plunged into the park despite it being night. It was as if I was challenging New York.

'Come on, you motherfucking city,' I was saying. 'Come and mug me.'

But the only people about were old Jewish ladies walking their poodles and late-night joggers completing the loop.

I walked as far as the lake and sat on one of the small wooden boat-landings. The lake was still, with just the occasional breezy ripple wobbling the reflection of the East Side apartment towers.

'I wonder where all the ducks go in the night-time,' I mused.

Of course I didn't really wonder that – I couldn't give a shit. It just seemed an appropriate thought, given my mood. But I was a bit old to be paraphrasing Holden Caulfield. I didn't feel his anger at the phoneys. I was one myself, for Chrissake.

From behind the towers the sky erupted into fantastic colours. Great cascades of red, white and blue exploded like expanding universes before plunging south.

Fuck me, it was the fourth of July – no wonder the bar was empty and no wonder the radio was banging on about life, liberty and the pursuit of all that crap. I'd been so self-absorbed I'd missed the most important day of the American year.

I laughed out loud. It was really only a quiet chuckle as I realized I was on my own in Central Park at night. I was keen not to be seen as a complete nutter and laughing at fireworks must be in the same league as barking at the moon.

Mind you, there was nothing laughable about the show. It was magnificent – and all the greater when reflected off the lake. The smiley-face fireworks were the best and they broke my mood.

I realized the next day was a holiday and I walked home, cheered. I'd devote the day to a long Manhattan bike ride. And I needed to start looking for a new apartment – maybe a nice block with a doorman.

Notes From A Big Country

by Bill Bryson

'ONE OF HIS BEST BOOKS'
Scott Bradfield, *Independent*

Bill Bryson has the rare knack of being out of his depth
wherever he goes – even (perhaps especially) in the land of
his birth. This became all too apparent when, after nearly
two decades in England, the world's best-loved travel
writer upped sticks with Mrs Bryson, little Jimmy et al.
and returned to live in the country he had left as a youth.

Of course there were things Bryson missed about Blighty
but any sense of loss was countered by the joy of re-
discovering some of the forgotten treasures of his
childhood: the glories of a New England autumn; the
pleasingly comical sight of oneself in shorts; and motel
rooms where you can generally count on being awakened
in the night by a piercing shriek and the sound of a female
voice pleading, 'Put the gun down, Vinnie, I'll do anything
you say.'

Whether discussing the dazzling efficiency of the garbage
disposal unit, the exoticism of having your groceries
bagged for you, the jaw-slackening direness of American
TV or the smug pleasure of being able to eat your beef
without having to wonder if when you rise from the table
you will walk sideways into the wall, Bill Bryson brings
his inimitable brand of bemused wit to bear on that
strangest of phenomena – the American way of life.

'DELIGHTFUL BITE-SIZE ESSAYS THAT EXUDE
AFFECTION WHILE DEBUNKING THE RIDICULOUS
WITH WONDERFUL SUCCINCTNESS . . . THIS IS NOT A
BOOK TO BE READ IN A SINGLE SITTING. IT IS ONE TO
BE SAVOURED'
Martin Fletcher, *The Times*

'BILL BRYSON'S ANSWER TO ALASTAIR COOKE'S
LETTER FROM AMERICA . . . NOT ONLY HILARIOUS
BUT ALSO INSIGHTFUL AND INFORMATIVE'
Jeremy Atiyah, *Independent on Sunday*

0 552 99786 2

BLACK SWAN

GO
by Simon Lewis

Heartbroken?
Family problems?
Ripped off your boss?
Think you've killed someone?

It's time to GO

Lee, Sol and Vix are on the run — from police, gangsters, parents . . . themselves. As they travel through Asia on separate quests, their paths cross. But it doesn't matter how far you go, reality always catches up with you . . .

'Alongside Alex Garland and William Sutcliffe, Lewis is one of the pioneers of new travel fiction. And of the three he is the most in tune with the experience of travelling and the possibilities it offers fiction'
Observer

'Fast, sharp, funny'
I-D

'The pace and wit of Elmore Leonard with Alan Bennettish realism . . . Highly accomplished and enjoyable'
The Times

'Confident, sharp as a tack, fast paced and blackly funny from beginning to end'
Big Issue

'Sweet, sour, surprising'
Observer

'South London gunplay and backpacker slack, jet trash characters – Simon Lewis mixes it all with style'
Toby Litt

0 552 14717 6

THE WRONG WAY HOME
by Peter Moore

When Peter Moore announced he was going to travel home from London to Sydney without stepping on to an aeroplane he was met with a resounding Why? The answer was a severe case of hippie envy: hippies had the best music, the best drugs, the best sex. But most of all, they had the best trips.

Knowing that his funds were woefully inadequate and that his chances of actually making it through such notorious hot-spots as the Balkans, Iran and Afghanistan were, in a word, slim, Peter was never one to err on the side of caution and over the next eight months (and twenty-five countries) he followed the trail overland to the East. It would prove to be a journey of exhilarating highs and, on occasions, frustrating lows, of diverse experiences – including the world's most expensive disco (in Albania), the bombed-out villages of Croatia, the opium fields of Laos, student riots in Jakarta, an all-night beach rave on a small island in Thailand – and memorable encounters with a wonderful cast of often eccentric, at times exasperating and, once in a while, overly amorous characters.

Funny, irreverent and acutely observed, *The Wrong Way Home* will strike a chord with anyone who has ventured on such a life-enhancing Grand Tour. It will also entertain (and perhaps alarm) all those who love to read about such adventures but would never be fool enough to grab that rucksack and go.

'Peter Moore is the genuine article . . . Inspirational stuff'
FHM

'A perceptive, subversive and hilarious book'
Sydney Morning Herald

'It will certainly make you laugh'
Sunday Mirror (Book of the Week)

A Bantam Paperback
055 3 81238 6